All in One Teaching Resources

Earth's Waters

PRENTICE HALL Science Explorer

D1370810

PEARSON

Prentice Hall

Needham, Massachusetts
Upper Saddle River, New Jersey

Pearson Prentice Hall™ is a trademark of Pearson Education, Inc.

Pearson® is a registered trademark of Pearson plc.

Prentice Hall® is a registered trademark of Pearson Education, Inc.

Lab zone™ is a trademark of Pearson Education, Inc.

Planet Diary® is a registered trademark of Addison Wesley Longman, Inc.

Discovery Channel School® is a registered trademark of Discovery Communications, Inc., used under license. The Discovery Channel School logo is a trademark of Discovery Communications, Inc.

SciLinks® is a trademark of the National Science Teachers Association. The SciLinks® service includes copyrighted materials and is owned and provided by the National Science Teachers Association. All rights reserved.

Science News® is a registered trademark of Science Services, Inc.

ISBN 0-13-190280-6   1 2 3 4 5 6 7 8 9 10   08 07 06 05 0

All in One Teaching Resources

Everything you need for daily planning is in one place! *Science Explorer* blackline masters, teaching support, and all answer keys are organized by chapter, making it easy for you to find what you need—when you need it.

Teaching Support

Lesson Plans—Streamline your path through every section with a core set of activities and teaching suggestions.

Color Transparency Planner—Provides you with easy access to the transparencies to help you plan your lessons.

Teacher Notes—Includes support for hands-on teaching for projects, labs, and assessment.

Complete Answer Keys—Find all the answers at the end of each chapter.

Reading & Review

Target Reading Skills Handbook—Guides student understanding of target reading skills and shows how to apply them.

Guided Reading and Study Worksheets—Promote active reading and help enhance students' study skills with worksheets that apply Target Reading Skills and guide students through the text with questioning strategies and exercises.

Section Summaries—Support all readers and English language learners with easily accessible content summaries.

Review & Reinforce Worksheets—Motivate students to build vocabulary, review main ideas, and interpret diagrams, charts, and graphs.

Enrichment

Enrich Worksheets—Encourage all students to read, write, and visualize as they apply core concepts in a new context.

Interdisciplinary Exploration Worksheets—Explore a topic from the perspective of four disciplines: science, mathematics, social studies, and language arts.

Labs & Activities

Laboratory Safety—Offers teacher support and safety symbols for ready reference.

Laboratory Investigations—In-depth labs apply and extend key concepts for each chapter and include teaching support, pre-lab discussions, and critical-thinking questions.

Student Edition Lab Worksheets—Help students get organized with blackline masters of Student Edition labs—each in an easy-to-grade format.

Chapter Project Support—Guide students through the Chapter Projects in the student text with extensive teacher notes, scoring rubrics, and student worksheets with project rules and checklists.

Assessment

Performance Assessment—Assess student problem-solving and process skills using scoring rubrics and suggested outcomes.

Chapter and Book Tests—Monitor student mastery of standards-driven content and skills with a variety of questions. Thousands more questions can be found on the *ExamView*® Computer Test Bank CD-ROM.

Earth's Waters

Contents

PRENTICE HALL

TeacherEXPRESS™

Plan • Teach • Assess

The TeacherExpress CD-ROM is a new suite of instructional tools to help teachers plan, teach, and assess.

- Powerful lesson planning
- Resource management
- Testing
- Interactive teacher's edition
- **All in One** *Teaching Resources*

Having everything in one place makes class preparation quick and easy!

Name _____ Date _____ Class _____

Finding Locations on a Map

Identify each place described below. Use the map of the Mississippi River in your textbook to find the answers.

1. This state is bordered on the north by Missouri and on the east by the Mississippi River. _____

2. This city is on the west bank of the Mississippi River, near where the Missouri River joins the Mississippi.

   _____

3. This city is on the east bank of the Mississippi River, near the boundary between Tennessee and Mississippi.

   _____

4. These "twin cities" are on the east and west banks of the Mississippi River near its headwaters. One city is the state capital.

   _____

5. This state is bordered on the west by the Mississippi River and on the south by the Ohio River.

   _____

6. This river flows southward across the state of Mississippi and joins the Mississippi River near Vicksburg.

   _____

7. This city is located where the Ohio River joins the Mississippi.

   _____

8. This river joins the Mississippi River about halfway between Memphis and Vicksburg.

   _____

9. This city is on the west bank of the Mississippi River, across from the state boundary between Wisconsin and Illinois.

   _____

10. Mark Twain's home town of Hannibal is in this state.

   _____

Name _____ Date _____ Class _____

Reading a Data Table

The table below compares the populations of eight cities along the Mississippi, Missouri, and Ohio Rivers. Use the table to answer the questions that follow.

Population Change

	1970	1980	1990	Rank in U.S. (1990)
Baton Rouge, Louisiana	166,000	220,000	220,000	74
Evansville, Indiana	139,000	130,000	126,000	144
Kansas City, Missouri	507,000	448,000	435,000	31
Louisville, Kentucky	362,000	299,000	270,000	58
Memphis, Tennessee	624,000	646,000	610,000	18
Minneapolis, Minnesota	434,000	371,000	368,000	43
New Orleans, Louisiana	593,000	558,000	497,000	24
Omaha, Nebraska	347,000	314,000	336,000	48

1. Which city had the largest population in 1990? _____

2. Which city had the largest population in 1970? _____

3. Which city is not one of the 100 largest U.S. cities? _____

4. Which city had a larger population in 1990 than in 1970? _____

5. How did the population of Omaha, Nebraska, change between 1970 and 1990?

_____

_____

6. Rank Kansas City, Minneapolis, and New Orleans in order from most population to least population for 1970, 1980, and 1990.

_____

_____

7. How many people did the city of Louisville gain or lose between 1970 and 1990?

_____

8. What is the percentage of population lost or gained in Louisville between 1970 and 1990?

_____

9. Which city lost the most population between 1970 and 1990? _____

10. Which two cities gained the most population between 1970 and 1980?

_____

Interdisciplinary Exploration · *Social Studies*

Making a Bar Graph

The table below shows the amount of freight carried on the Mississippi River system between 1970 and 1990. "Domestic freight" means goods that are bought and sold within the United States. "Foreign freight" means goods that the United States buys from other countries or sells to other countries.

Freight Carried on the Mississippi River System (millions of tons)

	1970	**1975**	**1980**	**1985**	**1990**
Domestic freight	341	360	408	420	490
Foreign freight	51	94	177	108	170

Use the table to make a bar graph on a sheet of graph paper. Label the vertical axis "Freight (millions of tons)." Label the horizontal axis "Years." Draw two bars for each year, one for domestic freight and one for foreign freight. When you finish the graph, answer the following questions.

1. What was the total amount of freight carried each year? _____

   _____

2. In what year was the largest amount of foreign freight carried on the river?

   _____

3. In what year was the largest amount of domestic freight carried on the river?

   _____

4. Describe how the amounts of domestic freight and foreign freight changed from 1970 to 1990.

   _____

   _____

   _____

   _____

Name _____ Date _____ Class _____

Finding Your Way Around New Orleans

Use this map of downtown New Orleans to answer the questions below. Write your answers on a separate sheet of paper.

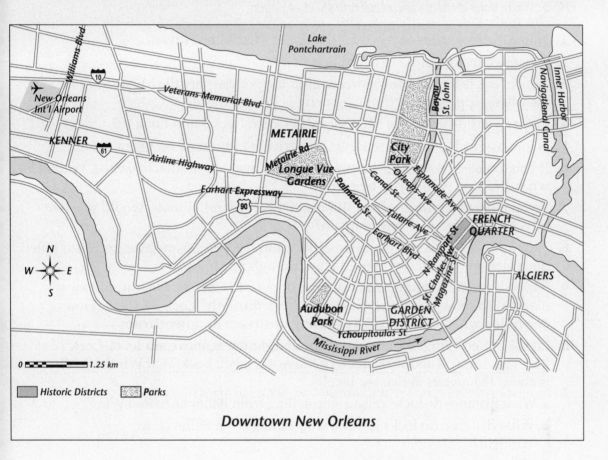

Downtown New Orleans

1. In which general direction does the Mississippi River flow here?
2. What body of water borders New Orleans on the north?
3. What waterway connects the Mississippi River with the body of water on the north?
4. Why do you think the waterway was built?
5. What body of water extends south from Lake Pontchartrain into the city?
6. What historic district is shown on the map?
7. Name the four streets that form the historic district's boundaries.
8. Use the map scale to determine about how long a walk it is along Esplanade Avenue from the French Quarter to City Park.
9. In which area of New Orleans is the airport located?
10. Which area of New Orleans is south of the Mississippi River?

Interdisciplinary Exploration · *Science*

Traveling the Upper Mississippi

The map on the next page shows the locks and dams on the upper Mississippi River. Areas shaded dark gray indicate major cities. Use the map to answer the questions below. Write your answers on a separate sheet of paper.

1. Name the five states that border the upper Mississippi River.

2. What two major cities are near Lock 1?

3. Which lock is the first downstream after the point where the Missouri River enters the Mississippi River? What major city is located there?

4. What river flows into the Mississippi between Lock 9 and Lock 10?

5. Name two lock-and-dam systems that are not numbered on the map.

6. If you traveled on the Mississippi from Hastings, Minnesota, to Genoa, Wisconsin, what direction would you be going?

7. If you took a boat from Alton, Illinois, to Rock Island, Illinois, would you be traveling upstream or downstream?

8. Suppose a boat entered the Mississippi from the Wisconsin River and then sailed downstream. Which lock would it go through first?

9. Suppose a boat is sailing from Quincy, Illinois, to Canton, Missouri. Draw a diagram to show how the boat would "lock through" Lock 20. (*Hint:* First determine whether the boat is traveling upstream or downstream.)

10. Lock 3 at Red Wing, Minnesota, is about 234 meters above sea level. Lock 12 at Bellevue, Iowa, is about 189 meters above sea level. Lock 24 at Winfield, Missouri, is about 143 meters above sea level.

    a. What distance do locks raise a ship sailing from Bellevue to Red Wing?

    b. What distance do locks lower a ship sailing from Bellevue to Winfield?

    c. What is the total distance that locks raise or lower ships between Red Wing and Winfield?

Interdisciplinary Exploration ▪ *Science*

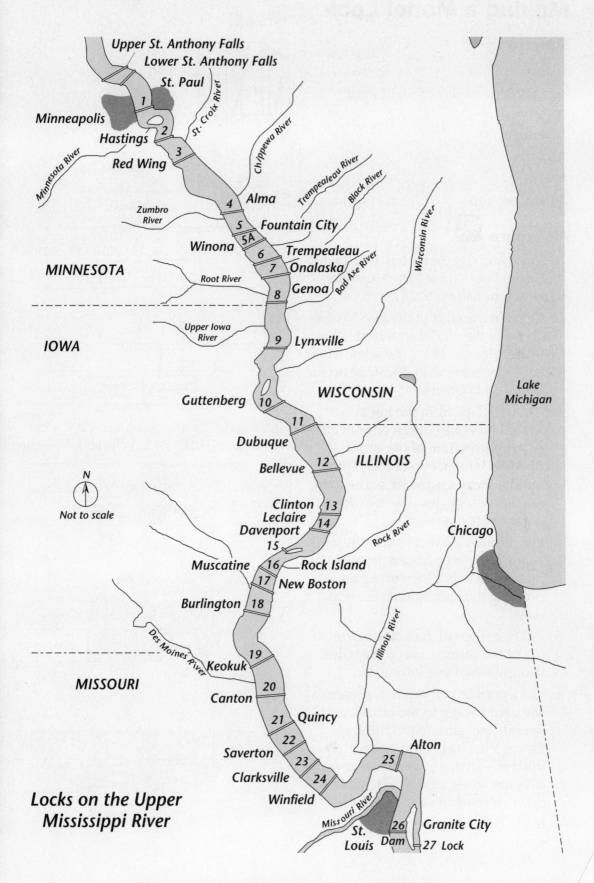

Upper St. Anthony Falls
Lower St. Anthony Falls
St. Paul
St. Croix River
Minneapolis
Hastings
Red Wing
Chippewa River
Minnesota River
Zumbro River
Alma
Fountain City
Trempealeau River
Black River
Winona
Trempealeau
Onalaska
Bad Axe River
Wisconsin River
MINNESOTA
Root River
Genoa
Upper Iowa River
Lynxville
IOWA
WISCONSIN
Lake Michigan
Guttenberg
Dubuque
Bellevue
ILLINOIS
N
Not to scale
Clinton
Leclaire
Davenport
Rock River
Chicago
Muscatine
Rock Island
New Boston
Burlington
Des Moines River
Keokuk
Illinois River
MISSOURI
Canton
Quincy
Saverton
Alton
Clarksville
Winfield
Missouri River
St. Louis
Dam
Granite City
Lock

Locks on the Upper Mississippi River

Interdisciplinary Exploration · *Science*

Making a Model Lock

Materials

scissors

half-gallon waxed cardboard juice
or milk carton

modeling wax

duct tape

water

cork or pen cap

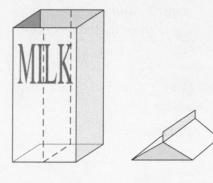

Procedure

1. Wash and dry the carton. Cut the top off, and save it for Step 3. Cut the carton in half vertically.

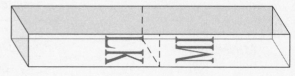

2. Overlap the ends of the two halves. To make the model watertight, put modeling wax along the seam. Then cover the seam with duct tape on the inside and outside.

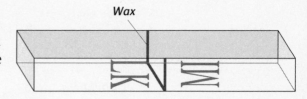

3. Cut two flaps from the top you saved. Tape the bottom edge of each flap to the bottom of the carton to divide it into three sections. The middle section is the lock. The flaps are the lock's gates. The two outer sections are the river.

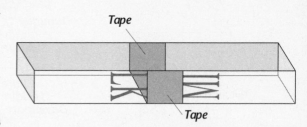

4. Use modeling wax to make the gates watertight. To operate a gate, just fold it down and then up again, pressing it firmly against the wax seals.

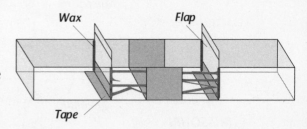

5. Put two strips of duct tape across the top of the carton to keep the sides straight when you add water.

6. Use a cork or pen cap to represent a ship. Add water to the model, and operate the gates to sail the ship through the lock. First, move it upriver—from a lower water level to a higher water level. Next, move it downriver—from a higher level to a lower level.

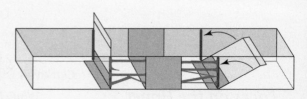

Interdisciplinary Exploration • *Mathematics*

Calculating Distances Between Locks

This table lists the distance from each lock to the point where the Ohio River joins the Mississippi River. Use the table to answers the questions below.

Distances Between Locks

Lock	Distance Above Ohio River (km)	Nearby Community
1	1364	Minneapolis–St. Paul, Minnesota
2	1312	Hastings, Minnesota
3	1282	Red Wing, Minnesota
4	1211	Alma, Wisconsin
5	1188	Winona, Minnesota
6	1149	Trempealeau, Wisconsin
7	1130	Onalaska, Wisconsin
8	1093	Genoa, Wisconsin
9	1042	Lynxville, Wisconsin
10	990	Guttenberg, Iowa

1. If you traveled from Genoa, Wisconsin, to Minneapolis, Minnesota, would you be going upstream or downstream? _____

2. What is the distance between Lock 1 and Lock 10? _____

3. What is the distance between Lock 4 and Lock 10? _____

4. Which two consecutive locks are farthest apart? _____

_____

5. Which two consecutive locks are closest together? _____

_____

6. Which is greater—the distance between Locks 1 and 2 or the distance between Locks 7 and 8?

_____

7. What is the distance between Red Wing, Minnesota, and Onalaska, Wisconsin?

_____

8. What is the distance between Guttenberg, Iowa, and Winona, Minnesota?

_____

Name _____ Date _____ Class _____

Graphing Population Changes

The table below shows the populations of three cities on the Mississippi River in each U.S. census from 1950 to 1990. Use the table to make a line graph on a sheet of graph paper. Label the vertical axis "Population (thousands)." Label the horizontal axis "Years." Use a different color to plot the data for each city. When you finish the graph, answer the questions that follow.

Population Changes

	1950	1960	1970	1980	1990
Minneapolis	521,700	482,900	434,400	371,000	368,400
St. Louis	856,800	750,000	622,200	452,800	396,700
Memphis	396,000	497,500	624,000	646,200	610,300

1. Which city or cities gained population between 1950 and 1970? _____

2. Which city or cities lost population during that same period?

3. Which city had the greatest drop in population between 1970 and 1990?

   _____

4. In which 10-year period did the population in these cities change the least?

   _____

5. Choose one city on the graph. Write one sentence that summarizes its population changes between 1950 and 1990.

   _____

   _____

   _____

Name _____ Date _____ Class _____

Paddlewheel Steamboat Cruises

Three steamboats offer cruises on the Mississippi River and its tributaries. Table 1 gives information about the boats. Use the table to answer the questions below.

TABLE 1: Steamboat Sizes and Capacity

	Length	Staterooms	Passengers	Crew
American Queen	418 feet	222	436	161
Delta Queen	285 feet	87	174	81
Mississippi Queen	382 feet	208	422	156

1. The steamboat company's brochure gives each boat's length in feet. What is the approximate length of each boat in meters? (*Hint:* 1 foot equals about 0.3 meter.)

   _____

2. What is the passenger-to-crew ratio on each boat? That is, how many passengers are there for each crew member? (*Hint:* Divide the number of passengers by the number of crew members. Round your answers to the nearest whole number.)

   _____

   _____

3. What is the average number of passengers per stateroom on each steamboat? (*Hint:* Round your answers to the nearest whole number.)

   _____

   _____

4. What other information might you like to have before choosing which boat to travel on?

   _____

   _____

   _____

Interdisciplinary Exploration · *Language Arts*

Mississippi River Vocabulary

Complete each sentence with a term from the list below.

cargo	silt
delta(s)	lock(s)
flood plain	steamboat(s)
headwaters	tributary
keelboat(s)	watershed(s)

5. Near its _____ in Minnesota, the Mississippi River is only a small, shallow stream.

6. The lower Mississippi flows through a broad, flat _____.

7. Grain from the Midwest is one important _____ shipped downriver on the Mississippi.

8. The Ohio River is an important _____ of the Mississippi River.

9. Before boats were powered by engines, people used long poles to push narrow _____ upstream against the current.

10. When the Mississippi River reaches the ocean, it deposits the silt and sand it carries, forming a _____.

11. Boats traveling on the upper Mississippi must pass through _____ that raise or lower them to a different water level.

12. The Mississippi's _____ includes all the land area drained by the Ohio River, the Missouri River, and other rivers flowing into the Mississippi River.

13. When Mark Twain was growing up in a small town on the Mississippi River, he wanted to become a _____ pilot.

14. The Missouri River is nicknamed the "Big Muddy" because it carries a large amount of _____.

Interdisciplinary Exploration • *Language Arts*

The Mound Builders

Read the paragraphs below. Then answer the following questions on a separate sheet of paper.

Early Native Americans known as Mound Builders lived in the Mississippi River valley from about 1000 B.C. to about A.D. 1600. These people are called Mound Builders today because they built earthen mounds for burials and other purposes. Some of these mounds were shaped like snakes, birds, turtles, and other animals.

One group of Mound Builders, the Mississippian culture, lived in villages and towns of 500 to 10,000 people. These societies constructed public buildings such as temples on top of rectangular, flat-topped mounds. The largest group of mounds still surviving today, the Cahokia Mounds, is located near St. Louis, Missouri. Of the 200 mounds in this group, the biggest is 32 meters high and about 6.5 hectares in area.

The Mississippian people still thrived when European explorers first arrived in the Mississippi valley in the mid-1500s. But by the mid-1600s, their population had greatly declined, and they had stopped building mounds. However, the people did not disappear entirely. They were the ancestors of many modern-day tribes, including the Chickasaw, Creek, and Natchez.

1. When did Mound Builders begin living in the Mississippi River valley?
2. Why do we call these people Mound Builders?
3. Which group of Mound Builders built the flat-topped mounds with buildings on them?
4. Where is the mound group called Cahokia Mounds located? How many mounds are in this group?
5. How many years passed between the arrival of Europeans and the end of mound building?
6. Why do you think the Mississippian people stopped building mounds?
7. Why is it inaccurate to say that all of the Mississippian people died out?

Interdisciplinary Explorations

Social Studies: Finding Locations on a Map

1. Arkansas
2. St. Louis
3. Memphis
4. Minneapolis and St. Paul
5. Illinois
6. Yazoo River
7. Cairo
8. Arkansas River
9. Dubuque
10. Missouri

Social Studies: Reading a Data Table

1. Memphis
2. Memphis
3. Evansville
4. Baton Rouge
5. It decreased between 1970 and 1980 and increased between 1980 and 1990 to end with a slightly smaller population in 1990 than in 1970.
6. Each year: 1. New Orleans, 2. Kansas City, 3. Minneapolis
7. lost 92,000
8. about 25 percent
9. New Orleans
10. Baton Rouge and Memphis

Social Studies: Making a Bar Graph

1. 1970: 392 million tons; 1975: 454 million tons; 1980: 585 million tons; 1985: 528 million tons; 1990: 660 million tons
2. 1980
3. 1990
4. The amount of domestic freight increased fairly steadily; the amount of foreign freight increased until 1985, when it decreased, and then it almost regained its 1980 level in 1990.

Social Studies: Finding Your Way Around New Orleans

1. from west to east
2. Lake Pontchartrain
3. the Inner Harbor Navigational Canal
4. To allow boats to move between the lake and the river
5. Bayou St. John
6. French Quarter

7. Esplanade Avenue, Canal Street, North Rampart Street, Tchoupitoulas Street
8. about 1.75 km
9. Kenner
10. Algiers

Science: Traveling the Upper Mississippi

1. Minnesota, Wisconsin, Illinois, Iowa, Missouri
2. Minneapolis and St. Paul
3. Lock 26; St. Louis
4. the Wisconsin River
5. Upper St. Anthony Falls, Lower St. Anthony Falls
6. southeast
7. upstream
8. Lock 10 (Guttenberg)
9. Sketches should show the lock raising the boat.
10. **a.** 45 m
    b. 46 m
    c. 91 m

Science: Making a Model Lock

The two end sections should be filled to different levels, with the lower level representing downriver. *To move the ship upriver:* Open the downriver gate, move the ship into the lock, close and seal the gate, fill the lock to the same level as upriver, open the upriver gate, move the ship out. *To move the ship downriver:* Open the upriver gate, move the ship into the lock, close and seal the gate, empty the lock to the same level as the downriver section, open the downriver gate, move the ship out.

Mathematics: Calculating Distances Between Locks

1. upstream
2. 374 km
3. 221 km
4. Locks 3 and 4 (71 km)
5. Locks 6 and 7 (19 km)
6. the distance between Locks 1 and 2 (52 km compared with 37 km)
7. 152 km
8. 198 km

Mathematics: Graphing Population Changes

1. Memphis
2. Minneapolis, St. Louis
3. St. Louis
4. 1980–1990
5. *Sample answers:* Minneapolis had a slow, steady loss in population from 1950 to 1980 and then declined slightly from 1980 to 1990. St. Louis's population dropped rapidly from 1950 to 1980 and then declined less severely from 1980 to 1990. Memphis's population grew fairly quickly from 1950 to 1970, increased a bit from 1970 to 1980, and then declined a bit more.

Mathematics: Paddlewheel Steamboats

1. *American Queen:* 125.4 m, *Delta Queen:* 85.5 m, *Mississippi Queen:* 114.6 m
2. *American Queen:* 3 to 1, *Delta Queen:* 2 to 1, *Mississippi Queen:* 3 to 1
3. *American Queen:* 2, *Delta Queen:* 2, *Mississippi Queen:* 2
4. *Sample answers:* Price per passenger or price per stateroom, meals, schedules, special features of boat

Language Arts: Mississippi River Vocabulary

1. headwaters
2. flood plain
3. cargo
4. tributary
5. keelboats
6. delta
7. locks
8. watershed
9. steamboat
10. silt

Language Arts: The Mound Builders

1. about 1000 B.C.
2. They built earthen mounds, many of which were shaped like animals.
3. the Mississippian culture
4. near St. Louis, Missouri; 200
5. about 100 years
6. Accept all reasonable responses. *Sample answer:* Their population declined greatly, so there weren't enough people to build mounds.
7. Some must have survived to become the ancestors of later Indian tribes.

Science Explorer • *Target Reading Skills Handbook*

🦉 Target Reading Skills

Identifying Main Ideas

Identifying the main idea helps you understand what you are reading. Sometimes the main idea can be easy to find. For example, suppose that you are reading just one paragraph. Very often you will find the main idea in the first sentence, the topic sentence. The other sentences in the paragraph provide supporting details or support the ideas in the topic sentence.

Sometimes, however, the first sentence is not the topic sentence. Sometimes you may have to look further. In those cases, it might help to read the paragraph and summarize what you have read. Your summary can give you the main idea.

A textbook has many paragraphs, each one with its own main idea. However, just as a paragraph has a main idea and supporting details, so does the text under each heading in your textbook. Sometimes the main idea is the heading itself. Other times it is more difficult to find. You may have to infer a main idea by combining information from several paragraphs.

To practice this skill, you can use a graphic organizer that looks like this one.

Main Idea		
Detail	Detail	Detail
a.	b.	c.

Outlining

Outlining shows you how supporting details relate to main ideas. You can make an outline as you read. Using this skill can make you a more careful reader.

Your outline can be made up of sentences, simple phrases, or single words. What matters is that you follow a formal structure. To outline while you read, use a plan like this one.

I. Section Title
  A. Main Heading
    1. Subheading
      a. Detail
      b. Detail
      c. Detail

The main ideas or topics are labeled as Roman numerals. The supporting details or subtopics are labeled A, B, C, and so on. Other levels of supporting information can be added under heads. When you outline in this way, you are deciding just how important a piece of information is.

Science Explorer • *Target Reading Skills Handbook*

Comparing and Contrasting

You can use comparing and contrasting to better understand similarities and differences between two or more concepts. Look for clue words as you read. When concepts or topics are similar, you will probably see words such as *also, just as, like, likewise,* or *in the same way.* When concepts or topics are different, you will see *but, however, although, whereas, on the other hand,* or *unlike.*

To use this skill, it sometimes helps to make a Venn diagram. In this type of graphic organizer, the similarities are in the middle, where the two circles overlap.

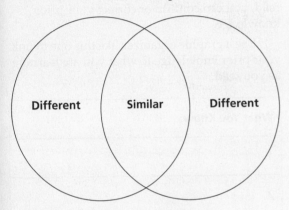

Relating Cause and Effect

Identifying causes and effects can help you understand the relationships among events. A cause is what makes something happen. An effect is what happens. In science, many actions cause other actions to occur.

Sometimes you have to look hard to see a cause-and-effect relationship in reading. You can watch for clue words to help you identify causes and effects. Look for *because, so, since, therefore, results, cause,* or *lead to.*

Sometimes a cause-and-effect relationship occurs in a chain. For example, an effect can have more than one cause, or a cause can have several effects. Seeing and understanding the relationships helps you understand science processes. You can use a graphic organizer like this one.

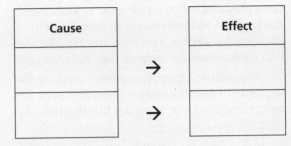

Asking Questions

Your textbook is organized using headings and subheadings. You can read the material under those headings by turning each heading into a question. For example, you might change the heading "Protecting Yourself During an Earthquake" to "How can you protect yourself during an earthquake?" Asking questions in this way will help you look for answers while reading. You can use a graphic organizer like this one to ask questions.

Question	Answer

Science Explorer ▪ *Target Reading Skills Handbook*

Sequencing

Sequencing is the order in which a series of events occurs. As you read, look for clue words that tell you the sequence or the order in which things happen. You see words such as *first, next, then,* or *finally.* When a process is being described, watch for numbered steps. Sometimes there are clues provided for you. Using the sequencing reading skill will help you understand and visualize the steps in a process. You can also use it to list events in the order of their occurrence.

You can use a graphic organizer to show the sequence of events or steps. The one most commonly used is a flowchart like this one.

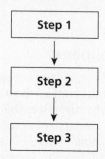

Sometimes, though, a cycle diagram works better.

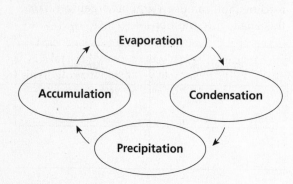

Using Prior Knowledge

Use prior knowledge to relate what you are reading to something that you already know. It is easier to learn when you can link new ideas to something that is already familiar to you. For example, if you know that fish are actually breathing oxygen that is dissolved in water, you wil be able to understand how or why gills work.

Using prior knowledge can help you make logical assumptions or draw conclusions about what you are reading. But be careful. Your prior knowledge might sometimes be wrong. As you read, you can confirm or correct your prior knowledge.

Use a graphic organizer like this one to link your prior knowledge to what you are learning as you read.

What You Know
1.
2.
3.

What You Learned
1.
2.
3.

Science Explorer ▪ *Target Reading Skills Handbook*

Previewing Visuals

Looking at visuals before you read can help you better understand a topic. Preview the visuals by reading labels and captions. For example, if you preview the visuals in a chapter about volcanoes, you will see more than just photographs of erupting volcanoes. You will see maps, diagrams, and photographs of rocks. These might tell you that you will learn where volcanoes are found, how they form, and what sort of rock is created when volcanoes erupt. Previewing visuals helps you understand and enjoy what you read.

One way to apply this strategy is to choose a few photographs, diagrams, or other visuals to preview. Then write questions about what you see. Answer the questions as you read.

Identifying Supporting Evidence

In science, you will read about hypotheses. A hypothesis is a possible explanation for scientific observations made by scientists or an answer to a scientific question. A hypothesis is tested over and over again. The tests may produce evidence that supports the hypothesis. When enough supporting evidence is collected, a hypothesis may become a theory.

Identifying supporting evidence in your reading can help you understand a hypothesis or theory. Evidence is made up of facts. Facts are information that can be confirmed by testing or observation.

When you are identifying supporting evidence, a graphic organizer like this one can be helpful.

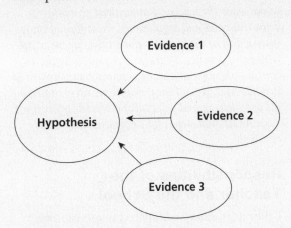

Building Vocabulary

To understand what someone is saying, you have to know the language that person is speaking. To understanding science, you need to know what the words mean.

There are many ways to build your vocabulary. You can look up the meaning of a new word in a dictionary or glossary. Then you can write its definitin in your own words. You can use the new word in a sentence. To figure out the meaning of a new word, you can use context clues or surrounding words. Look for prefixes and suffixes in the new word to help you break it down. Building vocabulary will get easier with practice.

Guidelines for Laboratory Safety

This section on laboratory safety is included as a resource for the teacher. Rather than providing definitive rules and regulations, the information is intended to be the basis for the establishment of safe laboratory practice. Pearson Prentice Hall and its consultants make no claims as to the completeness of this material. Not all the precautions necessitated by the use, storage, and disposal of materials are covered here. Additional steps and safeguards may be required.

Responsibilities of the Teacher and the School

Laboratory safety is a shared responsibility. Both the school and the teacher need to be sure that all educational activities protect and promote the health and safety of students and the environment. To accomplish this goal, teachers need to understand the hazards, precautions, and emergency procedures associated with laboratory activities. When schools or teachers fail to live up to this responsibility, their behavior may be considered negligent. As a result, they may be liable for resulting injuries.

The best way to avoid being considered negligent is to ask yourself four simple questions:

1. What are the hazards?
2. What are the worst things that could happen?
3. What do I need to do if they do happen?
4. What are the prudent practices, protective facilities, and protective equipment needed to minimize the risk?

Be sure that you can answer all four of these questions before starting any science activity or demonstration. Then you can reduce the risks to an acceptable level—a level where the educational benefits of the activity outweigh the risks.

General Safety Strategies

Teachers should promote a "safety first" philosophy through personal example and by the careful planning and implementation of safety strategies.

The following strategies will help create an enjoyable, instructional, and safe environment.

1. Set up a safety committee made up of both teachers and administrators. Arrange to meet regularly to set safety policies for the school, discuss any safety problems that might arise, and organize periodic inspections of classrooms and laboratory equipment.
2. Establish a safety and health reference shelf in a resource center.
3. Develop detailed plans explaining what to do in case of emergency, including spills, cuts, burns, electric shock, poisoning, and fire. Review the procedures periodically throughout the school year.
4. Inform students of these emergency plans and carry out unannounced drills.
5. Explain to students how to use the intercom or other available means of communication to get help during an emergency.
6. Keep up to date in first aid and CPR (cardiopulmonary resuscitation) training.
7. Post emergency phone numbers for ambulance, fire, police, hospital, and the poison control center next to the telephone.
8. Perform laboratory investigations before assigning them to students. Take note of any potential hazards; devise plans for dealing with any possible mishaps or emergencies.
9. Emphasize safety considerations in pre-lab discussions. Display posters dealing with safety issues in the classroom as reminders.
10. Keep classroom aisles and exits free of obstructions.

11. During an investigation, move about the classroom to keep a constant watch for potentially dangerous situations.

12. Curtail inappropriate behavior immediately. Wild play and practical jokes are forbidden during labs. Once students realize that the practice of safety is a required part of the course, they will accept a serious approach to laboratory work.

13. Never leave students unattended while they are engaged in science activities.

14. Require proper clothing at all times. Insist that long hair, dangling jewelry, and loose clothing be restrained; do not allow students to wear open shoes.

15. Insist that students wear safety goggles when the lab requires it.

16. Encourage students to keep lab work space neat and clear of extraneous objects, such as books and jackets.

17. Make sure that investigations utilizing toxic, fuming, or flammable materials are performed under a fume hood.

18. Keep the fume hood clear of unnecessary chemicals and equipment. Have the fume hood checked periodically to ensure that it is operating safely and efficiently.

19. Demonstrate to students the proper handling of glass materials, such as beakers and graduated cylinders.

20. Only wastepaper should be discarded in wastepaper receptacles. Keep a separate container for broken glass.

21. Substitute plastic containers for glass ones whenever possible, including graduated cylinders and beakers.

22. Consider the use of dispensing containers for liquids. They help prevent spills, skin contact with chemicals, and waste.

23. Use hot plates in place of open flames whenever possible. Never use open flames or hot plates when flammables are present in the room.

24. Use only nonmercury thermometers in investigations that call for the measurement of temperature.

25. Do not permit students to insert glass tubing or thermometers into rubber stoppers. If necessary, do this task yourself. When inserting these items into rubber stoppers, use safety stoppers, which have holes with beveled edges and are easier to use. Use glycerin or water to lubricate the glass.

26. All electrical equipment used in the lab should have GFI (Ground Fault Interrupter) switches.

27. Do not leave equipment that is operating or plugged in unattended.

28. When working with live animals or plants, check ahead of time for students who may have allergies to the specimens.

29. Students should wear disposable nitrile, latex, or food-handling gloves when handling live animals or nonliving specimens.

30. Wearing safety equipment is required of all students.

31. Report in writing unsafe conditions to the department head, maintenance director, and principal.

32. Have clearly defined penalties for violations of safety rules. Have these penalties approved and supported by the principal.

33. Document safety training, rules violations, and penalties in your records.

34. Keep a record of injuries and incidents (close calls), no matter how minor they may seem. Discuss these events at a department meeting to avoid similar occurrences.

Laboratory Safety

Guidelines for Laboratory Safety *(continued)*

35. As a class, review the safety rules and symbols. Make sure students understand the safety rules.
36. Require students to sign the safety contract.
37. Conduct quarterly inspections of the classrooms and storage areas to maintain safe conditions.

Safety Equipment

Any classroom where laboratory investigations are performed should contain at least one each of the following pieces of safety equipment: (1) fire extinguisher, (2) fire blanket, (3) fire alarm, (4) phone or intercom to the office, (5) eyewash station, (6) safety shower, (7) safety hood, and (8) first-aid kit. If any of these basic pieces of safety equipment are not available, you may need to modify your laboratory program until the situation is remedied.

Make sure students know the location and proper use of all safety equipment. Where appropriate and practical, have students handle or operate the equipment so that they become familiar with it. Make sure all safety equipment is in good working order. All malfunctions should be promptly reported in writing to the proper school or district administrator.

Fire equipment At the beginning of the school year, you may wish to give each student the opportunity to actually operate a fire extinguisher, as the sound and action of a CO_2 fire extinguisher can be quite alarming to those who have never used one. You may also want to have students practice smothering imaginary flames on one another with the fire blanket.

Eyewash station The eyewash station should be used if chemicals are splashed onto the face or eyes. The exposed area should be left in the running water for five to ten minutes.

Safety shower The shower is used when chemicals have been spilled on a student's body or clothing. The student should stand under the shower until the chemical is completely diluted. Have a bathrobe or some type of replacement clothing handy in case the student's clothing is so badly contaminated that it must be removed.

You may want to set up one or two spill kits in your laboratory. The contents of a spill kit are used to neutralize chemicals, such as acids and bases, so that they can be cleaned up more easily. Baking soda (sodium bicarbonate) can be used to neutralize acids. Vinegar (acetic acid) can be used to neutralize bases. Commercial spill kits for acids, bases, and a number of other chemicals are available from supply houses.

Safety hood Use a safety hood whenever students are working with volatile or noxious chemicals. Make sure that the room is well ventilated when students are using any kind of chemicals or are working with preserved specimens. Warn students of the flammability and toxicity of various chemicals.

First-aid kit A typical first-aid kit contains an assortment of antiseptics, bandages, gauze pads, and scissors. Most also contain simple instructions for use. Be sure to read the instructions if you are not familiar with basic first-aid procedures. A first-aid kit should be taken on all field trips. For field trips, you may wish to add such items as a bee-sting kit, meat tenderizer, tweezers, and calamine lotion. Do not dispense medication (including aspirin).

Guidelines for the Use and Care of Animals

Animals are an essential part of a science curriculum. The judicious use of live or preserved animals can help students realize that the study of science is relevant, fascinating, and rewarding. It is important to be aware of and sensitive to ethical and practical concerns when studying animals. The purpose of this section is to discuss some realistic guidelines for using animals in the classroom.

1. Whenever possible, live animals should be observed in their natural habitats or in zoos, parks, and aquariums.

2. Check the state and federal codes regarding animal welfare that apply in your area. You may also wish to refer to guidelines published by the National Science Teachers Association, the National Association of Biology Teachers, and the International Science Fair. Make students aware of all safety rules and regulations regarding animals.

3. Before bringing a live animal into the classroom, determine whether a proper habitat can be maintained in the classroom. Such a habitat includes temperature, space, and type of food. Students should have a clear understanding of the appropriate care needed by the live animals brought into the classroom. Do not allow students to tap on animal enclosures or otherwise disturb the animals.

4. No wild vertebrate animals should be brought into the classroom. Purchase animals from a reputable dealer only.

5. Live animals should be nonpoisonous and healthy. Any mammals used in the classroom should be vaccinated against rabies unless the animals were purchased recently from a reliable scientific supply company. Quarantine any animal to make sure it is disease-free before bringing it into the classroom.

6. Make sure that the living quarters of classroom animals are clean, located away from stressful situations, appropriately spacious, and secure enough to confine the animal. You may wish to lock cages to prevent the accidental release of animals; the small padlocks used on luggage are good for this purpose.

7. Remove wastes from animal living quarters daily. Thoroughly clean animal living quarters periodically to ensure that they are odor and germ-free. Provide a daily supply of fresh water and any other needs specific to the particular animal.

8. Provide for the care of animals during weekends and school vacations. Inform the custodial staff of the presence of animals and warn them of any special requirements. For example, turning off the aquarium pump to save electricity or spraying the classroom for insects can be fatal to animals.

9. Students should be instructed how to handle each species brought into the classroom. Make students aware that they can receive painful wounds from the improper handling of some animals.

10. Animals should be handled only if necessary. If an animal is frightened or excited, pregnant, feeding, or with its young, special handling is required.

11. Students should thoroughly clean their hands after handling animals or the quarters containing animals.

12. Animals should be returned to their natural habitat after an observation period of not longer than 14 days. However, laboratory-bred animals or species that are not native to an area should not be released into the environment.

13. If an animal must be euthanized, do not allow students to watch. Contact the local humane society for advice.

© Pearson Education, Inc., publishing as Pearson Prentice Hall. All rights reserved.

Laboratory Safety

Guidelines for the Use and Care of Animals *(continued)*

14. Before performing any experiment involving live animals, check local and state regulations. In some states, certification is required before a teacher is permitted to experiment with animals.

15. No animal studies involving anesthetic drugs, pathogenic organisms, toxicological products, carcinogens, or radiation should be performed.

16. Any experiment requiring live animals should have a clearly defined objective relating to the teaching and learning of some scientific principle.

17. No experimental procedures that will cause pain, discomfort, or harm to animals should be done in the classroom or at home.

18. Surgical procedures should not be performed on live animals.

19. If fertilized bird eggs are opened, the embryo should be destroyed humanely two days before it would have hatched, at the latest.

20. When working with preserved animals, make sure that students maintain a serious and respectful attitude toward the specimens.

Handling Ethical Issues

There is much controversy regarding the use of animals in scientific research. This controversy extends to preserved animals in dissections as well as to live animals in experiments. Although the debate over what uses of animals are appropriate in a science classroom can be emotionally charged, it can also provide an opportunity for students to closely examine a current issue. You may wish to have students read current literature on the subject and contact groups and individuals with varying points of view.

Stress that it is important to make a rational, informed decision before taking a stand on any issue. Point out that it is vital to know and understand the arguments on all sides of an issue. Help students analyze the sources they find in terms of bias and the reliability and objectivity of the author(s). Help them to distinguish between fact and opinion. Encourage them to question what they read and hear. Challenge them to discover the hidden assumptions and implications of different points of view.

If dissections are a part of your curriculum and a student chooses to avoid dissections because of ethical concerns, respect that student's opinion. Point out, however, that no simulation or videotape can completely replace hands-on experience.

Guidelines for Safe Disposal of Laboratory Wastes

Every effort should be made to recover, recycle, and reuse materials used in the laboratory. When disposal is required, however, specific procedures should be followed to ensure that your school complies with local, state, and federal regulations.

1. Discard only dry paper into ordinary wastebaskets.

2. Discard broken glass into a separate container clearly marked "For Broken Glass Only."

3. Acidic or basic solutions need to be neutralized before disposal. Slowly add dilute sodium hydroxide to acids and dilute hydrochloric acid to bases until pH paper shows that they are no longer strongly acidic or basic. Then flush the solutions down the drain with a lot of water.

4. Before each investigation, instruct your students concerning where and how they are to dispose of chemicals that are used or produced during the investigation. Specific teacher notes addressing disposal are provided on each lab as appropriate.

5. Keep each excess or used chemical in a separate container; do not mix them. This allows for possible recycling or reuse. It also eliminates unexpected reactions or the need for expensive separation by a contractor if the wastes must be disposed of professionally.

6. Only nonflammable, neutral, nontoxic, nonreactive, and water-soluble chemicals should be flushed down the drain.

7. When growing bacterial cultures, use only disposable petri dishes. After streaking, the dishes should be sealed and not opened again by students. After the lab, students should return the unopened dishes to you and wash their hands with antibacterial soap.

8. For the safe disposal of bacterial cultures, autoclave the petri dishes and discard them without opening. If no autoclave is available, carefully open the dishes (never have a student do this), pour full-strength bleach into the dishes, and let them stand for a day. Then pour the bleach from the petri dishes down a drain and flush the drain with lots of water. Tape the petri dishes back together and place them in a sealed plastic bag. Wrap the plastic bag with a brown paper bag or newspaper and tape securely. Throw the sealed package in the trash. Thoroughly disinfect the work area with bleach.

9. To grow mold, use a new, sealable plastic bag that is two to three times larger than the material to be placed inside. Seal the bag and tape it shut. After the bag is sealed, students should not open it. To dispose of the bag and mold culture, make a small cut near an edge of the bag and cook the bag in a microwave oven on a high setting for at least one minute. Discard the bag according to local ordinance, usually in the trash.

Laboratory Safety

Science Safety Rules

To prepare yourself to work safely in the laboratory, read the following safety rules. Then read them a second time. Make sure you understand and follow each rule. Ask your teacher to explain any rules you do not understand.

Dress Code

1. To protect yourself from injuring your eyes, wear safety goggles whenever you work with chemicals, flames, glassware, or any substance that might get into your eyes. If you wear contact lenses, notify your teacher.

2. Wear an apron or a lab coat whenever you work with corrosive chemicals or substances that can stain.

3. Tie back long hair to keep it away from any chemicals, flames, or equipment.

4. Remove or tie back any article of clothing or jewelry that can hang down and touch chemicals, flames, or equipment. Roll up or secure long sleeves.

5. Never wear open shoes or sandals.

General Precautions

6. Read all directions for an experiment several times before beginning the activity. Carefully follow all written and oral instructions. If you are in doubt about any part of the experiment, ask your teacher for assistance.

7. Never perform activities that are not assigned or authorized by your teacher. Obtain permission before "experimenting" on your own. Never handle any equipment unless you have specific permission.

8. Never perform lab activities without direct supervision.

9. Never eat or drink in the laboratory.

10. Keep work areas clean and tidy at all times. Bring only notebooks and lab manuals or written lab procedures to the work area. All other items, such as purses and backpacks, should be left in a designated area.

11. Do not engage in horseplay.

First Aid

12. Always report all accidents or injuries to your teacher, no matter how minor. Notify your teacher immediately about any fires.

13. Learn what to do in case of specific accidents, such as getting acid in your eyes or on your skin. (Rinse acids from your body with plenty of water.)

14. Be aware of the location of the first-aid kit, but do not use it unless instructed by your teacher. In case of injury, your teacher should administer first aid. Your teacher may also send you to the school nurse or call a physician.

15. Know the location of the emergency equipment such as the fire extinguisher and fire blanket.

16. Know the location of the nearest telephone and whom to contact in an emergency.

Heating and Fire Safety

17. Never use a heat source, such as a candle, burner, or hot plate, without wearing safety goggles.

18. Never heat anything unless instructed to do so. A chemical that is harmless when cool may be dangerous when heated.

19. Keep all combustible materials away from flames. Never use a flame or spark near a combustible chemical.

20. Never reach across a flame.

21. Before using a laboratory burner, make sure you know proper procedures for lighting and adjusting the burner, as demonstrated by your teacher. Do not touch the burner. It may be hot. Never leave a lighted burner unattended. Turn off the burner when it is not in use.

22. Chemicals can splash or boil out of a heated test tube. When heating a substance in a test tube, make sure that the mouth of the tube is not pointed at you or anyone else.

23. Never heat a liquid in a closed container. The expanding gases produced may shatter the container.

24. Before picking up a container that has been heated, first hold the back of your hand near it. If you can feel heat on the back of your hand, the container is too hot to handle. Use an oven mitt to pick up a container that has been heated.

Science Explorer • *Science Safety Rules*

Using Chemicals Safely

25. Never mix chemicals "for the fun of it." You might produce a dangerous, possibly explosive substance.

26. Never put your face near the mouth of a container that holds chemicals. Many chemicals are poisonous. Never touch, taste, or smell a chemical unless you are instructed by your teacher to do so.

27. Use only those chemicals needed in the activity. Read and double-check labels on supply bottles before removing any chemicals. Take only as much as you need. Keep all containers closed when chemicals are not being used.

28. Dispose of all chemicals as instructed by your teacher. To avoid contamination, never return chemicals to their original containers. Never pour untreated chemicals or other substances into the sink or trash containers.

29. Be extra careful when working with acids or bases. Pour all chemicals over the sink or a container, not over your work surface.

30. If you are instructed to test for odors, use a wafting motion to direct the odors to your nose. Do not inhale the fumes directly from the container.

31. When mixing an acid and water, always pour the water into the container first and then add the acid to the water. Never pour water into an acid.

32. Take extreme care not to spill any material in the laboratory. Wash chemical spills and splashes immediately with plenty of water. Immediately begin rinsing with water any acids that get on your skin or clothing, and notify your teacher of any acid spill at the same time.

Using Glassware Safely

33. Never force glass tubing or a thermometer into a rubber stopper or rubber tubing. Have your teacher insert the glass tubing or thermometer if required for an activity.

34. If you are using a laboratory burner, use a wire screen to protect glassware from any flame. Never heat glassware that is not thoroughly dry on the outside.

35. Keep in mind that hot glassware looks cool. Never pick up glassware without first checking to see if it is hot. Use an oven mitt. See rule 24.

36. Never use broken or chipped glassware. If glassware breaks, notify your teacher and dispose of the glassware in the proper broken-glassware container.

37. Never eat or drink from glassware.

38. Thoroughly clean glassware before putting it away.

Using Sharp Instruments

39. Handle scalpels or other sharp instruments with extreme care. Never cut material toward you; cut away from you.

40. Immediately notify your teacher if you cut your skin when working in the laboratory.

Animal and Plant Safety

41. Never perform experiments that cause pain, discomfort, or harm to animals. This rule applies at home as well as in the classroom.

42. Animals should be handled only if absolutely necessary. Your teacher will instruct you how to handle each animal species brought into the classroom.

43. If you know that you are allergic to certain plants, molds, or animals, tell your teacher before doing an activity in which these are used.

44. During field work, protect your skin by wearing long pants, long sleeves, socks, and closed shoes. Know how to recognize the poisonous plants and fungi in your area, as well as plants with thorns, and avoid contact with them. Never eat any part of a plant or fungus.

45. Wash your hands thoroughly after handling animals or a cage containing animals. Wash your hands when you are finished with any activity involving animal parts, plants, or soil.

End-of-Experiment Rules

46. After an experiment has been completed, turn off all burners or hot plates. If you used a gas burner, check that the gas-line valve to the burner is off. Unplug hot plates.

47. Turn off and unplug any other electrical equipment that you used.

48. Clean up your work area and return all equipment to its proper place.

49. Dispose of waste materials as instructed by your teacher.

50. Wash your hands after every experiment.

Laboratory Safety

Science Explorer · *Science Safety Symbols*

Safety Symbols

These symbols appear in laboratory activities. They warn of possible dangers in the laboratory and remind you to work carefully.

Safety Goggles Wear safety goggles to protect your eyes in any activity involving chemicals, flames or heating, or glassware.

Lab Apron Wear a laboratory apron to protect your skin and clothing from damage.

Breakage Handle breakable materials, such as glassware, with care. Do not touch broken glassware.

Heat-Resistant Gloves Use an oven mitt or other hand protection when handling hot materials such as hot plates or hot glassware.

Plastic Gloves Wear disposable plastic gloves when working with harmful chemicals and organisms. Keep your hands away from your face, and dispose of the gloves according to your teacher's instructions.

Heating Use a clamp or tongs to pick up hot glassware. Do not touch hot objects with your bare hands.

Flames Before you work with flames, tie back loose hair and clothing. Follow instructions from your teacher about lighting and extinguishing flames.

No Flames When using flammable materials, make sure there are no flames, sparks, or other exposed heat sources present.

Corrosive Chemical Avoid getting acid or other corrosive chemicals on your skin or clothing or in your eyes. Do not inhale the vapors. Wash your hands after the activity.

Poison Do not let any poisonous chemical come into contact with your skin, and do not inhale its vapors. Wash your hands when you are finished with the activity.

Fumes Work in a ventilated area when harmful vapors may be involved. Avoid inhaling vapors directly. Only test an odor when directed to do so by your teacher, and use a wafting motion to direct the vapor toward your nose.

Sharp Object Scissors, scalpels, knives, needles, pins, and tacks can cut your skin. Always direct a sharp edge or point away from yourself and others.

Animal Safety Treat live or preserved animals or animal parts with care to avoid harming the animals or yourself. Wash your hands when you are finished with the activity.

Plant Safety Handle plants only as directed by your teacher. If you are allergic to certain plants, tell your teacher; do not do an activity involving those plants. Avoid touching harmful plants such as poison ivy. Wash your hands when you are finished with the activity.

Electric Shock To avoid electric shock, never use electrical equipment around water, or when the equipment is wet or your hands are wet. Be sure cords are untangled and cannot trip anyone. Unplug equipment not in use.

Physical Safety When an experiment involves physical activity, avoid injuring yourself or others. Alert your teacher if there is any reason you should not participate.

Disposal Dispose of chemicals and other laboratory materials safely. Follow the instructions from your teacher.

Hand Washing Wash your hands thoroughly when finished with the activity. Use antibacterial soap and warm water. Rinse well.

General Safety Awareness When this symbol appears, follow the instructions provided. When you are asked to develop your own procedure in a lab, have your teacher approve your plan before you go further.

Name _____ Date _____ Class _____

Science Explorer · *Laboratory Safety*

Laboratory Safety Contract

I, _____ ,

(please print full name)

have read the Science Safety Rules and Safety Symbols
sections, understand their contents completely, and agree to
demonstrate compliance with all safety rules and guidelines
that have been established in each of the following categories:

(please check)

❑ Dress Code

❑ General Precautions

❑ First Aid

❑ Heating and Fire Safety

❑ Using Chemicals Safely

❑ Using Glassware Safely

❑ Using Sharp Instruments

❑ Animal and Plant Safety

❑ End-of-Experiment Rules

_____

(signature)

Date _____

Earth's Waters • *Book Test*

Earth's Waters

Multiple Choice

Write the letter of the correct answer on the line at the left.

_____ 1. The tiny algae and animals that float on the ocean's surface are called
   a. sewage.
   b. plankton.
   c. nekton.
   d. benthos.

_____ 2. The process of supplying water to areas of land to make them suitable for growing crops is called
   a. irrigation.
   b. erosion.
   c. condensation.
   d. upwelling.

_____ 3. Icebergs are dangerous to ships because
   a. over 90 percent of an iceberg lies below the surface.
   b. more snow falls on an iceberg than melts.
   c. most icebergs are less than 90 percent ice.
   d. most present-day glaciers are valley glaciers.

_____ 4. What causes ocean currents to curve to the right in the Northern Hemisphere?
   a. El Niño
   b. seafloor spreading
   c. Coriolis effect
   d. surface tension

_____ 5. All of the following could result in a water shortage EXCEPT
   a. when the demand for water is greater than the supply.
   b. when the supply of water falls below the demand.
   c. when a drought affects the supply of groundwater.
   d. when demand for water is less than the supply.

_____ 6. Fertilizers and pesticides are examples of which source of water pollution?
   a. agricultural wastes
   b. industrial wastes
   c. road runoff
   d. human wastes

_____ 7. An estuary is
   a. a crescent-shaped body of water near a river.
   b. an underground layer of sediment that holds water.
   c. a coastal area where fresh water mixes with ocean water.
   d. a ring-shaped reef surrounding a shallow lagoon.

____ 8. The total amount of dissolved salts in water is called
   a. concentration.
   b. density.
   c. salinity.
   d. water vapor.

____ 9. Water is the only substance on Earth that commonly exists in all of its different
   a. solutions.
   b. states.
   c. molecules.
   d. sediments.

____ 10. A watershed is
   a. a ridge of land that separates river systems.
   b. the land area that supplies water to a river system.
   c. an area where fresh water mixes with ocean water.
   d. the layer of rocks and soil above the water table.

Matching

Match each term with its correct definition. Write the letter of the correct answer on the line.

____ 11. conservation

____ 12. evaporation

____ 13. transpiration

____ 14. concentration

____ 15. aquaculture

a. the process by which water is given off through the leaves of plants

b. The Farming of Saltwater and Freshwater organisms.

c. the wise use of a resource so that it will not be used up

d. The process by which molecules at the surface of a liquid absorb enough energy to change to the gaseous state.

e. the amount of one substance in a certain volume of another substance

True or False

If the statement is true, write true. *If it is false, change the underlined word or words to make the statement true.*

_____ 16. Most waves form when <u>salts</u> transmit their energy to water.

_____ 17. Overfishing causes the supply of fish in a fishery to <u>decrease</u>.

_____ 18. The undersea mountains of the mid-ocean ridge have been formed by the interactions of Earth's <u>plates</u>.

_____ 19. Most of Earth's water is <u>fresh</u> water.

_____ 20. Near shore, wave height <u>decreases</u> as wavelength decreases.

Earth's Waters · *Book Test*

Using Science Skills: Interpreting Diagrams

Use the figure below to answer the questions that follow. Write your answers in the spaces provided.

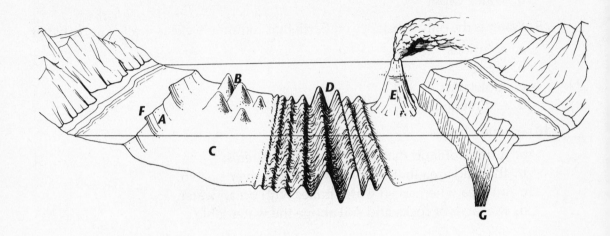

21. Identify the features of the ocean floor at points A through G.

_____

_____

_____

22. Describe the process by which the feature at point D is formed.

_____

_____

_____

_____

Essay

On a separate sheet of paper, write an answer for each of the following.

23. What are tides, and what causes them?

24. What is the purpose of wastewater treatment? Describe at least three steps in a typical wastewater treatment process.

25. How does salinity, temperature, and pressure change as you descend through the water column?

Earth's Waters · *Book Test*

Using Science Skills

Use the figure below to answer the following questions. Write your answers on a separate sheet of paper.

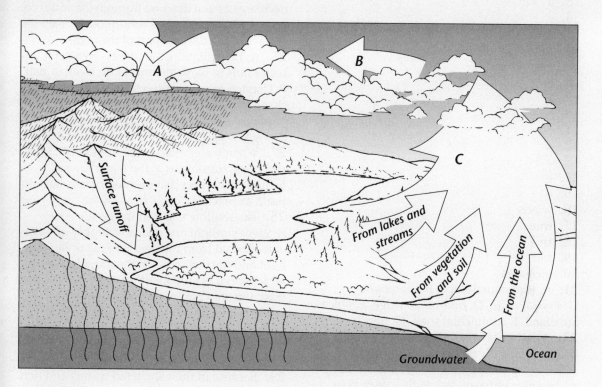

26. **Classifying** Identify and define the three processes shown in the figure at points A, B, and C. Then write a title for the figure that identifies the continuous process shown.

27. **Applying Concepts** How does this continuous process renew the usable supply of fresh water on Earth?

Essay

Write an answer for each of the following on a separate sheet of paper.

28. Explain why the neritic zone supports more life than the open-ocean zone.

29. How do wetlands play an important role in the environment?

30. How does the structure of water molecules affect its ability to dissolve other substances?

Book Test

1. b
2. a
3. a
4. c
5. d
6. a
7. c
8. c
9. b
10. b
11. c
12. d
13. a
14. e
15. b
16. winds
17. true
18. true
19. salt
20. increases
21. **A.** continental slope, **B.** seamount, **C.** abyssal plain, **D.** mid-ocean ridge, **E.** volcanic island, **F.** continental shelf, **G.** trench
22. A mid-ocean ridge is formed along the boundaries of diverging plates as magma squeezes up through the cracks and hardens, adding new strips of rock to the ocean floor.
23. Tides are the daily rise and fall of Earth's waters on its coastlines. They are caused by the interactions of Earth, the moon, and the sun.
24. The purpose of wastewater treatment is to make water safe to return to the environment. A typical wastewater treatment process includes primary treatment, which involves settling; secondary treatment, which involves filtering the water through gravel covered with bacteria; and additional treatment, which may involve the adding of chemicals, additional filtering, and purifying in open pools.
25. Salinity varies near the surface but below the surface zone remains fairly constant. Temperature varies near the surface depending on the weather. Below the surface, the temperature decreases as you descend through the water column. Pressure increases continuously from the surface to the deepest part of the ocean.
26. **A.** Precipitation, the process by which water falls to Earth as rain, snow, sleet, or hail **B.** Condensation, the process by which a gas changes to a liquid **C.** Evaporation, the process by which molecules at the surface of a liquid absorb enough energy to change to a gaseous state
27. When water evaporates from Earth, salts and other substances in the water are left behind. The water that eventually falls back to Earth as precipitation is fresh water.
28. The shallow water in the neritic zone receives sunlight and a steady supply of nutrients washed from the land into the ocean. The light and nutrients enable the growth of algae, which serve as food for other organisms. In contrast, the only part of the open ocean that receives enough sunlight to support algae growth is the surface zone. Most of the rest of the open ocean does not have the light and nutrients to support many organisms.
29. Because of their sheltered waters and rich supply of nutrients, wetlands provide habitats for many living things. Wetlands also provide natural water filtration of waste materials and help control floods by absorbing extra runoff from heavy rains.
30. In a water molecule, the oxygen end has a slight negative charge and the hydrogen ends have a slight positive charge. Thus, water consists of polar molecules. One reason that water is able to dissolve many substances is that it is a polar substance. The charged ends of the water molecule attract the molecules of other polar substances, such as sugar and salt.

Earth: The Water Planet

Lab zone Chapter **Project** Every Drop Counts

The following steps will walk you through the Chapter Project. Use the hints and detailed directions as you guide your students through the gathering of information, presentation, and reflection.

Chapter Project Overview

As you introduce the project, ask students to brainstorm a list of uses of water in and around the house. Write their suggestions on the board and ask them to copy the list. Tell students that they will be investigating how much water is used in their homes during the project.

In introducing the project, do the following demonstration.

1. Ask students to estimate how many liters each person uses each day in the United States.
2. After students have made their estimates, tell them that residential water use averages about 300 liters per person per day.
3. Have students illustrate that figure with 2-liter soda bottles. For example, 15 bottles represents one-tenth of the average daily use.

Distribute the Chapter Project Overview. Review the project's rules. You may also wish to hand out the Chapter Project Scoring Rubric, which you will use for assessing students' work.

Divide students into small groups. Make sure they understand that each student will individually collect data for water use at home, both personal data and data for their households. Groups will collaborate in collecting data about another building in their community and in making a class presentation.

Set a deadline for the project presentation and some interim dates for the Check Your Progress at the end of Sections 1 and 3.

Point out that each student will make a table of the data they collect about water use in the home. At the end of the first week, each student must calculate a total water use. Students who get water from wells or do not have access to their water meters will have to rely on their estimates.

Demonstrate for students how to make their own estimates of how much water is typically used during a certain task, such as washing hands.

1. In discussion with students, come to some reasonable conclusion about how long it takes to wash hands, such as 1 minute.
2. Open a faucet for 30 seconds, collecting the water in a bucket.
3. Measure the amount of water in the bucket by pouring the liquid into a graduated cylinder repeatedly.
4. Multiply the measurement by 2 to find the amount of water that would be used in a 1-minute washing.

For students who plan to use water-meter readings to complete their projects, distribute the Chapter Project Worksheet 1. After students have read the worksheet and completed the examples, find out if they have any questions. If possible, provide other practice examples.

Some students will need to read a straight-line water meter rather than a round-dial meter. Straight-line meters are very similar to the odometer of a car. Advise students to read the number on the meter from left to right to get the correct daily figure. Remind them to note the unit the figure indicates, usually either cubic feet or gallons.

Distribute the Chapter Project Worksheet 2. Make sure students understand that they should record their daily meter readings on the worksheet.

Review with students how to make conversions to liters from other units, including cubic feet and gallons: 1 gallon = 3.8 liters; 1 cubic foot = 28.5 liters. Emphasize that they will have to convert all readings to liters. Provide some conversion examples for them to work.

Anticipate that some groups may have trouble finding the water use for the community building they choose to study. You might check on a few locations in advance to hold in reserve if student efforts fail. Try to find a wide range of buildings to compare, such as office buildings, hospitals, factories, and various retail buildings.

Keep Students on Track— Section 1

As you review students' data tables, make sure that each student has kept a daily record of water use and has several types of uses on the table.

Help students who have trouble making the calculations necessary to find daily water use. Guide them through the process of adding the figures for each use, adding all the figures together, and dividing by the number of days in the survey.

Help students with any problems in reading the water meters at home. In some cases, students may take the figures correctly but fail to make the subtractions necessary to determine daily use. Also provide support for students in calculating household water use based on estimates instead of meter readings.

Meet with each group to discuss a plan for contacting people at another building in their community. Encourage students who have not made a decision about this task to make a choice quickly. Guide some groups to buildings where you know they will gain cooperation. Advise group members to work together in contacting and visiting buildings.

Keep Students on Track— Section 3

Review with each group a plan for determining water use in a community building. For those students who have not been able to make a contact, provide information about a building you have already contacted.

If possible, make sure no building is being audited by more than one group. Try to have groups audit different types of buildings.

Review with students the kind of data they need to gather, using the list on the Chapter Project Overview as a reference.

Advise students to organize their questions before making contact with someone at a building. In class, have some students role-play the situation. Then discuss how they should introduce themselves and what questions they should ask.

Work with students on how to graph the household-use data they have in their data tables. Demonstrate how to make circle and bar graphs on the board. Bar graphs can be set up to show days or types of use on the x-axis and total use on the y-axis.

Chapter 1 Project Wrap Up

As you review students' data tables, graphs, and other materials, you may wish to have each group "talk you through" the presentation. Make suggestions for organizing the materials for a coherent and logical report.

Provide class time for group presentations. Allow each group to present the findings, and then encourage class members to ask questions.

After all the presentations have been made, discuss with students what conclusions they can draw from all the data they have gathered. Focus on household tasks that use the most water, businesses or industries that have particularly high water use, and methods of conservation.

Encourage students to evaluate how well they accomplished what they set out to do and to make suggestions that they think would have made the project better.

Extension

Students might want to compare the data they collect during this period with water use at another time of year. For example, residential water use may increase during summer months.

Earth: The Water Planet · *Chapter Project*   **Overview**

Lab zone **Chapter Project** **Every Drop Counts**

How important is water to your life? In this project, you have a chance to examine how much water you and others use in a week. You'll probably be surprised!

First, you will determine how much water you personally use at home during one week. Second, you will find out how much water your household uses during that same week. Then, you will work with other students to find out how much water a building in your community—such as a business, hospital, or government building—uses in one week. At the end of the project, your group will present your data to the class.

Data Table of Personal Water Use

Water uses	Day 1	Day 2	Day 3	Day 4	Day 5	Day 6	Day 7
Brushing teeth	3	3	3				
Washing hands	5	6	5				
Flushing toilet	3	5	4				
Washing dishes	1	2	1				

Project Rules

- Keep a daily record of your personal water use in the form of a data table. The table above is a brief example. You will have to show this data table at the Check Your Progress at the end of Section 1.

- Take readings of your water meter to determine how much water your household uses on a daily basis. You will have to show evidence of this work at the Check Your Progress at the end of Section 1. If taking meter readings is not possible, you can estimate your total household use instead. You will need to keep daily records of estimated water use for all family members.

- With your group, choose a building in the community to study, and find someone connected with that building to provide you with water-use data for the building. You should choose the building you will study before the Check Your Progress at the end of Section 3.

- With your group, prepare a class presentation of the data you have collected. As part of this presentation, you will prepare a graph of your household water use with the data you collected from a water meter.

Earth: The Water Planet • *Chapter Project*   **Overview**

Hints for Determining Home Water Use

- For each water use, determine how much water is actually used.

- You may not have access to the water meter, especially if you live in an apartment. A building superintendent or manager might be able to help. You can also determine average daily use from a household water bill. Be sure to divide the total amount used by the correct number of days.

- You can follow these steps to determine how much water you and your family use.

  1. Make a list of your daily personal uses of water.
  2. Set up a data table on a separate sheet of paper.
  3. Determine how much water to assign to each type of use.
  4. Use your table to make daily records of your water use.
  5. Calculate the total amount of water you use in a week by multiplying the amount of water used for each kind of use by the number of times you used water for that purpose. Then add all the numbers together.
  6. If possible, take daily readings of the water meter in your home. Calculate the total amount used in a week based on your meter readings or on your estimates if you do not have access to a water meter.
  7. Make a graph that shows daily household water use.

Hints for Determining Water Use in Another Building in the Community

- Begin immediately to find a building in your community to study. Ask family members and friends for suggestions of buildings and people to contact.

- Your group should collect all of the following information.

  1. Name, location, and kind of building studied
  2. Name and job title of the person who helped you obtain the data
  3. All ways water is used in this building
  4. Amount of water used per month in the building

Project Timeline

Task	Due Date
1. Complete personal water-use inventory	_____
2. Calculate total household water use	_____
3. Obtain all information from building in community	_____
4. Complete graphs and presentation	_____

Earth: The Water Planet · *Chapter Project*   **Worksheet 1**

Reading Round-Dial Water Meters

Round-dial water meters have several small, round dials, as shown in Figure 1 below. Notice that beside each small dial is a number that is a multiple of 10. In reading a round-dial meter, begin with the dial that has the highest number beside it. In most cases, that number is 100,000. On each dial, a pointer points to a number, which is the reading for that dial. If the pointer is between two numbers, the reading is the *smaller* number. Also note the units in which the water is measured. Now follow the steps below to learn how to read the meter in Figure 1.

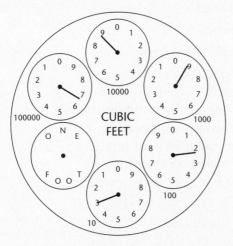

Figure 1   **Figure 2**

1. Read the 100,000 dial. Multiply that number by 10,000. Write the product on a sheet of paper. *For Figure 1, you would write 60,000.*

2. Read the 10,000 dial. Multiply that number by 1,000 and write the product below the first number. *For Figure 1, you would write 8,000.*

3. Read the 1,000 dial. Multiply that number by 100 and write the product below the second number. *For Figure 1, you would write 900.*

4. Read the 100 dial. Multiply that number by 10 and write the product below the third number. *For Figure 1, you would write 20.*

5. Read the 10 dial. Write that number down last. Then add all the numbers together to get the reading. *For Figure 1, you would write 3 and then add all the numbers together.* Write the final reading in the blank.

_____ cubic feet

6. Now follow the steps again to read the meter in Figure 2. Write the final reading in the blank. _____ cubic feet

Determining Household Water Use

To determine household water use, take a meter reading at the beginning of each day, as well as a final meter reading at the end of the week. Each morning, do your calculations on a separate sheet of paper, and then record the results here. Remember to convert your readings from the units on the meter to liters.

Meter Reading	Water Used
Day 1 _____	
Day 2 _____	Difference = _____
Day 3 _____	Difference = _____
Day 4 _____	Difference = _____
Day 5 _____	Difference = _____
Day 6 _____	Difference = _____
Day 7 _____	Difference = _____
Day 8 _____	Difference = _____
	Total Use = _____

Making Conversions

The measurement unit that you will use in this project is liters. Yet you will likely discover that water meters and amounts supplied by building managers will be in cubic feet or gallons. This means you will have to convert those numbers to liters. The following conversion factors will help you do this.

   1 gallon = 3.8 liters

   1 cubic foot = 28.5 liters

For practice, convert the readings you determined for the round-dial meters on Worksheet 1. Since those dials record water use in cubic feet, you need to divide the final figures by 28.5 to convert the readings into liters. Do your calculations on a separate sheet of paper and then write the answers in the blanks.

Figure 1: _____ liters

Figure 2: _____ liters

Earth: The Water Planet • *Chapter Project* **Scoring Rubric**

Lab zone Chapter Project Every Drop Counts

In evaluating how well you complete the Chapter Project, your teacher will judge your work in four categories. In each, a score of 4 is the best rating.

	4	3	2	1
Collecting Data in the Home	Collects data for at least 12 different types of household uses of water and accurately computes household use from daily water-meter readings.	Collects data for at least 9 household uses of water and computes household use from daily water-meter readings.	Collects data for at least 6 household uses of water and computes household use from at least 4 water-meter readings.	Collects data for 4 or fewer household uses of water and makes little or no attempt to compute household use from water-meter readings.
Collecting Data from Another Building in the Community	Collects all necessary data to compute the building's water use.	Collects most necessary data about the building's water use.	Collects only partial data about the building's water use.	Collects little or no data about the building's water use.
Presenting the Results	Makes a thorough and interesting presentation with a well-constructed graph of home water use and complete data about water use in a community building.	Makes an interesting presentation with a well-constructed graph and mostly complete data about water use in a community building.	Makes an adequate presentation with a well-completed graph and some data about water use in a community building.	Makes a poor presentation with an incomplete graph and little or no data about water use in a community building.
Working Cooperatively	Takes a lead in group planning and in the collection of data.	Participates in all aspects of group planning and in the collection of data.	Participates in most group planning and collection of data.	Participates minimally in group planning and collection of data.

The Properties of Water

1–2 periods, 1/2–1 blocks

Ability Levels Key
L1 Basic to Average
L2 For All Students
L3 Average to Advanced

Objectives

H.1.1.1 Describe how the chemical structure of water molecules causes them to stick together.

H.1.1.2 Describe some of water's unusual properties.

H.1.1.3 Identify the three states in which water exists on Earth.

Key Terms

- polar molecule • capillary action
- surface tension • solution • solvent
- specific heat • evaporation • condensation

Local Standards

PRETEACH

Build Background Knowledge

Show a glass of liquid water containing ice, and relate that to the states of water and why ice floats.

 **Discover Activity** *What Are Some Properties of Water?* L1

Targeted Resources

❏ **All in One Teaching Resources**
   L2   Reading Strategy: Building Vocabulary
❏ ⊙ **Presentation-Pro CD-ROM**

INSTRUCT

The Structure of Water Use an illustration to analyze how the charges on water molecules attract one another to stick together.

Key Properties of Water Relate the polarity of water to why water dissolves other substances.

Changing State Use labeled diagrams to identify and explain the differences in the three states of water.

Targeted Resources

❏ **All in One Teaching Resources**
   L2   Guided Reading, pp. 47–50
   L2   Transparencies H1, H2, H3
❏ ▭ **www.SciLinks.org** Web Code: scn-0811
❏ ⊙ **Student Edition on Audio CD**

ASSESS

Section Assessment Questions

Have students use their definitions of key terms to answer the questions.

Reteach

Use illustrations to relate the structure of water to its properties and changes of state.

Targeted Resources

❏ **All in One Teaching Resources**
   Section Summary, p. 46
   L1   Review and Reinforce, p. 51
   L3   Enrich, p. 52

Earth: The Water Planet · *Section Summary*

The Properties of Water

Guide for Reading

■ How does the chemical structure of water molecules cause them to stick together?

■ What are some of water's unusual properties?

■ What are the three states in which water exists on Earth?

A water molecule is made up of two hydrogen atoms bonded to an oxygen atom. Each end of a water molecule has a slight electric charge. A molecule that has electrically charged areas is called a **polar molecule. The positive hydrogen ends of one water molecule attract the negative oxygen ends of nearby water molecules. As a result, the water molecules tend to stick together.**

Many of water's unusual properties occur because of the attraction among its polar molecules. **The properties of water include capillary action, surface tension, the ability to dissolve many substances, and high specific heat. Capillary action** is the combined force of attraction among water molecules and with the molecules of surrounding materials. **Surface tension** is the tightness across the surface of water that is caused by polar molecules pulling on each other.

A **solution** is a mixture that forms when one substance dissolves another. The substance that does the dissolving is called the **solvent.** Many substances dissolve in water because water is polar. The charged ends of the water molecule attract the molecules of other polar substances.

Specific heat is the amount of heat needed to increase the temperature of a certain amount of a substance. Compared to other substances, water requires a lot of heat to increase its temperature.

Water exists in three **states,** or forms: solid, liquid, and gas. **Ice is a solid, the familiar form of water is a liquid, and water vapor in the air is a gas.** Change of state is related to temperature, which is a measurement of the average speed of molecules. When the temperature reaches 0°C, the solid ice melts and becomes liquid water. At 100°C, liquid water boils and the molecules have enough energy to escape the liquid and become water vapor. Liquid water also becomes a gas through **evaporation,** which is the process by which molecules at the surface of a liquid absorb enough energy to change to the gaseous state.

The process by which a gas changes to a liquid is called **condensation**. As the temperature of the gas cools down to 100°C, the molecules slow down and begin to change back to the liquid state. When water cools below 4°C, the molecules line up in a crystal structure. Water molecules take up more space in this crystal structure than as a liquid. This means that ice is less dense than liquid water, and thus floats on liquid water.

Earth: The Water Planet ▪ *Guided Reading and Study*

The Properties of Water

This section describes the structure and properties of water. It also describes the way water changes state, or form.

Use Target Reading Skills

After reading the passages that contain key terms, use all the information you have learned to write a definition of each key term in your own words.

polar molecule:

_____

_____

capillary action:

_____

_____

surface tension:

_____

_____

solution:

_____

_____

solvent:

_____

_____

specific heat:

_____

_____

evaporation:

_____

_____

condensation:

_____

_____

Earth: The Water Planet · *Guided Reading and Study*

The Properties of Water *(continued)*

The Structure of Water

1. Circle the letter of each sentence that is true about water's structure.
   a. Water is made up of atoms bonded to form molecules.
   b. Water contains half as many hydrogen atoms as oxygen atoms.
   c. Water molecules tend to push away from each other.
   d. The chemical formula for water is H_2O.

Key Properties of Water

2. A molecule that has electrically charged areas is called a(n)
   _____ molecule.

3. Circle the letter of each sentence that is true about capillary action.
   a. It explains how water moves against the force of gravity.
   b. It is due to the attraction among molecules of water and surrounding materials.
   c. It prevents water from moving through materials with pores.
   d. It causes clothing to stay dry.

4. How does capillary action allow water to climb up the sides of a straw?

   _____

   _____

5. Circle the letter of each sentence that is true about water's surface tension.
   a. It helps some insects "skate" across the surface of the water.
   b. It refers to the tightness across the surface of the water.
   c. It is caused by polar molecules repelling each other.
   d. It causes raindrops to form round beads.

6. How does surface tension force the surface of water to curve?

   _____

   _____

7. A mixture that forms when one substance dissolves another is called
   a(n) _____. The substance that does the dissolving
   is called a(n) _____.

8. Why can water dissolve many substances?

   _____

   _____

   _____

   _____

Earth: The Water Planet • *Guided Reading and Study*

9. Circle the letter of each substance that dissolves in water.

   a. salt
   b. oil
   c. oxygen
   d. wax

10. The amount of heat needed to increase the temperature of a certain mass of a substance by 1°C is its _____.

11. Is the following sentence true or false? Compared with other substances, water requires a lot of heat to increase its temperature. _____

12. Circle the letter of each sentence that is true about water's specific heat.

   a. It is due to the many attractions among water molecules.
   b. It makes large bodies of water heat up more quickly than nearby land.
   c. It makes large bodies of water cool off more slowly than nearby land.
   d. It leads to warmer air over land than over water on summer days.

Changing State

13. List the three states of matter.

   a. _____   **b.** _____

   c. _____

14. Solid water is called _____.

15. Complete this compare/contrast table.

How Water Changes State

Type of Change	Starting State	Ending State
Melting	Solid	Liquid
Boiling	**a.**	**b.**
Evaporation	**c.**	**d.**
Condensation	**e.**	**f.**
Freezing	**g.**	**h.**

Earth: The Water Planet ▪ *Guided Reading and Study*

Match the state of water with the statement that is true about it.

State of Water	Statement
____ **16.** ice	**a.** It is invisible.
____ **17.** liquid water	**b.** It takes the shape of its container.
____ **18.** water vapor	**c.** It has a temperature less than 0°C.

19. Circle the letter of each sentence that is true about evaporation.

    a. It occurs as water molecules absorb energy.

    b. It occurs as water molecules slow down.

    c. It occurs at the surface of a liquid.

    d. An example of it is air drying your hair after swimming.

20. Circle the letter of each sentence that is true about condensation.

    a. It occurs as water molecules slow down.

    b. It occurs as the temperature of water molecules reaches the boiling point.

    c. It turns water from a visible state to an invisible state.

    d. An example of it is clouding up a cold window with your breath.

The Properties of Water

Understanding Main Ideas

Label the parts of this water molecule by writing the name of the element and the electrical charge in items 1 through 3.

Answer the following questions on a separate sheet of paper.

4. Why is water considered a polar substance?

5. Which state of water allows fish to remain in a lake when winter temperatures are below 0°C? Explain.

6. What happens to the molecules of water vapor when the temperature of the gas cools to 100°C?

7. Why is water often called the "universal solvent"?

1. Element _____
   Charge _____

2. Element _____
   Charge _____

3. Element _____
   Charge _____

Building Vocabulary

Match each term with its definition by writing the letter of the correct definition in the right column on the line beside the term in the left column.

_____ 8. capillary action

_____ 9. condensation

_____ 10. evaporation

_____ 11. specific heat

_____ 12. solution

_____ 13. solvent

_____ 14. state

_____ 15. surface tension

a. a mixture that forms when one substance dissolves another

b. form of a substance, including solid, liquid, or gas

c. the tightness across the surface of water caused by the polar molecules pulling on each other

d. the process by which molecules at the surface of a liquid absorb enough energy to change to the gaseous state

e. the combined force of attraction among water molecules and with the molecules of surrounding materials

f. the process by which a gas changes to a liquid

g. a substance that dissolves another substance

h. the amount of heat needed to increase the temperature of a certain amount of a substance by 1°C

Earth: The Water Planet • *Enrich*

The Ends Make the Difference

If you get grease on a piece of clothing, what do you do? You wash it in water with a detergent. The reason detergent helps clean the cloth has to do with the structure of detergent molecules and how they mix with water. As you can see in Figure 1, a detergent molecule has two very different ends. The rounded end has a positive charge. This charged end of the detergent molecule is attracted to the polar water molecules. The other end of the detergent molecule has no charge. Instead of being attracted to polar water molecules, the end without a charge is attracted to the nonpolar grease and dirt molecules.

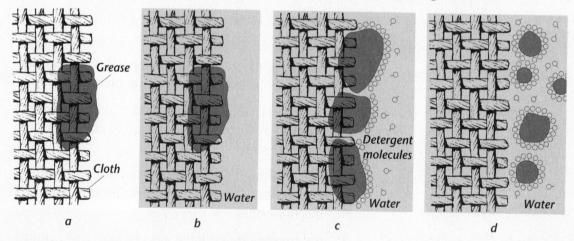

Charged end   Uncharged end

Figure 1

When you add detergent to the water in a washing machine, the nonpolar ends of detergent molecules dissolve into the grease on the cloth and break the grease apart into tiny droplets. The action of the washing machine helps dislodge the grease droplets from the cloth. The detergent molecules surround the grease droplets, with their polar ends sticking out from the droplet. These polar ends dissolve in water. When the water flows out of the washing machine, the grease droplets are carried along with it.

Figure 2

Answer the following questions on a separate sheet of paper.

1. Write a caption for each of the illustrations in Figure 2, using what you have learned about how a detergent works.

2. In your own words, describe how a greasy pair of pants gets clean by being washed in a washing machine.

Water on Earth

🕐 *2–3 periods, 1–1 1/2 blocks*

**Earth:
The Water Planet**

Objectives

H.1.2.1 State how people and other living things use water.

H.1.2.2 Describe how Earth's water is distributed.

H.1.2.3 Explain how Earth's water moves through the water cycle.

Key Terms

• photosynthesis • habitat • groundwater
• water cycle • transpiration • precipitation

Local Standards

PRETEACH

Build Background Knowledge
Elicit reasons that the human body needs water and elicit which other living things need water.

 **Discover Activity** *Where Does the Water Come From?* **L1**

Targeted Resources

❏ **All in One Teaching Resources**
   L2 Reading Strategy Transparency H4: Identifying Main Ideas

❏ ⊙ **Presentation-Pro CD-ROM**

INSTRUCT

All Living Things Need Water Use a questioning strategy to help students consider how living things use water.
Distribution of Earth's Water Use an illustration to identify where Earth's water is distributed and in what forms.
The Water Cycle Use a labeled diagram to sequence the flow of water through the water cycle.

 Skills Lab *Water From Trees* **L2**

Targeted Resources

❏ **All in One Teaching Resources**
   L2 Guided Reading, pp. 55–59
   L2 Transparency H5
   L2 Lab: *Water From Trees*, pp. 62–63

❏ 📼 **Lab Activity Video/DVD**
   Skills Lab: *Water From Trees*
❏ **PHschool.com** Web Code: cfp-4024
❏ ⊙ **Student Edition on Audio CD**

ASSESS

Section Assessment Questions
🔄 Have students use their graphic organizers with main ideas and details to answer the questions.

Reteach
Use the figures to summarize the distribution of Earth's water and the parts of the water cycle.

Targeted Resources

❏ **All in One Teaching Resources**
Section Summary, p. 54
   L1 Review and Reinforce, p. 60
   L3 Enrich, p. 61

Earth: The Water Planet • *Section Summary*

Water on Earth

Guide for Reading

- How do people and other living things use water?

- How is Earth's water distributed?

- How does Earth's water move through the water cycle?

Earth is unique among the planets in the solar system because its surface is nearly covered with liquid water. The water on Earth is essential to life. **All living things need water in order to carry out their body processes. In addition, many living things use water for shelter.** One of the body processes that needs water is **photosynthesis.** This is the process by which plants use water, carbon dioxide, and energy from the sun to make their food. Animals and other living things depend on food made by plants. Bodies of water also provide many organisms with **habitats,** or places to live and obtain what is necessary to survive.

Most of the Earth's water—roughly 97 percent—is found in salty oceans. Only 3 percent is fresh water. The huge expanses of ice near the North and South Poles account for about three quarters of that 3 percent. The oceans—actually, a single world ocean—cover nearly 71 percent of Earth's surface. The fresh water that is available for humans to use includes the water in lakes and rivers. But far more fresh water is located underground. **Groundwater** is water that fills the cracks and spaces in underground soil and rock layers.

Water on Earth is naturally recycled through the **water cycle. Water moves from bodies of water, land, and living things on Earth's surface to the atmosphere and back to Earth's surface.** The sun is the source of energy that drives the water cycle.

The water cycle has no beginning or end. It includes evaporation, condensation, and precipitation. Large amounts of water continually evaporate from oceans and lakes. More water vapor is given off through the leaves of plants in a process called **transpiration.**

As warm air carries water vapor upward, the air cools. Cold air holds less water vapor than warm air, so the water condenses into droplets, which clump around dust particles and form clouds. As the droplets grow bigger and heavier, they fall back to Earth as rain, snow, sleet, or hail, also called **precipitation.**

Most precipitation falls directly into the oceans. Some water that falls on land evaporates immediately. Some runs off the surface into rivers, lakes, or oceans, or trickles down into the ground. The total amount of water on Earth has remained fairly constant for millions of years. In the world as a whole, the rates of evaporation and precipitation are balanced.

Name _____ Date _____ Class_____

Water on Earth

This section explains how all living things need water. It also describes how water is distributed on Earth.

Use Target Reading Skills

As you read the Distribution of Earth's Water section, complete the graphic organizer. Write the main idea in the graphic organizer. Then write four supporting details that further explain the main idea.

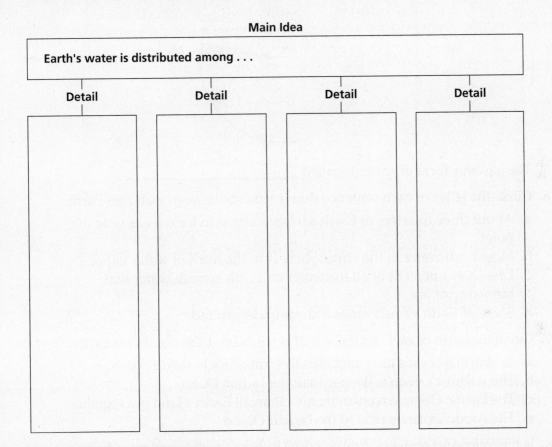

Main Idea

Earth's water is distributed among . . .

| Detail | Detail | Detail | Detail |

All Living Things Need Water

1. Is the following sentence true or false? Water makes up one third of the human body. _____

2. The place where an organism lives and that provides the things it needs to survive is its _____.

3. Is the following sentence true or false? Neither fresh water nor salt water provide habitats for many living things. _____

Earth: The Water Planet · *Guided Reading and Study*

Water on Earth *(continued)*

Distribution of Earth's Water

4. Label the circle graph to show the percentage of Earth's water that is salt water and the percentage that is fresh water.

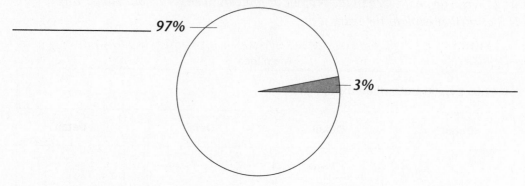

Distribution of Water on Earth

_____ 97%

3% _____

5. The gaseous form of water is called _____.

6. Circle the letter of each sentence that is true about fresh water on Earth.

   a. About three quarters of Earth's fresh water is in ice masses near the poles.

   b. Most fresh water in the atmosphere is in the form of water vapor.

   c. Less than 1 percent of all the water on Earth is fresh water that humans can use.

   d. Some of Earth's fresh water is deep underground.

7. Circle the letter of each sentence that is true about the oceans on Earth.

   a. All Earth's oceans are connected to form a single world ocean.

   b. The Atlantic Ocean is deeper than the Indian Ocean.

   c. The Pacific Ocean covers more area than all Earth's land put together.

   d. The Arctic Ocean is next to the Indian Ocean.

8. Is the following sentence true or false? Icebergs are formed from frozen salt water. _____

9. Water that fills the cracks and spaces in underground soil and rock layers is called _____.

Earth: The Water Planet · *Guided Reading and Study*

The Water Cycle

10. Circle the letter of each sentence that is true about the water cycle.
    a. It naturally recycles water.
    b. It is powered by energy from the sun.
    c. It is a continuous process.
    d. It does not involve living things.

11. Is the following sentence true or false? All the water on Earth has been through the water cycle. _____

12. Is the following sentence true or false? The water cycle has a beginning and an end. _____

13. How do plants take in water?

    _____

    _____

14. Add arrows to the diagram to show how water moves through the water cycle.

The Water Cycle

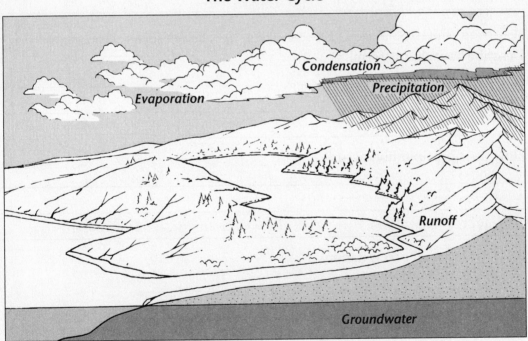

Condensation

Precipitation

Evaporation

Runoff

Groundwater

Earth: The Water Planet • *Guided Reading and Study*

Water on Earth *(continued)*

15. Why isn't water vapor that comes from the ocean salty?

_____

_____

16. Complete the table.

Processes in the Water Cycle

Process	Role in the Water Cycle
Evaporation	Produces water vapor from bodies of water
	Produces water vapor from plants
	Forms clouds from water vapor

17. Why does water vapor condense when it travels far above Earth?

_____

_____

_____

18. Describe how clouds form.

_____

_____

_____

19. How does precipitation occur?

_____

_____

_____

20. List four forms of precipitation.

a._____   b._____

c._____   d._____

Earth: The Water Planet ▪ *Guided Reading and Study*

21. Is the following sentence true or false? Little precipitation actually falls directly into the oceans. _____

22. Circle the letter of each sentence that is true about Earth's water supply.

    a. Precipitation is the source of all fresh water on Earth.

    b. The water cycle uses up Earth's fresh water supply.

    c. Earth's total water supply has decreased greatly over the past million years.

    d. In the world as a whole, rates of evaporation and precipitation are balanced.

Earth: The Water Planet · *Review and Reinforce*

Water on Earth

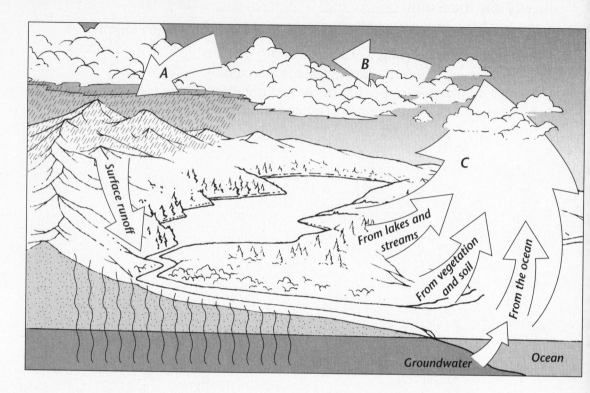

Study the illustration, and then answer the questions on a separate sheet of paper.

1. Give this illustration a title by writing the name of the continuous process it shows.

2. What three processes does this illustration show at points A, B, and C?

3. What is the source of energy that drives the continuous process shown in the illustration?

4. Name and describe the process by which water moves from plants to the atmosphere.

5. Describe how clouds form in the continuous process shown.

6. What role does the ocean play in the continuous process shown?

Name _____ Date _____ Class _____

Evaporation, Precipitation, and Runoff

The diagram below shows the yearly global flow of water through the water cycle. The numbers represent the amounts of evaporation and precipitation over the oceans and over the land. Use the diagram to answer the questions that follow.

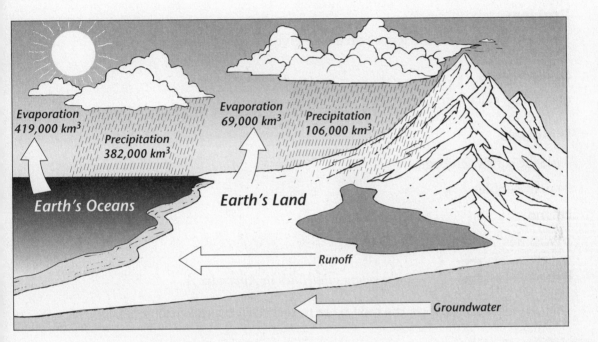

Answer the following questions on a separate sheet of paper.

1. What is the total amount of global evaporation?

2. What is the total amount of global precipitation?

3. How does the total amount of global precipitation compare to the total amount of global evaporation?

4. Where does more evaporation occur, from the oceans or from the land? Explain.

5. Where does more precipitation occur, over the oceans or over the land? Explain.

6. Do Earth's oceans gain or lose water, considering evaporation and precipitation together? How much?

7. Do Earth's continents gain or lose water, considering evaporation and precipitation together? How much?

8. Compare the differences in evaporation and precipitation over Earth's oceans and land. How are they related?

Earth: The Water Planet • *Skills Lab*

Water From Trees

Trees play many important roles in the environment—they keep the soil from washing away, remove carbon dioxide from the air, and produce oxygen. Trees are also a vital part of the water cycle. In this lab you will discover how trees help to keep water moving through the cycle.

Problem

How much water do the leaves on a tree give off in a 24-hour period?

Skills Focus

observing, calculating, inferring

Materials

3 plastic sandwich bags

3 small pebbles

balance

3 twist ties

Procedure 🔬 *Review the safety guidelines in Appendix A.*

1. Use the data table on the next page to record your measurements of mass.
2. Place the sandwich bags, twist ties, and pebbles on a balance. Determine their total mass to the nearest tenth of a gram.
3. Select an outdoor tree or shrub with leaves that are within your reach.
4. Put one pebble into a sandwich bag and place the bag over one of the tree's leaves. Fasten the twist tie around the bag, forming a tight seal around the stem of the leaf.
5. Repeat Step 4 with the other plastic bags on two more leaves. Leave the bags in place on the leaves for 24 hours.
6. The following day, examine the bags and record your observations in your notebook.
7. Carefully remove the bags from the leaves and refasten each twist tie around its bag so that the bag is closed tightly.

Earth: The Water Planet ▪ *Skills Lab*

Data Table

Starting mass of bags, ties, and pebbles	
Mass of bags, ties, and pebbles after 24 hours	
Difference in mass	

8. Place the three bags, including pebbles and twist ties, on the balance. Determine their total mass to the nearest tenth of a gram.

9. Subtract the original mass of the bags, ties, and pebbles that you found in Step 2 from the mass you found in Step 8.

Analyze and Conclude

Write your answers on the back of this sheet or on a separate sheet of paper.

1. Use the observations you made in Step 6 to account for the difference in mass you found in Step 9.

2. What is the name of the process that caused the results you observed? Explain the role of that process in the water cycle.

3. A single birch tree may transpire as much as 260 liters of water in a day. How much water would a grove of 1,000 birch trees return to the atmosphere in a year?

4. **Think About It** Based on what you learned from this investigation, write a paragraph explaining why some people are concerned about the destruction of forests around the world.

Design an Experiment

Write a hypothesis about what would happen if you repeated this activity with a different type of tree. Design a plan to test your hypothesis. *Obtain your teacher's permission before carrying out your investigation.*

Surface Water

🕐 *2–3 periods, 1–1 1/2 blocks*

Ability Levels Key
L1 Basic to Average
L2 For All Students
L3 Average to Advanced

Objectives
H.1.3.1 Tell what a river system is.
H.1.3.2 Explain how ponds and lakes form.
H.1.3.3 Describe the changes that occur in
ponds and lakes.

Key Terms
• tributary • watershed • divide • reservoir
• nutrient • eutrophication

Local Standards

PRETEACH

Build Background Knowledge
Encourage students to describe rivers, lakes, and
ponds they have seen.

 **Discover Activity** *What's in Pond Water?* **L1**

Targeted Resources

❏ **All in One Teaching Resources**
  L2 Reading Strategy Transparency H6:
  Outlining
❏ 💿 **Presentation-Pro CD-ROM**

INSTRUCT

River Systems Use a diagram to define a
river system and identify its parts.
Ponds and Lakes Ask leading questions
to help students explain how ponds and
lakes form.
How Lakes Can Change Describe how ponds
and lakes change with the seasons and how the
buildup of nutrients leads to eutrophication.

Targeted Resources

❏ **All in One Teaching Resources**
  L2 Guided Reading, pp. 66–69
  L3 Transparencies H7, H8, H9
❏ **PHSchool.com** Web Code: cfd-3013

ASSESS

Section Assessment Questions
🔄 Have students use their completed outlines
of the section to answer the questions.
Reteach
As a class, make a chart comparing and
contrasting rivers, ponds, and lakes.

Targeted Resources

❏ **All in One Teaching Resources**
  Section Summary, p. 65
  L1 Review and Reinforce, p. 70
  L3 Enrich, p. 71

Earth: The Water Planet • *Section Summary*

Surface Water

Guide for Reading

- What is a river system?

- How do ponds and lakes form?

- What changes occur to ponds and lakes?

Fresh water on Earth may be moving, as in streams and rivers, or still, as in pond and lakes. All fresh water, however, comes from precipitation. The many small streams that come together to form a river are called the headwaters. These streams flow into a small river. The streams and rivers that feed into a main river are called **tributaries.** Tributaries flow downward toward the main river, pulled by the force of gravity. **A river and all of its tributaries together make up a river system.**

The land area that supplies water to a river system is called a **watershed.** One watershed is separated from another by a ridge of land called a **divide.** Streams on each side of the divide flow in different directions.

Ponds and lakes are bodies of fresh water. Unlike the moving water of streams and rivers, ponds and lakes contain still, or standing water. **Ponds and lakes form when water collects in hollows and low-lying areas of land**. People can also create a lake by building a dam across a river. The lake may be used for supplying drinking water, for irrigating fields, or for recreation. A lake that stores water for human use is called a **reservoir.**

Lakes change for many reasons. **In addition to seasonal changes, a lake can undergo long-term changes that may eventually lead to its death.** Seasonal changes are common in cool, northern areas of North America. In summer, the sun warms the upper layer of water in a lake. As the top layer cools, it becomes denser and sinks. This causes the lake waters to mix. This mixing, also called turnover, causes materials to rise from the lake bottom. Lake turnover refreshes the supply of nutrients throughout the lake. **Nutrients** are substances such as nitrogen and phosphorus that enable plants and algae to grow.

The second type of change that may occur in a lake happens over a long period of time. Over many years, the nutrients build up in the lake in a process called **eutrophication.** As eutrophication causes more algae to grow, a thick, green scum forms on the surface of the water. When the algae becomes so thick that it begins to block out the sunlight, plants living in the lake or pond cannot carry out photosynthesis. Eutrophication may lead to the death of a pond or a lake.

Earth: The Water Planet • *Guided Reading and Study*

Surface Water

This section describes how streams and rivers begin and how they flow. it also describes ponds and lakes, the habitats they provide, and how lakes change over time.

Use Target Reading Skills

As you read, make an outline of this section. Use the red headings for the main ideas and the blue headings for the supporting ideas.

Surface Water

I.   River systems
   A. Tributaries
   B.
   C.
 	
II. Ponds and lakes
   A.
   B.
   C.
 	
III.
   A.
   B.
   C.

River Systems

1. How do rivers begin?

   _____

   _____

Match the term with its definition.

Term   **Definition**

_____ **2.** tributary   **a.** A river and all its tributaries together

_____ **3.** river system   **b.** The land area that supplies water to a river system

_____ **4.** watershed   **c.** A smaller stream or river that feeds into a main river

_____ **5.** divide   **d.** The ridge that separates one watershed from another

6. The many small streams that come together at the source of a river are called the _____.

7. The broad, flat valley through which a river flows is called the _____. Looping curves in a river formed by erosion and deposition are called _____.

Name _____ Date _____ Class _____

Earth: The Water Planet · *Guided Reading and Study*

8. Number the pictures to show the correct sequence in which an oxbow lake forms.

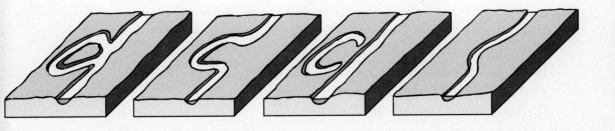

_____ _____ _____ _____

9. The point where a river flows into another body of water is called the

_____.

Ponds and Lakes

10. Complete the Venn diagram by labeling each circle.

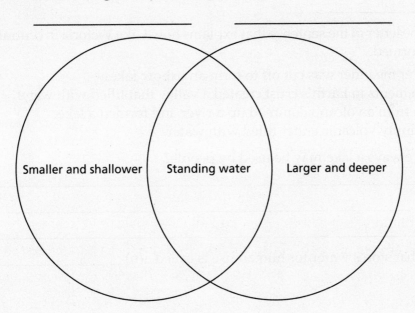

_____   _____

Smaller and shallower   Standing water   Larger and deeper

Earth: The Water Planet ▪ *Guided Reading and Study*

Surface Water *(continued)*

11. When do ponds and lakes form?

   _____

   _____

   _____

12. Circle the letter of each sentence that is true about ponds.

   a. Ponds provide only one type of habitat.
   b. All ponds exist year-round.
   c. Algae are the basic food producers in ponds.
   d. Pond animals include fish.

13. Circle the letter of the sentence that explains why plants grow throughout a pond.

   a. Pond water is shallow.
   b. Animals live throughout a pond.
   c. A pond is muddy on the bottom.
   d. Algae grow in a pond.

14. Is the following sentence true or false? Lakes form in many ways.

   _____

15. Circle the letter of the sentence that explains how Lake Victoria in central Africa formed.

   a. A river meander was cut off to form an oxbow lake.
   b. Movements in Earth's crust created a valley that filled with water.
   c. Lava from a volcano dammed up a river and formed a lake.
   d. An empty volcanic crater filled with water.

16. What are ways a lake may be used by people?

   _____

   _____

   _____

17. A lake that stores water for human use is called a(n) _____.

Earth: The Water Planet · *Guided Reading and Study*

18. Is the following sentence true or false? Wildlife near the shore of a lake are similar to wildlife in a pond. _____

19. Is the following sentence true or false? Compared with the center of a pond, the center of a lake has more organisms.

_____

How Lakes Can Change

20. Circle the letter of each sentence that is true about lake turnover.

    a. It occurs in cool northern areas of North America.
    b. It happens each year.
    c. It occurs in the summer.
    d. It causes nutrients to rise from the bottom to the surface.

21. Circle the letter of each sentence that is true about eutrophication.

    a. It happens over a long period of time.
    b. It prevents algae from growing in a lake.
    c. It is a process of using up nutrients in a lake.
    d. It keeps lake water clear.

Earth: The Water Planet ▪ *Review and Reinforce*

Surface Water

Understanding Main Ideas

1. What river feature is shown between Points A and B in the diagram above?

   _____.

2. How are a lake and a pond alike? How are they different?

   _____

   _____

3. What is eutrophication and how might this process bring change to a pond?

   _____

   _____

Building Vocabulary

Write a definition for each of the following terms..

4. tributary _____

5. divide _____

6. watershed _____

7. headwater _____

8. reservoir _____

9. nutrient _____

10. eutrophication _____

The Columbia River Debate

The Columbia River is the fourth largest river in North America. Its watershed includes seven northwestern states and two Canadian provinces. The Columbia River system is important to both the people and wildlife of the area, but sometimes their needs conflict. Government officials are now trying to decide how to balance the needs of humans and wildlife.

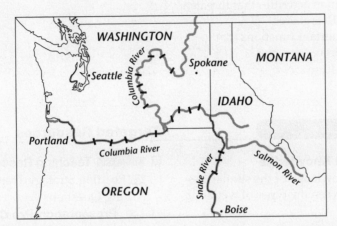

People need the Columbia River system. There are more than 100 dams along the Columbia and its tributaries. These dams help control flooding and create reservoirs that are used for swimming, boating, fishing, and other activities. Many of the dams generate inexpensive electric power for homes and businesses. This inexpensive power has encouraged the growth of industry in the area. The dams provide irrigation water that has turned arid land into productive farmland. The Columbia River also supplies water for cities and industries. In addition, the river system is used for shipping and for commercial salmon fishing, a $2 billion industry in the Northwest.

Salmon need the Columbia River system. Salmon reproduce in the Columbia's headwaters. The young fish, called smolts, swim downriver to the Pacific Ocean, where they grow to adulthood. The adults return to their birth-streams to reproduce and die. The river system's dams act as barriers to migrating smolts and adult salmon, since the fish cannot swim over or around them. Along some dams, people have built fish ladders so adult salmon can bypass the dams as they migrate upstream. Fish ladders are a series of steps in the water that allow fish to make several small jumps to get over the dam. But fish ladders do not help the smolts migrating downstream. They become stranded in lakes behind dams, are eaten by predators in the lakes, or are killed by the dams' turbines. Of every five smolts that start the downstream trip, only one reaches the ocean.

Choose one of the following viewpoints or another viewpoint of your own. On a separate sheet of paper, write a persuasive argument to support your viewpoint.

A. The Columbia River system is a valuable resource that should be used to meet the needs of people.

B. The Columbia River system should be returned to its natural state so it can serve the needs of salmon and other wildlife.

Wetland Environments

1–2 periods, 1/2–1 blocks

Ability Levels Key
- **L1** Basic to Average
- **L2** For All Students
- **L3** Average to Advanced

Objectives
H.1.4.1 Describe the common types of freshwater wetlands.
H.1.4.2 Identify human activities that threaten the Florida Everglades.
H.1.4.3 Explain important functions that wetlands serve.

Key Terms
- wetland

Local Standards

PRETEACH

Build Background Knowledge
Assess students' knowledge of the similarities and differences between the types of wetlands.

 **Discover Activity** *Wet or Dry?* **L1**

Targeted Resources

- ☐ **All in One Teaching Resources**
  L2 Reading Strategy Transparency H10: Asking Questions
- ☐ 💿 **Presentation-Pro CD-ROM**

INSTRUCT

Types of Wetlands Compare and contrast the three types of wetlands.
The Everglades: A Wetland Analyze how farming, development, and the introduction of new species are threatening the Everglades.
Importance of Wetlands Ask questions to help students consider the ways that wetlands help wildlife and people.

Targeted Resources

- ☐ **All in One Teaching Resources**
  L2 Guided Reading, pp. 74–76
- ☐ 💿 **www.SciLinks.org** Web Code: scn-0814

ASSESS

Section Assessment Questions
Have students use their flowcharts with questions and answers to answer the questions.
Reteach
Use photos and illustrations to review the organisms that live in wetlands and how wetlands are important to people.

Targeted Resources

- ☐ **All in One Teaching Resources**
  Section Summary, p. 73
  L1 Review and Reinforce, p. 77
  L3 Enrich, p. 78

Earth: The Water Planet · *Section Summary*

Wetland Environments

Guide for Reading

- What are the common types of freshwater wetlands?

- Which human activities threaten the Florida Everglades?

- What important functions do wetlands serve?

A **wetland** is an area of land that is covered with a shallow layer of water during some or all of the year. **The three common types of freshwater wetlands are marshes, swamps, and bogs.** Marshes are generally grassy, while swamps contain trees and shrubs. Bogs generally are characterized by many types of mosses. Wetlands along coasts usually contain a mixture of fresh and salt water. Coastal wetlands include salt marshes and mangrove forests.

The Everglades is a huge wetland area in southern Florida where a shallow, slow moving stream of water runs from Lake Okeechobee to Florida Bay. Although it is a habitat for many rare and endangered species, the wetland is threatened by human activities. **Agriculture, development, and the introduction of new species are some human activities that threaten the Florida Everglades.** Canals and levees have changed the flow of water in the Everglades, drying up some areas and flooding others. Conservation efforts by the National Park Service, the state of Florida, and the U.S. Army Corps of Engineers have been made to manage the supply of water around and in the Everglades.

Because of their sheltered waters and rich supply of nutrients, wetlands provide habitats for many living things. Wetlands have important functions for people, as well as for wildlife. As water moves slowly through wetlands, solid materials settle out. Other wastes are absorbed by the plants. The plants' roots also trap mud and silt. **In this way, wetlands act as natural water filters. They also help control floods by absorbing extra runoff from heavy rains.**

Earth: The Water Planet · *Guided Reading and Study*

Wetland Environments

This section describes wetlands and the habitats they provide. The section also explains why wetlands are important and why the Everglades, a wetland region in Florida, is a unique environment.

Use Target Reading Skills

Before you read, preview the red headings. Ask a what or how question for each heading. As you read, answer your questions.

Wetland Environments

Question	Answer
What are the types of wetlands?	The three types of wetlands are . . .

Types of Wetlands

1. Circle the letter of each sentence that is true about a wetland.

    a. It is an area of land covered with shallow water.

    b. It can be small or large.

    c. It may dry up in the summer.

    d. It may form where groundwater seeps onto the surface.

Earth: The Water Planet · *Guided Reading and Study*

2. Complete the concept map.

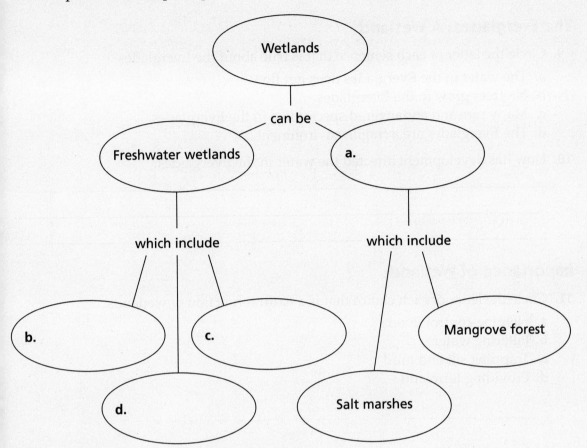

Match the type of wetland with its description.

Type of Wetland

_____ 3. marsh

_____ 4. swamp

_____ 5. bog

_____ 6. salt marsh

_____ 7. mangrove forest

Description

a. It has trees and shrubs growing in the water.

b. It has tall, strong grasses and a rich, muddy bottom.

c. It has cattails, rushes, and other tall grasslike plants.

d. It has short trees with a thick tangle of roots.

e. It has acidic water and mosses.

8. Circle the letter of each sentence that is true about wetland habitats.

a. They have sheltered waters.
b. They provide a poor supply of nutrients.
c. They have very different animal life from other freshwater habitats.
d. They have many temporary residents.

Wetland Environments (continued)

The Everglades: A Wetland

9. Circle the letter of each sentence that is true about the Everglades.
   a. The water in the Everglades does not flow.
   b. No trees grow in the Everglades.
   c. Many rare and endangered species live in the Everglades.
   d. The Everglades are a fragile environment.

10. How has development affected the water in the Everglades?

   _____

   _____

   _____

Importance of Wetlands

11. Circle the letter of each choice that is a natural function of wetlands.
   a. Helping control floods
   b. Filtering water
   c. Trapping silt and mud
   d. Providing farmland

Earth: The Water Planet • *Review and Reinforce*

Wetland Environments

Understanding Main Ideas

Answer the following questions on a separate sheet of paper.

1. Why do wetlands have a rich supply of nutrients? What other feature makes wetlands good habitats for so many organisms?

2. How are wetlands important to migrating birds?

3. Identify three human actions that pose a threat to the Everglades.

4. How can paving over a wetland area cause flooding?

Building Vocabulary

Answer the following questions in the spaces provided.

5. What is a wetland?

_____

_____

6. What type of freshwater wetland is shown in this picture? Explain your answer.

_____

_____

_____

Earth: The Water Planet · *Enrich*

The Shrinking Everglades

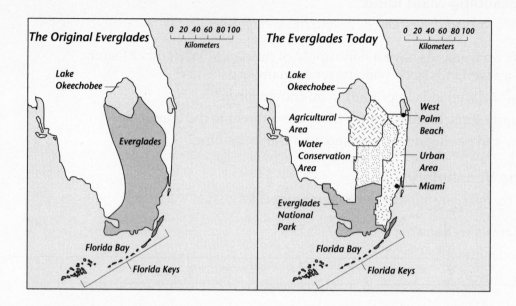

If you look at the maps above, you can see that the Everglades have changed. The original Everglades covered 1.6 million hectares. Today the Everglades are about half that size. What has caused the Everglades to shrink?

Up until the 1920s, Lake Okeechobee overflowed during heavy rains. These floodwaters brought a fresh supply of water to the Everglades. Then a 12-meter-high levee was constructed along the lake's eastern shore to prevent flooding. Later, canals were built to drain a huge area of land south of the lake and convert it to farmland.

In the 1940s, a system of canals, levees, and pumping stations was built to provide drainage and supply water to South Florida's growing population. This system channels excess water into the Atlantic Ocean instead of into the Everglades. The system also created large areas of dry land for agriculture and urban growth.

Answer the following questions on a separate sheet of paper.

1. About how large are the Everglades today?
2. What Florida city shown on the map was built on land that used to be part of the Everglades?
3. How could the urban area on the map pose a threat to the Everglades?
4. What effect could the nearby agricultural area have on the Everglades?
5. Briefly describe in your own words the pros and cons of the changes people have made to the land in South Florida.

Water Underground

 3–4 periods, 1–2 blocks

Objectives

H.1.5.1 Describe how water moves through underground layers of soil and rock.
H.1.5.2 Explain how people obtain water from an aquifer.

Key Terms

• permeable • impermeable • saturated zone
• water table • unsaturated zone • aquifer
• artesian well

Local Standards

PRETEACH

Build Background Knowledge
Show a bottle of spring water, and ask students where spring water comes from.

 Discover Activity *Where Does the Water Go?* **L1**

Targeted Resources

❏ **All in One Teaching Resources**
  L2 Reading Strategy Transparency H11: Previewing Visuals

❏ ◉ **Presentation-Pro CD-ROM**

INSTRUCT

How Water Moves Underground Use a labeled cross section of soil layers to describe how water moves underground.
Bringing Up Groundwater Use a diagram to explain how people get water from an aquifer.

 Design Your Own Lab *Soil Testing* **L2**

Targeted Resources

❏ **All in One Teaching Resources**
  L2 Guided Reading, pp. 81–83
  L2 Transparencies H12, H13
  L2 Lab: *Soil Testing*, pp. 86–88

❏ ▭ **Lab Activity Video/DVD**
  Design Your Own Lab: *Soil Testing*
❏ **www.SciLinks.org** Web Code: scn-0815
❏ ◉ **Student Edition on Audio CD**

ASSESS

Section Assessment Questions
⟳ Have students use the questions and answers they developed for previewing a visual to answer the questions.

Reteach
Summarize the connection between saturated and unsaturated zones and permeable and impermeable layers beneath Earth's surface.

Targeted Resources

❏ **All in One Teaching Resources**
  Section Summary, p. 80
  L1 Review and Reinforce, p. 84
  L3 Enrich, p. 85

Earth: The Water Planet ▪ *Section Summary*

Water Underground

Guide for Reading

- How does water move through underground layers of soil and rock?

- How do people obtain water from an aquifer?

Underground water comes from precipitation that soaks into the ground. **The water underground trickles down between particles of soil and through cracks and spaces in layers of rock.**

Different types of rock and soil have different-sized spaces, or pores, between their particles. Materials that allow water to pass through easily are called **permeable.** Materials that do not allow water to pass through easily are called **impermeable.**

When water soaks down into the ground, it passes through permeable materials. Eventually it reaches an impermeable layer. There, it stops trickling down and begins to fill the spaces in the permeable layer above it. The permeable layer that becomes filled with water is called the **saturated zone.** The level of the top of the water in the saturated zone is called the **water table.** The layer of rocks and soil above the water table is called the **unsaturated zone.**

An **aquifer** is an underground layer of rock or sediment where water has collected. The water in an aquifer seeps through the permeable rock layers where it is stored. **With mechanical equipment people can obtain groundwater from an aquifer by drilling a well below the water table.** Pumping water out of an aquifer lowers the water level near the well. The aquifer refills when new water from the surface, called recharge, enters the aquifer.

In some aquifers, the water that has collected between impermeable layers is under great pressure. If a hole is drilled in the impermeable layer above it, the water flows out of the aquifer without being pumped. A well in which water rises because of pressure within the aquifer is called an **artesian well.**

A spring is a place where groundwater bubbles or flows out of cracks in the rock. The water in some springs is warm or even hot. The water is heated by hot rocks deep underground. A geyser is a hot spring in which the water is under pressure. From time to time, the pressure causes the hot water and steam to erupt into the air.

Earth: The Water Planet ▪ *Guided Reading and Study*

Water Underground

This section explains how water moves underground from the surface and how underground water is stored in rock layers. The section also describes how underground water moves back to the surface.

Use Target Reading Skills

Before you read, preview the figure, "Bringing Up Groundwater." Then write questions that you have about the diagram. As you read, answer your questions.

Bringing Up Groundwater

Q. What is an artesian well?
A.
Q.
A.

How Water Moves Underground

1. Precipitation that soaks into the ground trickles downward due to
_____.

Match the term with its definition.

Term

_____ 2. pore

_____ 3. permeable

_____ 4. impermeable

_____ 5. saturated zone

_____ 6. water table

_____ 7. unsaturated zone

Definition

a. Allows water to pass through

b. Area that is totally filled with water

c. Space between rock and soil particles

d. Does not let water pass through

e. Layer above the water table

f. Top of the saturated zone

Earth: The Water Planet · *Guided Reading and Study*

Water Underground *(continued)*

8. In the drawing, label the water table and the saturated and unsaturated zones.

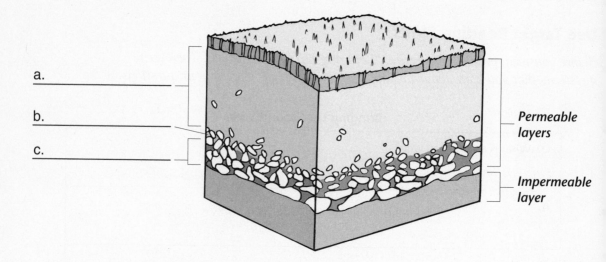

a. _____

b. _____

c. _____

Permeable layers

Impermeable layer

Earth: The Water Planet ▪ *Guided Reading and Study*

9. Any underground layer of rock or sediment that holds water is called
a(n) _____.

10. Circle the letter of each sentence that is true about aquifers.

   a. All of them are very large.
   b. They can provide drinking water.
   c. They can provide water for crops.
   d. They contain moving water.

Bringing Up Groundwater

11. Is the following sentence true or false? The depth of the water table is
always the same, even over a large area of land.

_____

12. Circle the letter of the choice that best explains how to get water from an
aquifer with a well.

   a. By drilling below the water table
   b. By drilling below the aquifer
   c. By drilling through impermeable rock
   d. By drilling near a dry well

13. A well in which water rises because of pressure within an aquifer is
called a(n) _____.

14. Places where groundwater bubbles or flows out of cracks in the rock are
called _____.

15. A type of hot spring from which the water bursts periodically into the
air is called a(n) _____.

Earth: The Water Planet · *Review and Reinforce*

Water Underground

Understanding Main Ideas

Answer the following questions on a separate sheet of paper.

1. What two factors determine how easily water moves through a material?
2. Why doesn't water have to be pumped out of an artesian well?
3. What might cause a well to run dry?

Building Vocabulary

Look carefully at this diagram. Then answer the questions below.

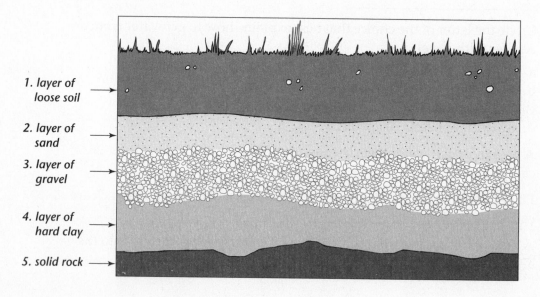

1. layer of loose soil
2. layer of sand
3. layer of gravel
4. layer of hard clay
5. solid rock

4. Which layers are permeable?

   _____

   _____

5. Which layers are impermeable?

   _____

   _____

6. What is an underground layer that holds water called?

   _____

   _____

7. Use a blue pencil or marker to add groundwater to the diagram. You may choose how much groundwater you add, but make sure you put the groundwater in a logical place on the diagram. Then add the following labels: saturated zone, water table, unsaturated zone.

Name _____ Date _____ Class _____

Earth: The Water Planet · *Enrich*

A Model Aquifer

Mrs. Cohen's science class is making displays for Parents' Night at the school. One student has decided to make a model of an aquifer. This drawing shows the student's plan for the model.

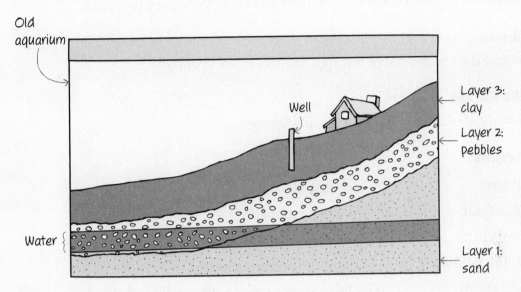

Write an answer for each of the following questions in the spaces provided.

1. Study the layers in the diagram. How would Layer 3 affect runoff?

   _____

   _____

2. Would water collect where it is shown on the diagram? Explain your answer.

   _____

   _____

3. Would the well shown on the plan work in real life? Explain.

   _____

   _____

4. Redraw the plan for the model, showing any changes you would make. Include the underground layers, the well, and the water table. Label the layers to show the materials you would use if you were building the model.

Earth: The Water Planet • *Design Your Own Lab*

Soil Testing

In what type of soil is it best to site a well? This is a question that hydrologists, scientists who study groundwater, need to answer before new houses or other buildings can be constructed. In this lab, you will compare different soil types to learn more about their water-holding properties.

Problem

How fast does water move through sand, clay, and pebbles?

Skills Focus

observing, developing hypotheses, designing

Materials

hand lens

sand, 100 mL

stopwatch

3 100-mL beakers

water, 300 mL

pebbles, 100 mL

3 rubber bands

powdered potter's clay, 100 mL

3 squares of cheesecloth

3 large funnels or cut-off plastic soda bottle tops

Procedure *Review the safety guidelines in Appendix A.*

Part 1 Observing the Flow of Water Through Sand

1. Copy the data table into your notebook.
2. Use a hand lens to observe the sand sample closely. Record your observations in the data table.
3. Place a piece of cheesecloth over the bottom of one funnel or bottle top and secure it with a rubber band.
4. Place the sand in the funnel, the pebbles in another, and the clay in another. Be sure that there is about 5 cm of space above the material in the funnel.
5. Place the funnel on top of a beaker.
6. Slowly pour 100 mL of water into the funnel. Do not let the water overflow the funnel.
7. Start the stopwatch when the water begins to flow or drip out of the bottom of the funnel.

Earth: The Water Planet · *Design Your Own Lab*

8. Stop the stopwatch when the water stops dripping out of the funnel or after 5 minutes. Record the time to the nearest second in the data table.

Data Table

Material	Observations	Time for Water to Stop Dripping
Sand		
Pebbles		
Clay		

Part 2 Comparing the Flow of Water Through Different Soil Samples

9. Use a hand lens to observe each of the two other material samples closely. Record your observations in the data table.

10. Using the procedures you followed in Part 1, design an experiment to compare the flow of water through sand, clay, and pebbles. Be sure to write a hypothesis and control all necessary variables.

11. Submit your experimental plan to your teacher. After making any necessary changes, carry out your experiment. Record your observations in your data table.

12. When you are finished with this activity, dispose of the materials according to your teacher's instructions. Wash your hands thoroughly with soap.

Earth: The Water Planet · *Design Your Own Lab*

Soil Testing *(continued)*

Analyze and Conclude

Write the answers for the following questions in the space provided or on a seperate sheet of paper.

1. In Part 1, how did the sand look under the hand lens? How long did it take the water to flow through the sand?

   _____

   _____

2. What hypothesis did you test in Part 2? On what did you base your hypothesis?

   _____

   _____

3. What was the manipulated variable in Part 2? What was the responding variable?

   _____

   _____

4. Through which material did water move the fastest? The slowest? What can you conclude about the permeability of the three materials?

   _____

   _____

5. Based on the results of this lab, would you expect to get more water from a well dug in sand, pebbles, or clay? Explain.

   _____

   _____

6. **Think About It** You and your neighbor are discussing your gardens. You're explaining that it's important for a gardener to know the permeability of different soils. Write your conversation in dialogue form. Use quotation marks for each speaker.

   _____

   _____

More to Explore

Of the soil samples you tested, which do you think most resembles the soil of the grounds at your school? Explain your reasoning. How might you test your hypothesis?

_____

_____

_____

Name _____ Date _____ Class_____

Key Terms

Test your knowledge of key terms from the chapter by completing the crossword puzzle.

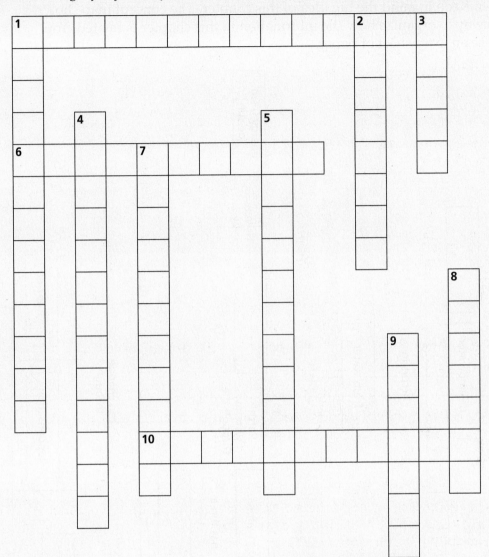

Clues across

1. Process by which plants make food
6. Process of supplying water to the land for growing crops
10. Process by which liquid water changes to water vapor

Clues down

1. Water that falls from clouds
2. Mixture of one substance dissolved in another
3. Form of matter
4. Process by which plants release water vapor
5. Process by which water vapor changes to liquid water
7. Water in underground soil and rock layers
8. Substance that dissolves another substance
9. Place where an organism lives

Earth: The Water Planet · *Connecting Concepts*

Connecting Concepts

Develop a concept map that uses the key concepts and key terms from this chapter. Keep in mind the big idea of this chapter. The concept map shown is one way to organize how the information in this chapter is related. You may use an extra sheet of paper.

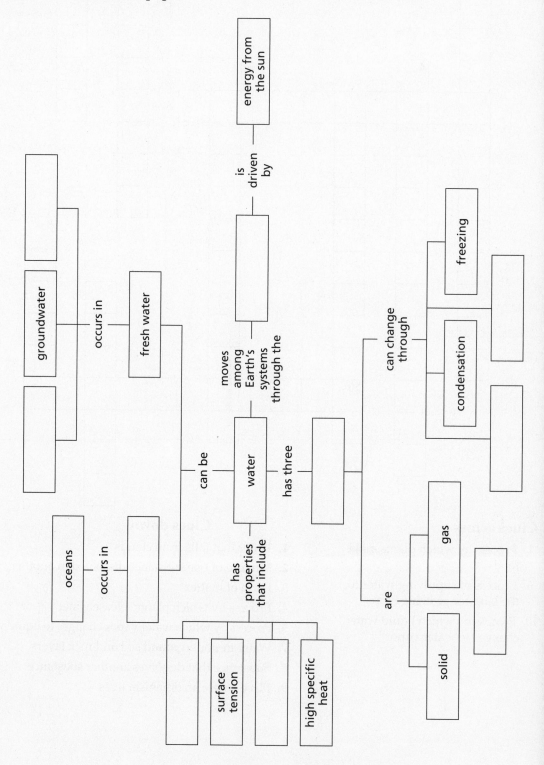

Properties of Water

Key Concept

The properties of water make it a unique substance on Earth.

Skills Focus

observing, inferring, predicting

Time

60 minutes

Materials (per group)

plastic cup

tap water

3-cm square of metal window screening

dark food coloring

paper towel

scissors

250-mL beaker

distilled water

hot plate

thermometer, metal

spoon

salt

hot pad

wax pencil

Alternate Materials

If possible, use alcohol thermometers rather than mercury thermometers.

Advanced Preparation

You may want to form the screening containers for Part A ahead of time. Consider setting up separate stations for Parts A, B, and C.

Teaching Tips

- Dark food coloring will make the water movement easier to see.

- Students can complete Part C while waiting to observe the results from Part B.

Earth: The Water Planet ▪ *Laboratory Investigation*

Properties of Water

Pre-Lab Discussion

Water is the only substance on Earth that commonly exists in all three states—solid, liquid, and gas. Water also has some other unusual properties. In this investigation, you will examine some properties of the substance that covers most of Earth's surface.

1. What are three properties of water that are caused by the attractions among water molecules?

   _____

   _____

2. Why can water dissolve so many other substances?

   _____

   _____

Problem

What are some of the unique properties of water?

Materials (*per group*)

plastic cup

tap water

3-cm square of metal window screening

dark food coloring

paper towel

scissors

250-mL beaker

distilled water

hot plate

thermometer, metal

spoon

salt

hot pad

wax pencil

Safety   *Review the safety guidelines in appendix A of your textbook.*

Handle the thermometer carefully. If it breaks, do not touch it and immediately tell your teacher. Use tongs or a hot pad when handling hot objects. Always wear safety goggles when heating objects.

Name _____ Date _____ Class _____

Earth: The Water Planet • *Laboratory Investigation*

Procedure

Part A: Surface Tension

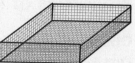

Figure 1

1. Fill a plastic cup three-fourths full with tap water.
2. Bend up the sides of the window screening to form the shape shown in Figure 1. Be careful of any sharp edges on the screen.
3. Predict what will happen if you place the screening on the water's surface. Explain your reasoning.

_____

_____

4. Carefully set the bottom of the container flat on the surface of the water in the cup. Do not touch the water with your hand. Observe whether the container sinks or floats. Record your observations under Observations.

Part B: Capillary Action

1. Put about 2 cm of tap water in the plastic cup. Add 2 or 3 drops of food coloring to the water.
2. Cut a strip of paper towel about 1 cm wide. Drape it over the lip of the cup so that one end is in the water. See Figure 2.
3. Predict what will happen to the paper strip. Explain your reasoning. **Figure 2**

_____

_____

4. Set the cup aside. After about 20 minutes, observe the strip of paper towel. Record your observations under Observations.

Part C: Changing States

1. **CAUTION:** *Put on your safety goggles and apron.* Fill a 250-mL beaker two-thirds full of distilled water. Place the beaker on a hot plate.
2. Heat the water until it boils. Measure the temperature of the boiling water. **CAUTION:** *Handle the thermometer carefully; it is breakable.*
3. Let the water cool slightly. Add a spoonful of salt to the water. Predict how adding salt will affect the water's boiling point. Explain your reasoning.

_____

_____

4. Heat the water until it boils and record the temperature of the boiling water in the Data Table under Observations.
5. Repeat Steps 3 and 4 three more times. **CAUTION:** *Use a hot pad or beaker tongs to handle the beaker.*

Earth: The Water Planet · *Laboratory Investigation*

Properties of Water *(continued)*

Observations

Part A

1. What happened when you placed the screening on the water's surface?

   _____

   _____

Part B

1. What did you observe about the end of the paper towel that was outside the cup?

   _____

Part C

Data Table

	Boiling-Point Temperature
Distilled water	
Distilled water + 1 spoon of salt	
Distilled water + 2 spoons of salt	
Distilled water + 3 spoons of salt	
Distilled water + 4 spoons of salt	

Analyze and Conclude

1. Explain your observations in Part A based on what you know about the surface tension of water.

   _____

   _____

2. Explain your observations in Part B based on what you know about capillary action.

   _____

   _____

3. How does dissolving salt in water affect the temperature at which the water boils?

   _____

   _____

   _____

Earth: The Water Planet · *Laboratory Investigation*

Critical Thinking and Applications

1. What do you think would happen if you put a penny on the screening? Give a reason for your answer.

   _____

   _____

2. If you cut off a centimeter from the bottom of a celery stalk and put the cut end into water colored with blue food coloring, in about an hour the stem would be streaked with blue. Explain what happens in terms of capillary action.

   _____

   _____

3. When some people cook vegetables, they add salt to the cooking water. They say this makes the vegetables cook faster. Are they correct? Give a reason for your answer.

   _____

   _____

More to Explore

New Problem Does dissolving salt in water change the freezing point of the water?

Possible Materials Consider what materials you will need. Write a list of your materials.

Safety Handle thermometers carefully. Wear your safety goggles and apron.

Procedure Write a procedure you could follow to find the answer to the problem. Have the teacher approve your procedure before you carry out the investigation. (Hint: You do not necessarily need to make salt water freeze to answer this question.)

Observations Make a data table and record your observations.

Analyze and Conclude

1. How does dissolving salt in water affect its freezing point?

   _____

   _____

2. Why do some communities spread salt on icy roads in winter?

   _____

   _____

Making Drops of Rain

Students are presented with the problem of creating a model for raindrop formation using the materials given. To solve this problem, students will apply the concepts they have learned about changes of states and the water cycle.

Expected Outcome

Students should devise a setup that allows water vapor to condense on a jar top. The most likely setup would include water in the bottom of the jar and the top turned upside down, covering the mouth of the jar. The upside-down top would hold several ice cubes. Once students put this setup together, droplets should form inside the jar on the jar lid within about 10 minutes as the liquid water evaporates and then condenses on the lid. The process will be speeded up if students place the setup in sunlight.

Content Assessed

This activity assesses students' understanding of evaporation and condensation and the water cycle.

Skills Assessed

developing hypotheses, designing experiments, drawing conclusions

Materials

Provide students with large, wide-mouthed glass jars.

Place containers of water and bowls of ice cubes on a table at a central location or on a few tables around the classroom. Advise students to use as much water and as many ice cubes as they need for their setups.

Advance Preparation

- Buy a bag of ice cubes on the morning students do this activity.

- Gather several containers, either pitchers or beakers, to hold the water needed for the activity.

Time

30 minutes

Safety

Caution students that they will be working with glass jars that are breakable. Instruct them to wear safety goggles and to handle the jars with care. Tell students that if glass does break, they should notify you immediately and not touch the broken pieces.

Monitoring the Task

- Review students' hypotheses and setup sketches before they try out their plans.

- Advise students that they do not need to fill their jars completely with water.

- Caution students to be careful when pouring the water and handling the ice cubes.

- Allow students who ask to place their setups on a window ledge where there is direct sunlight. This will speed up evaporation.

- Provide a place for students to dispose of the water and ice cubes they have used.

Making Drops of Rain

In assessing students' performance, use the following rubric.

	4	3	2	1
Constructing the Model	The student's hypothesis and sketch are complete and logical, and the model causes water vapor to condense in droplets.	The student's hypothesis and sketch are complete but flawed, and the model is partially effective in causing water vapor to condense in droplets.	The student's hypothesis and sketch are incorrect, but show that an attempt was made, and the model does not yield the expected outcome.	The student's hypothesis and sketch are incomplete or missing, and there was little or no attempt to construct a model.
Concept Understanding	The student demonstrates a mastery of the concepts that underlie the model, including changes of state and the water cycle.	The student demonstrates an adequate understanding of the concepts that underlie the model, including changes of state and the water cycle.	The student demonstrates only a partial understanding of the concepts that underlie the model, including changes of state and the water cycle.	The student demonstrates little or no understanding of the concepts that underlie the model, including changes of state and the water cycle.

Earth: The Water Planet • *Performance Assessment*

Making Drops of Rain

Problem

How can you construct a model to show how raindrops form in the atmosphere?

Suggested Materials

ice cubes

wide-mouthed jar

jar lid

water

Devise a Plan

1. Study the materials and think of a way that they could be used to make a model of how raindrops form in the atmosphere. Formulate a hypothesis about how you could make such a model. Consider the water cycle as you do this.

2. Make a drawing on a separate sheet of paper of the setup you plan to use.

3. Try out your plan. Experiment with your setup until you find how to use the materials to make a model of raindrop formation.

Analyze and Conclude

On a separate sheet of paper, respond to the items that follow.

1. Make a sketch of the model you made. Add as many arrows and labels as you can to your sketch, showing what changes occurred.

2. Describe how raindrops formed inside your model.

3. How is the process of raindrop formation different in your model than how it occurs in the atmosphere?

4. What changes of state occurred inside the model? Explain why.

5. Explain what property of water accounts for the shape of the water drops that formed in your model.

6. Describe how your model fits into the water cycle. What more would have to occur to complete the cycle?

Earth: The Water Planet

Multiple Choice

Write the letter of the correct answer on the line at the left.

_____ 1. A mixture that forms when one substance dissolves into another is a

    a. solvent.   **b.** solution.

    c. state.   **d.** solute.

_____ 2. What is the process by which plants give off water vapor through their leaves?

    a. condensation   **b.** transpiration.

    c. precipitation   **d.** irrigation

_____ 3. What property allows water to rise up in a narrow tube?

    a. surface tension   **b.** specific heat

    c. changing state   **d.** capillary action

_____ 4. The process of supplying water to areas of land to make them suitable for growing crops is called

    a. transpiration.   **b.** condensation.

    c. irrigation   **d.** evaporation.

_____ 5. What is the source of energy for the water cycle?

    a. gravity   **b.** transpiration.

    c. the oceans   **d.** the sun

_____ 6. A molecule that has electrically charged areas is called a(n)

    a. atom.   **b.** bond.

    c. polar molecule.   **d.** gas molecule.

_____ 7. What is a habitat?

    a. a place where an organism lives
    b. one part of the water cycle
    c. where water is supplied to make crops grow
    d. a place where groundwater is found

_____ 8. At what temperature do water vapor molecules begin to change back to the liquid state?

    a. 0°C   **b.** 10°C

    c. 50°C   **d.** 100°C

_____ 9. When clouds form, condensed droplets of water form around which of the following?

    a. water cycles   **b.** dust particles

    c. polar molecules   **d.** vapor molecules

Earth: The Water Planet • *Chapter Test (continued)*

_____ 10. The process by which molecules at the surface of a liquid absorb enough energy to change to the gaseous state is called

    a. evaporation.   **b.** transpiration.

    c. condensation.   **d.** precipitation.

Completion

Fill in the line to complete each statement.

11. Rain, snow, sleet, and hail are forms of _____.

12. A substance that dissolves another substance is a(n) _____.

13. The tightness across the surface of water is called _____.

14. Most water in the atmosphere is invisible _____.

15. The process by which a gas changes to a liquid is _____.

True or False

If the statement is true, write true. *If it is false, change the underlined word or words to make the statement true.*

_____ **16.** More than 97 percent of the water on Earth is <u>fresh water</u>.

_____ **17.** The <u>water cycle</u> renews the supply of fresh water on Earth.

_____ **18.** Compared to other substances, water has a <u>high</u> specific heat.

_____ **19.** <u>Capillary action</u> causes raindrops to form round beads when they fall on a car windshield.

_____ **20.** Water is the only substance on Earth that commonly exists in its three <u>states</u>.

Using Science Skills: Developing Hypotheses

For each of the following, write a hypothesis that would explain what occurred.

21. A snowstorm covered the ground on all sides of a house with about a foot of snow. The next day was sunny, and the temperature rose above freezing. The snow on the sunny side of the house melted, but the snow on the shaded side remained. Develop a hypothesis about the effect the sun has on melting.

_____

_____

_____

Earth: The Water Planet · *Chapter Test*

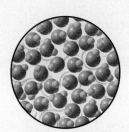 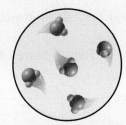

Water at 50°C   *Water at 100°C*

22. The drawings above show water molecules at 50°C and 100°C. Develop a hypothesis about the relationship of temperature and the distance between water molecules.

_____

_____

Essay

Write an answer for each of the following.

23. List five ways that people use water and give an example of each.

_____

_____

_____

_____

_____

24. Explain why water is known as the "universal solvent."

_____

_____

_____

_____

25. Describe the water cycle.

_____

_____

_____

_____

_____

_____

Name _____ Date _____ Class_____

Earth: The Water Planet • *Chapter Test*

Using Science Skills

Use the graph below to answer the following questions.

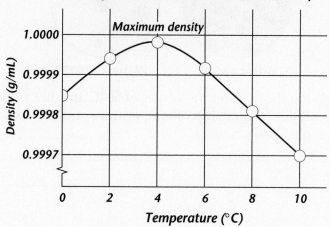

Temperature's Effect on Water Density

26. **Interpreting a Graph** Compare the density of water at 0°C and 4°C.

_____

_____

27. **Drawing Conclusions** How does this graph explain why ice floats?

_____

_____

_____

Essay

Write an answer for each of the following. Use the back of this sheet if you need more room.

28. What sources of water on Earth are available for human use? Explain why most water cannot be used.

_____

_____

29. Explain how the property of surface tension is related to the structure of the water molecule.

_____

_____

30. Describe how a cloud forms.

_____

_____

Chapter 1 Project Worksheet 1

The total reading for the dials in Figure 1: 68,923 cubic feet, in Figure 2: 37,049 cubic feet

Chapter 1 Project Worksheet 2

Figure 1: 68,923 cubic feet ÷ 28.5 = 2,420 liters;
Figure 2: 37,049 cubic feet ÷ 28.5 = 1,300 liters

The Properties of Water
Guided Reading and Study

Use Target Reading Skills
Check students' definitions.

1. a, d
2. polar
3. a, b
4. Water molecules stick to the sides of the straw and pull other water molecules up with them.
5. a, b, d
6. The molecules at the surface are pulled by the molecules next to them and below them, and this forces the surface of the water to curve.
7. solution; solvent
8. Water can dissolve many substances because it is polar, and the charged ends of water molecules attract the molecules of other polar substances.
9. a, c
10. specific heat
11. true
12. a, c, d
13. **a.** solid **b.** liquid **c.** gas
14. ice
15. **a.** liquid **b.** gas **c.** liquid **d.** gas **e.** gas **f.** liquid **g.** liquid **h.** solid
16. c
17. b
18. a
19. a, c, d
20. a, d

The Properties of Water
Review and Reinforce

1. Hydrogen, positive
2. Hydrogen, positive
3. Oxygen, negative
4. Water is a polar substance because its molecules have electrically charged areas.
5. Solid water, or ice, floats because it is less dense than liquid water. The fish live in the water below the ice.
6. The molecules slow down and begin to change back to the liquid state.

7. Water is often called the "universal solvent" because it is able to dissolve so many substances.
8. e
9. f
10. d
11. h
12. a
13. g
14. b
15. c

The Properties of Water
Enrich

1. Answers will vary. A typical answer: a. A piece of clothing becomes dirty when grease attaches to its fibers. b. Putting the cloth in water does not disturb the grease, because grease does not dissolve in water. c. When detergent is added to the water, the uncharged ends of the detergent molecules dissolve into the grease on the cloth, breaking the grease apart into droplets. d. Detergent molecules surround the droplets of grease with their charged ends sticking out. These charged ends allow the droplets of grease to dissolve in the water.
2. Answers will vary. A typical answer should mention the structure of detergent molecules, how detergent molecules interact with grease and water, and how the action of a washing machine helps to dislodge grease droplets surrounded by detergent molecules.

Water on Earth
Guided Reading and Study

This is one possible way to complete the graphic organizer. Accept all logical answers.
Detail: Earth's oceans in the form of salt water, in which 97 percent of Earth's water is found
Detail: Ice in the form of icebergs near the North and South Poles **Detail:** Rivers and lakes, which contain the smallest amount of fresh water on Earth **Detail:** Water below the surface, which fills cracks and spaces in underground soil and rock layers
1. false
2. habitat
3. false
4. 97 percent: salt water; 3 percent: fresh water
5. water vapor
6. a, b, c, d
7. a, c
8. false
9. groundwater

The Water Cycle

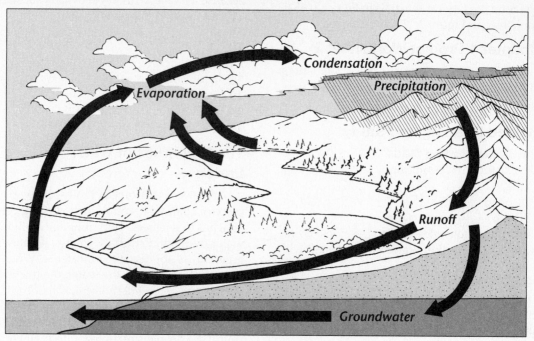

10. a, b, c
11. true
12. false
13. Plants draw in water from the soil through their roots.
14. See above.
15. It isn't salty because the salt remains in the ocean when the water evaporates.
16. Transpiration: produces water vapor from plants; condensation: forms clouds from water vapor
17. Higher up, the air is colder. Cold air holds less water vapor than warm air, so some of the water vapor condenses.
18. Clouds form when water droplets clump together around tiny dust particles in the the air.
19. Water droplets in a cloud grow larger and larger. Eventually they become so heavy that they fall to Earth.
20. rain, hail, snow, sleet
21. false
22. a, d

Water on Earth
Review and Reinforce

1. The Water Cycle
2. **A.** precipitation
   B. condensation
   C. evaporation
3. the sun

4. Plants draw in water from the ground through their roots. Eventually the water is given off through the leaves as water vapor in a process called transpiration.
5. Clouds form when water vapor cools in the colder air high in the atmosphere. The cold air causes water to condense, and water droplets clump together around tiny dust particles, causing clouds to form.
6. The ocean is where most precipitation falls and where most evaporation takes place.

Water on Earth
Enrich

1. $419{,}000 + 69{,}000 = 488{,}000$ km
2. $382{,}000 + 106{,}000 = 488{,}000$ km
3. Global evaporation equals global precipitation.
4. Much more evaporation occurs from the oceans ($419{,}000$ km^3 compared to $69{,}000$ km^3), because much more of Earth's surface is covered by ocean than land.
5. Much more precipitation occurs over the oceans ($382{,}000$ km^3 compared to $106{,}000$ km^3), because much more of Earth's surface is covered by ocean than land.
6. Since $419{,}000$ km3 of water evaporate while only $382{,}000$ km^3 of water fall as precipitation, Earth's oceans lose $37{,}000$ km^3 of water.

7. Since 106,000 km^3 of water fall as precipitation while only 69,000 km^3 of water evaporate, Earth's land gains 37,000 km^3 of water.

8. The oceans lose the same amount as the land gains. The water that flows into the oceans in runoff and groundwater balances the two out.

Water From Trees
Skills Lab

For answers, see the Teacher's Edition.

Surface Water
Guided Reading and Study

Use Target Reading Skills
Surface Water
I. River Systems
   A. Tributaries
   B. Watersheds
   C. Divides
II. Ponds and lakes
   A. Exploring a Pond
   B. Exploring a Lake
   C. Lake Formation
III. How Lakes Can Change
   A. Seasonal Changes
   B. Long-Term Changes
   C. Death of a Body of Fresh Water
1. Rivers begin when trickles of water run together over the ground and join in larger streams.
2. c
3. a
4. b
5. d
6. headwaters
7. flood plain, meanders
8. from left to right: 3, 2, 4, 1
9. mouth
10. from left to right: Pond, Lake
11. They form when water collects in hollows and low-lying areas.
12. c, d
13. a
14. true
15. b
16. A lake may be used for supplying drinking water, irrigation, and recreation.
17. reservoir
18. true
19. false

20. a, b, d
21. a, c

Surface Water
Review and Reinforce

1. A meander
2. A lake and a pond both form when water collects in hollows and low-lying areas of land. A pond is usually smaller than a lake and surrounded by land with no fresh water flowing in or out.
3. Eutrophication occurs when nutrients build up in a lake causing more algae to grow, forming a scum on the surface. This scum can block the sunlight, halting growth to plants in the water.
4. A stream or smaller river that feeds into a main river
5. A ridge of land separating watersheds
6. Land area that supplies water to a river system
7. Many small streams that come together at the source of a river
8. A lake that stores water for human use
9. Substances that enable plants and algae to grow
10. When nutrients build up in a lake causing more algae to grow, forming a scum on the surface

Surface Water
Enrich

Students' viewpoints and the arguments they use to support them will vary. Accept and encourage all viewpoints supported with *specific details*. Some students may recognize that people holding Viewpoint A include those whose livelihoods depend on commercial salmon fishing.

Wetland Environments
Guided Reading and Study

Use Target Reading Skills
What are the types of wetlands? The three types of wetlands are marshes, swamps, and bogs.
What is the Everglades? The Everglades is a region of wetlands stretching from Lake Okeechobee to Florida Bay.
How are wetlands important to wildlife? They provide habitats for many living things.

1. a, b, c, d
2. a. Coastal wetlands b. Marshes c. Bogs
   d. Swamps
3. c
4. a
5. e
6. b
7. d
8. a, d
9. c, d
10. Development has polluted and changed the flow of water in the Everglades.
11. a, b, c

Wetland Environments
Review and Reinforce

1. Dead leaves and other plant and animal material serve as natural fertilizer, adding nitrogen, phosphates, and other nutrients to the water and soil in wetlands. Wetlands provide sheltered, slow-moving waters.
2. Wetlands provide temporary homes for migrating birds that rest, feed, mate, and raise young in these habitats.
3. *Any three:* Farming has introduced new chemicals that upset the natural balance of nutrients. Developers have filled in surrounding areas to build new homes and roads. New organisms brought into the area by humans compete with native organisms for space and food. Water flowing into the Everglades has been diverted for farming. New canals and levees have changed the flow of water into and out of the Everglades, so areas dry up or are flooded.
4. Wetlands act like giant sponges, storing excess water and then gradually releasing it. When a wetland is paved over, the excess water cannot be absorbed. Instead, it runs off the land quickly and can cause floods.
5. A wetland is an area of land that is covered with shallow water during some or all of the year.
6. A swamp; it looks like a flooded forest, with trees growing in shallow water.

Wetland Environments
Enrich

1. about 0.8 million hectares
2. Miami

3. Answers will vary. Sample answer: As the area's population increases, people may want to drain even more of the Everglades to obtain land for development.
4. Agricultural fertilizers and pesticides could reach the Everglades in runoff from farmland. Fertilizers encourage overgrowth of plants and algae. Pesticides kill wetland insects and contaminate the animals that eat them.
5. Answers may vary. Sample answer: *Pro:* Changes in the land have made dry land available for agricultural and urban growth, enabling people to live and work in the area. *Con:* Changes have caused the Everglades to shrink in size by about half, have reduced the supply of fresh water to the Everglades, and have brought harmful chemicals that threaten wildlife.

Water Underground
Guided Reading and Study

Use Target Reading Skills
Bringing Up Groundwater
Q: What is an artesian well?
A: It is a well in which water rises because of pressure within an aquifer.
Q: Where does the water that supplies a well come from?
A: Underground water comes from precipitation that trickles down between particles of soil and through cracks and spaces in layers of rock.

1. gravity
2. c
3. a
4. d
5. b
6. f
7. e
8. a. Unsaturated zone
   b. Water table
   c. Saturated zone
9. aquifer
10. b, c, d
11. false
12. a
13. artesian well
14. springs
15. geyser

Water Underground
Review and Reinforce

1. The size of the pores (the spaces between the particles) and whether the pores are connected to each other

2. The water is under pressure from the weight of the rock above it, so it flows out on its own.

3. Too much water might have been taken out of the aquifer, lowering the water table, or dry weather might have limited the amount of recharge.

4. 1 (loose soil); 2 (sand); 3 (gravel)

5. 4 (hard clay); 5 (solid rock)

6. an aquifer

7. Students should add water above the layer of clay. The part filled with water should be labeled *saturated zone* (depth may vary). The top of the saturated zone should be labeled *water table*. The area above the water table should be labeled *unsaturated zone*.

Water Underground
Enrich

1. Since Layer 3 is clay, which is impermeable to water, runoff would flow over the land rather than sink into the ground.

2. No; sand is permeable and would not hold water in a layer as it is shown; the water would trickle down through the sand until it reached an impermeable layer.

3. 3. No; the bottom of the well is in an impermeable layer and does not reach the water.

4. Students' drawings should at least include the following corrections: Move Layer 3 down (use clay for the bottom layer). The "band" of water should not extend into the clay. The bottom of the well should extend down past the water table in Layer 2.

Soil Testing
Design Your Own Lab

For answers, see the Teacher's Edition.

Key Terms

DOWN
1. precipitation
2. solution
3. state
4. transpiration
5. condensation
6. groundwater
7. solvent
8. habitat

ACROSS
1. photosynthesis
2. irrigation
3. evaporation

Connecting Concepts

This concept map is only one way to represent the main ideas and relationships in this chapter. Accept other logical answers from students.

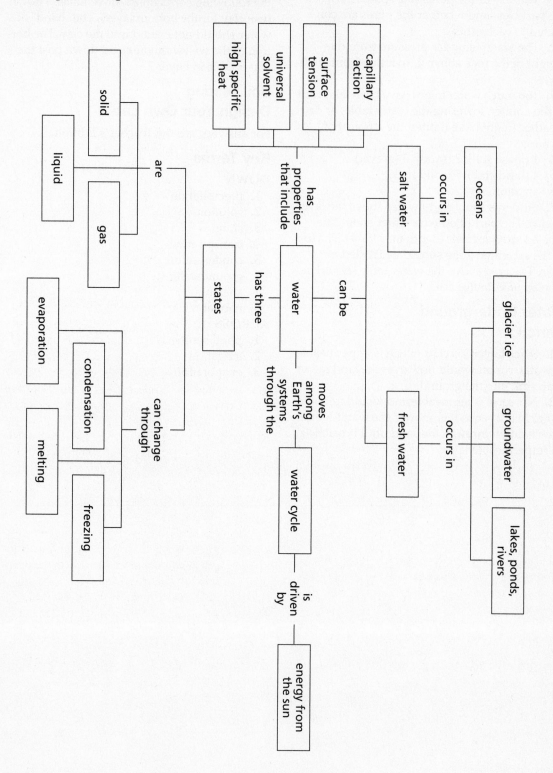

Laboratory Investigation

Properties of Water

1. Surface tension, capillary action, and high specific heat

2. The water molecule is polar, so its charged ends attract the molecules of other polar substances.

Procedure

Part A: Surface Tension

3. Unless students consider surface tension, they may predict the screening will sink.

Part B: Capillary Action

3. Students will likely predict the towel will absorb water, based on previous experience with cleaning up spills.

Part C: Changing States

3. Students will likely think adding salt will affect the water's boiling point in some way.

Observations

Part A

1. If the screening is set carefully on the water, with the flat bottom touching the surface of the water, it will float.

Part B

1. After 20 minutes, the end of the paper towel that was outside the cup was wet.

Part C

100°C

Boiling-point temperatures may vary, depending on accuracy of the laboratory thermometers and altitude, but in general, the more salt that is dissolved in the water, the higher its boiling point.

Analyze and Conclude

1. The container floated because it isn't heavy enough to break the surface tension of the water.

2. Water moves through the small spaces in the paper towel because of capillary action.

3. The more salt dissolved in the water, the higher the boiling point of the solution becomes.

Critical Thinking and Applications

1. The container would sink because the penny made it heavy enough to break the surface tension of the water. Suggest students test

their hypothesis by performing this experiment.

2. The colored water travels up tiny tubes in the celery stalk. Capillary action causes water molecules to cling to the insides of the narrow tubes and move through them.

3. Adding salt to water makes water boil at a higher temperature, and a higher temperature will cook the vegetables a little faster.

More to Explore

Students will need access to a freezer for this investigation. It will probably take several hours for the salt water to freeze, depending on the concentration. If a freezer isn't available or to save class time, have students do the project at home.

Analyze and Conclude

1. The more salt that is dissolved in the water, the lower the freezing point of the water will be.

2. Salt lowers the freezing point of water, so the ice will change to water even when the air temperature is below 0°C.

Chapter Performance Assessment

1. Students' sketches may vary. An excellent sketch should include the basic setup of the ice on the jar lid, an indication of the droplets that form inside the lid, arrows showing the incoming heat energy of the sun and the movement of water vapor as the water evaporates, and labels for evaporation and condensation.

2. Students' descriptions may vary. A typical description will mention that the energy of the sun caused the liquid water to evaporate. The water vapor then rose to the lid, which the ice had made cooler than the air. As a result, condensation occurred on the lid.

3. In the model, the water vapor condensed and formed droplets on the jar lid. In the atmosphere, water vapor condenses and forms droplets around tiny dust particles.

4. Evaporation occurred because the molecules of the liquid water gained enough energy to change to the gaseous state. Condensation occurred when the temperature of the air near the lid cooled enough for the water vapor to change to the liquid state.

5. The surface tension of water accounts for the droplet shapes on the lid.

6. The model shows only part of the water cycle. To complete the water cycle, the droplets would have to become larger and fall back into the jar as precipitation.

Chapter Test

1. b
2. b
3. d
4. c
5. d
6. c
7. a
8. d
9. b
10. a
11. precipitation
12. solvent
13. surface tension
14. water vapor
15. condensation
16. salt water
17. true
18. true
19. surface tension
20. true
21. Direct exposure to the sun raises the temperature of the air and causes frozen water to melt faster than it otherwise would.
22. The higher the temperature, the greater the distance between water molecules.
23. The five categories of water use are household purposes, agriculture, industry, transportation, and recreation. Students' examples may vary. Typical examples might include washing, irrigation, product manufacturing, boating, and swimming, respectively.

24. Water is known as the universal solvent because it can dissolve so many substances. Water is able to dissolve many substances because it is polar. The charged ends of water molecules attract molecules of other polar substances.

25. The water cycle is the continuous process by which water moves through the living and nonliving parts of the environment. It includes the processes of evaporation, condensation, and precipitation.

26. The graph shows that water reaches its maximum density at 4°C. As the temperature continues to drop, water becomes less dense. At 0°C, water is less dense than at 4°C.

27. Less dense substances float on more dense substances. The graph shows that ice is less dense than liquid water. Therefore, ice floats on liquid water.

28. Only the fresh water from lakes, rivers, and shallow groundwater is available for human use. Most other water is salt water, which humans cannot use, or ice, which is not available for use.

29. A water molecule has electrically charged areas. As a result, water molecules tend to stick together. On the surface of water, the molecules are being pulled by the molecules around them and by the molecules below them. The result is the tightness across the surface known as surface tension.

30. A cloud forms when water vapor cools in the colder air high in the atmosphere. The cool air causes water vapor to condense, and water droplets clump together around tiny dust particles, causing a cloud to form. If the air is cold enough, ice crystals form rather than water droplets.

Freshwater Resources

Chapter Project

Water Supply and Demand

Water to Drink

Freshwater Pollution

Droughts and Floods

Water Power

Chapter Support

⬛ Chapter Project ⬛ A Precious Resource

The following steps will walk you through the Chapter Project. Use the hints and detailed instructions as you guide your students through the planning, assembly, testing, and presentation of their water treatment systems.

Chapter Project Overview

In this project, students will assemble and demonstrate a model water treatment system that consists of at least two steps.

To introduce the project, show students a container of tap water and a container of dirty water. Encourage students to brainstorm a list of ways by which the dirty water could be cleaned to look as clear as the tap water. Write the list on the chalkboard. Point out to students that in this project, they will make a model water treatment system to clean this dirty water.

Distribute the two-page Chapter Project Overview and the Chapter Project Scoring Rubric. After students have read the pages, answer any questions they have and clarify what will be expected of them in this project.

Set a deadline for the project presentation and some interim dates for checkpoints. Students can fill in these dates on the Project Time Line.

As students observe, create a "cleanness scale" that they can use to judge how well their model treatment systems have cleaned the dirty water.

1. Have on hand a large container of dirty water and a large container of tap water or distilled water, as well as five large graduated cylinders. Also, prepare ahead of time a container that contains a mixture of half dirty water and half clean water.

2. Place the graduated cylinders in a row on a table. Fill the first cylinder with dirty water. Fill the second cylinder three quarters full with dirty water and then fill to the top with clean water. Fill the third cylinder half full with dirty water and then fill to the top with clean water. Fill the fourth cylinder a quarter full with dirty water and fill to the top with clean water. Fill the last cylinder full with clean water.

3. Have on hand a graduated cylinder that contains a half-and-half mixture of dirty water and clean water. Challenge students to compare this mixture to the mixtures in the "cleanness scale" and determine which it matches best. Point out that this will be the way in which they can determine how well they have cleaned water with their model treatment systems.

Distribute Chapter Project Worksheet 1. This activity can be done by pairs of students or in small groups.

Distribute Chapter Project Worksheet 2. This activity can be done by pairs of students or in small groups.

Materials and Preparation

You will need a supply of dirty water for both Worksheet 1 and for groups to use to test their systems. You can make dirty water by adding one teaspoon of fuller's earth per cup of tap water. (Fuller's earth is available at most hardware stores.) You can also collect a supply of dirty water from a local lake, river, or pond. Make or collect as much dirty water as you need at the beginning of the project so that the water will be consistently dirty for all groups and for every trial. Make sure that students understand that they should never taste this water, even after it is cleaned by their systems. Remind students to wash their hands with soap after they have handled the water.

For Worksheet 1, each group will need the following materials: dirty water, a 2-L clear plastic bottle with the bottom cut off, a large beaker to serve as a catch basin for filtered water, nylon fabric, a rubber band, fine sand, gravel of various sizes, activated charcoal, a coffee filter or some other kind of commercial filter, and various kinds of fabric.

Prepare the filtering apparatus for Worksheet 1 by cutting off the bottom of a 2-L clear plastic bottle, as shown in Figure 1a. Figure 1b shows how the neck of the bottle can be placed in a beaker, which will collect the filtered water.

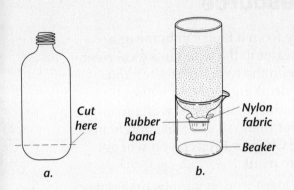

a. b.

Cut here — Rubber band — Nylon fabric — Beaker

Clarify who will supply the materials needed for the model treatment systems that the students design. Materials may include those needed for coagulation, distillation, and filtration. Help students find materials that you cannot supply.

Keep Students on Track— Section 1

Review each student's design and flowchart on Worksheet 2.

Help students who are having trouble designing a system of more than one step. Refer them to the activities on aeration, coagulation, and settling described in the Teacher's Edition for Section 1.

Keep Students on Track— Section 3

Review students' designs, making sure that each design has at least two steps. At this point, help students collect the materials they need to assemble and test their systems.

Advise students to use tap water for the first test of their treatment systems. They need to check for leaks or other problems. Encourage them to make necessary changes if leaks occur.

Keep Students on Track— Section 4

Provide each student with 1 L of dirty water to run through his or her model treatment system.

Encourage students to make changes and repairs in the system in preparation for the presentation to the class. Help students troubleshoot their models.

Chapter Project Wrap-Up

As you review students' model treatment systems, you may wish to have each student briefly walk you through his or her presentation to the class. Help students decide which process can be demonstrated and which process would take too long. For example, an aeration step could be presented, while a settling step would take too long.

Provide class time for presentations. Allow each student to present his or her model treatment system, demonstrate one part of the system, show the final product, and explain the processes involved in the steps of the system. Each student should indicate how much of the 1 L of dirty water the treatment system recovered and refer to the "cleanness scale" to show how well the system worked.

After all of the presentations have been made, discuss with students what conclusions they can draw from their work. Have them compare systems for similarities and differences as well as for how well each worked.

Encourage students to evaluate in their journals how well they accomplished what they set out to do and to make whatever suggestions they think could have made the project better.

Extensions

Challenge students to design a water treatment system by using the best ideas from the projects presented. Encourage a few students to build and test such a system and report their findings to the class.

Freshwater Resources

△Lab zone Chapter Project ▶ A Precious Resource

Think of the water that you drink every day from a faucet at home or a drinking fountain at school. Compare that water to the water in a local river or lake. There's an obvious difference between the two, isn't there? You probably drink water from home or from a drinking fountain without thinking about it, but you might not even bathe or shower in water from a river or lake, much less drink it. Yet the water in the river or lake might just be the source of your drinking water. In the Chapter Project, you will get some idea of how dirty water is made safe to drink.

First, you will explore the filtration of water through various materials. As you will see, filtration is one way to clean water. Second, you will design a two-step model water treatment system that cleans dirty water. Third, you will assemble and test the treatment system you've designed. Finally, you will present your water treatment system to the class.

Project Rules

■ Explore the filtration of water by completing Chapter Project Worksheet 1. After you have observed filtration, you may want to include this process as one of your steps. However, including filtration in your model treatment system is not required.

■ Complete Chapter Project Worksheet 1. Use this worksheet to make your own design of a model water treatment system. This design must include at least two steps. That is, it should have more than one process to clean dirty water. To complete the worksheet, describe the steps, make a flow-chart that represents the system, and make a sketch of the system. This design should include two steps for cleaning dirty water.

■ Assemble and test the model treatment system. Gather the materials you need to assemble the system. Your teacher can provide some materials, but you may want to bring some items from home. When the system is complete, test it with tap water for leaks and other problems.

■ Use your system to clean 1 L of dirty water. Find out how well your system works. Your treatment system will be evaluated according to how well it cleans water and how much water it recovers. The goal is to recover as much of the original 1 L of water as possible.

■ Make your presentation to the class. In making this presentation, you and your group should describe the steps of the system, demonstrate at least one of the steps, and explain the processes involved. Also report your results.

Freshwater Resources · *Chapter Project*   **Overview**

Project Hints

- Study the figure in this chapter that shows drinking-water treatment. The processes used by a drinking-water treatment plant are those you and your group will want to consider using in your model treatment system.

- Make a list of all the ways that substances in water can be removed. Then think of simple ways such processes could be done in a model.

- Don't limit yourself to the processes described in your text. Be open to new ideas.

- Make sure the system you assemble is watertight. You want to recover as much clean water as possible. Leaks are your enemy!

Project Timeline

Task	Due Date
1. Complete Chapter Project Worksheet 1.	_____
2. Complete Chapter Project Worksheet 2.	_____
3. Complete design.	_____
4. Assemble model treatment system.	_____
5. Test system for leaks.	_____
6. Test system with dirty water.	_____
7. Revise design as necessary.	_____
8. Make presentation to class.	_____

Freshwater Resources

Freshwater Resources • *Chapter Project*

What Materials Filter Water Best?

Problem
What combination of materials filter dirty water best?

Materials

dirty water

2-L clear plastic bottle with the bottom cut off

large beaker

nylon fabric

rubber band

fine sand

gravel of various sizes

charcoal

coffee filter

fabric pieces

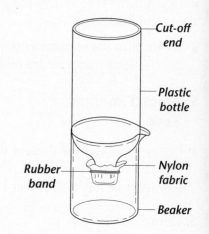

Cut-off end

Plastic bottle

Rubber band

Nylon fabric

Beaker

Devise a Plan   *Review the safety guidelines in Appendix A.*

1. Place the piece of nylon fabric over the narrow opening of the plastic bottle, and secure it with a rubber band. Then place the plastic bottle in the beaker, as shown in the figure.

2. Study the materials provided, and think of a way that they could be used to filter dirty water. You can have as many layers as you want and use them in the order you think will work best. You can use other materials you provide yourself.

3. Pour dirty water through your filter, and observe the results.

Analyze and Conclude
Answer the following items on a separate sheet of paper.

1. Make a sketch that shows the setup and the layers of materials you used.

2. Write a description of the dirty water before you filtered it through any materials.

3. Describe the difference in the water before and after filtration. Which mixture of the "cleanness scale" does the filtered water most resemble?

A Two-Step Design

What processes do you want to include in your model water treatment system? This worksheet will help you design your system.

1. Describe the first step of the treatment system. What will this step remove from the water? What materials will you need for this step?

_____

_____

_____

_____

_____

_____

2. Describe the second step of the treatment system. What will this step remove from the water? What materials will you need for this step?

_____

_____

_____

_____

_____

_____

3. Make a flowchart that explains the steps of your model system.

4. On a separate sheet of paper, make a sketch of your design, showing the two steps you have described.

Freshwater Resources • *Chapter Project*   **Scoring Rubric**

A Precious Resource

In evaluating how well you complete the Chapter Project, your teacher will judge your work in three categories. In each category, a score of 4 is the best rating.

	4	3	2	1
Design and Flowchart	Clearly describes and accurately sketches a treatment system with two excellent steps and makes a flowchart that explains how each step cleans water.	Describes and sketches a treatment system with two good steps and makes a flowchart that suggests how each step cleans water.	Describes and sketches a treatment system with at least one good step and makes a flowchart that vaguely suggests how the system cleans water.	Describes and sketches a treatment system that could not clean water and makes no flowchart or an incomplete one.
Model Treatment System	Model includes two distinct steps and thoroughly cleans and recovers close to 1 L of water.	Model includes two distinct steps and adequately cleans and recovers 3/4 L of water.	Model includes one good step and partially cleans and recovers 1/2 L of water.	Model includes one good step and minimally cleans and recovers less than 1/2 L of water.
Presenting the Model	Makes a thorough and interesting presentation of the system that includes a clear explanation of how each step cleans water.	Makes a thorough presentation of the system that includes an adequate explanation of how each step cleans water.	Makes a presentation of the system that includes a partial explanation of how the system cleans water.	Makes a presentation of the system that includes a weak or confused explanation of how the system could clean water.

Water Supply and Demand

Ability Levels Key
L1 Basic to Average
L2 For All Students
L3 Average to Advanced

 3–4 periods, 1–2 blocks

Objectives

H.2.1.1 Identify ways that people use water.
H.2.1.2 Describe some ways to conserve available fresh water.
H.2.1.3 Discuss some possible sources of water for the future.

Key Terms

• irrigation • conservation • desalination

Local Standards

PRETEACH

Build Background Knowledge
Challenge students to think of ways they directly and indirectly use water every day.

 **Discover Activity** *Can You Find a Balance?* **L1**

Targeted Resources

❑ **All in One Teaching Resources**
   L2 Reading Strategy Transparency H15:Using Prior Knowledge
❑ ⊙ **Presentation-Pro CD-ROM**

INSTRUCT

How People Use Water Use a map of an area where water is scarce to discuss how water is used.
Conserving Water Use the three R's to help students discuss ways to conserve water.
Fresh Water for the Future Discuss methods to obtain fresh water from ocean water and icebergs.

 Skills Lab *Getting the Salt Out* **L2**

Targeted Resources

❑ **All in One Teaching Resources**
   L2 Guided Reading, pp. 121–123
   L2 Transparency H16
   L2 Lab: *Getting the Salt Out*,
      pp. 126–127
❑ **Lab Activity Video/DVD**
   Skills Lab: *Getting the Salt Out*
❑ **PHSchool.com** Web Code: cfd-3021
❑ ⊙ **Student Edition on Audio CD**

ASSESS

Section Assessment Questions
⟳ Have students use their graphic organizers with what they know and have learned about water conservation to answer the questions.

Reteach
As a class, list the ways that water is used and ways to conserve water.

Targeted Resources

❑ **All in One Teaching Resources**
   Section Summary, p. 120
   L1 Review and Reinforce, p. 124
   L3 Enrich, p. 125

Freshwater Resources

Freshwater Resources • *Section Summary*

Water Supply and Demand

Guide for Reading

- How do people use water?

- What are some ways to conserve available fresh water?

- What are some possible sources of water for the future?

People use water for household purposes, industry, agriculture, transportation, and recreation. As you know, water is constantly recycled in the water cycle. However, sometimes water is used faster than it can be replaced by precipitation. A water shortage occurs when there is too little water or too great a demand on an area—or both. A water shortage may occur because of natural processes, or it can occur because of rapidly growing human needs.

Think of all the ways water is used in the home. There are many demands on water for home use. Industries use water. For example, power plants and steel mills need huge volumes of water to cool hot machinery.

Water has also been used transport people and goods since ancient times. If you look at a map of the United States, you will notice that many large cities are located on coasts. Ocean travel led to the growth of these port cities. In early America, rivers also served as natural highways.

Water is also needed for agriculture. However, some areas don't receive enough regular rainfall for agriculture. In such places, farmland must be irrigated. **Irrigation** is the process of supplying water to areas of land to make them suitable for growing crops.

During a water shortage, people often try to avoid wasting water. **Conservation** is the practice of using less of a resource so that it will not be used up. **Reducing water use, recycling water, and reusing water are three ways to conserve water.**

As the use of water in the world increases, so does the need for water. An obvious place to find a new source for water is the ocean. For thousands of years, people have tried to make fresh water from salt water. One possible method of obtaining fresh water from salt water is called **desalination.** A technique called distillation involves boiling water so that it evaporates, leaving the salt behind. The water vapor is then condensed to produce liquid fresh water. Freezing salt water, flowing salt water through a filter, and melting icebergs are also possible methods of meeting future water needs.

Name _____ Date _____ Class_____

Water Supply and Demand

This section explains how the supply of water and the demand for water can change. The section also describes ways to conserve water and new ways of obtaining fresh water that may be used in the future.

Use Target Reading Skills

Before you read, write what you know about water conservation. As you read, write what you learn.

What You Know
1. I can conserve water by taking shorter showers.
2.
3.

What You Learned
1.
2.
3.

How People Use Water

1. Is the following sentence true or false? Water is a nonrenewable resource. _____

2. When does a water shortage occur?

_____

_____

Freshwater Resources • *Guided Reading and Study*

Water Supply and Demand *(continued)*

3. The condition of scarce rainfall for a few years is known as a(n)
_____.

4. Circle the letter of each sentence that is true about droughts.
   a. They affect the supply of surface water.
   b. They affect the supply of groundwater.
   c. They cause the water table to rise.
   d. They may cause wells to run dry.

5. How can an aquifer be recharged naturally after a drought?
   _____

   _____

Conserving Water

6. Using a resource wisely so that it will not be used up is called
_____.

7. Circle the letter of each choice that helps conserve water in the home.
   a. Taking shorter showers
   b. Watering the lawn around noon instead of early or late in the day
   c. Keeping a pitcher of drinking water in the refrigerator
   d. Running the washing machine only when you have small loads

8. Is the following sentence true or false? In the United States, the biggest
use of water is for agriculture. _____

9. How do sprinkler and drip irrigation systems help conserve water?
   _____

10. Complete the concept map.

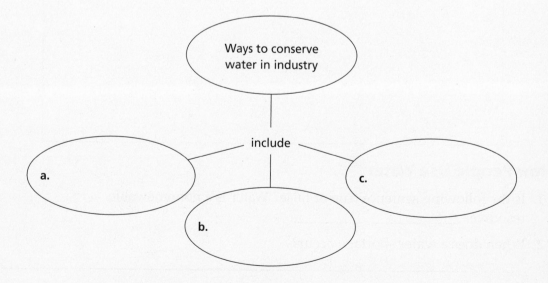

Name _____ Date _____ Class_____

Freshwater Resources · *Guided Reading and Study*

Fresh Water for the Future

11. Circle the letter of the choice that gives the correct sequence of steps in distillation.
    a. Evaporation, boiling, condensation
    b. Boiling, condensation, evaporation
    c. Boiling, evaporation, condensation
    d. Condensation, boiling, evaporation

12. The process of obtaining fresh water from salt water is called
    _____.

13. How could an iceberg be used to supply fresh water to a dry region on the coast of Africa or South America?
    _____
    _____
    _____
    _____

14. What environmental questions have been raised about using icebergs for fresh water?
    _____
    _____
    _____

Freshwater Resources · *Review and Reinforce*

Water Supply and Demand

Understanding Main Ideas

Complete the table below by stating whether each situation generally increases or reduces the water supply.

Situation	Affects Water Supply
A drought occurs throughout a region.	1. _____
A city builds a desalination plant.	2. _____
Water is pumped from an aquifer faster than the aquifer can be recharged.	3. _____
A new mining company begins using water to flush out the mines that it digs.	4._____
A wastewater treatment plant pumps water into shallow ponds to feed an aquifer.	5. _____

Answer the following on a separate sheet of paper.

6. How does carrying irrigation water into fields through open ditches waste water?

7. Give an example of water conservation in industry.

Building Vocabulary

Fill in the blank to complete each statement.

8. The process of obtaining fresh water from salt water is called _____.

9. A process of supplying water to areas of land to make them suitable for growing crops is called _____.

10. Using a resource wisely so that it will not be used up is called _____.

Freshwater Resources • *Enrich*

Whose Water Is It?

The Colorado River begins in the Rocky Mountains, flows through the Grand Canyon, and finally empties into the Gulf of California in northern Mexico. Dams have been built along the Colorado River, creating huge reservoirs such as Lake Powell. This river is a very important source of water for cities and towns in several states, including Arizona and California. Much of the river's water is used to irrigate large farms in this dry region of the country. Without this water, farming would be difficult, and people in many cities would not have enough water for business and home use. In most years, though, water shortages are common in the region. The table below provides clues as to why.

Distribution of Water from the Colorado River

Water Supply	Amount (millions of liters)
Average yearly flow of water, 1930–1980	16.1
Water Demand	
Water used near Colorado River	8.0
Water pumped to California	6.3
Water used in Phoenix, Arizona, area	1.2
Water lost to evaporation	1.9
Water absorbed into banks of Lake Powell	0.6
Water lost to shoreline plants	0.6
Water designated for Mexico	1.9

Answer the following questions on a separate sheet of paper.

1. How much of the Colorado River water is used by people in the western United States?
2. How much water is lost to natural processes (evaporation, absorbed into banks, lost to shoreline plants)?
3. What is the total yearly demand for the water in the Colorado River?
4. How does yearly demand for the water in the Colorado River compare with the yearly supply of water?
5. How would you propose to balance the supply and demand of water from the Colorado River?

Freshwater Resources • *Skills Lab*

Getting the Salt Out

Making Models

Desalination plants use many methods to produce fresh water from ocean water. In this lab, you will make a model of a desalination plant, using the method of distillation.

Problem

How can distillation be used to obtain fresh water from salt water?

Materials

hot plate	plastic tube
plastic spoon	rubber stopper
ice	250-mL beaker
stirring rod	shallow pan
rubber tubing, 50 cm	500-mL flask
aluminum foil	salt
water, 100 mL	

Procedure   *Review the safety guidelines in Appendix A.*

1. Pour 100 mL of water into the flask.
2. Add one spoonful of salt to the water in the flask and stir until dissolved. The solution should not be cloudy.
3. Gently insert the plastic tube through the hole of the rubber stopper. Do not force the tube into the hole; ask your teacher for help if you are having difficulty.
4. Insert one end of the plastic tube into the rubber tubing.
5. Put the rubber stopper in the flask. The bottom of the plastic tube should be above the surface of the solution.
6. Cover the beaker with aluminum foil. Press the edges of the foil against the beaker.
7. Push the free end of the rubber tubing through the center of the aluminum foil covering the top of the beaker.
8. Place the beaker, surrounded by ice, in the pan.

Freshwater Resources • *Skills Lab*

9. Put the flask on the hot plate, keeping it away from the pan of ice. (Your setup should look like the setup in the photo in your text.) Turn the hot plate on. Bring the solution to a boil. **CAUTION:** *Do not touch the hot plate or flask. Do not allow the solution to boil completely away.*

10. Observe what happens in the flask and the beaker. Continue heating the solution until a liquid has accumulated in the beaker.

11. Turn off the hot plate, and allow the flask and the beaker to cool. What is left behind in the flask? Record your observations.

Analyze and Conclude

Write an answer for each question. If you need more space, use the back of this sheet.

1. What happened to the water in the flask during the boiling process? What happened to the salt?

   _____

   _____

   _____

   _____

2. What did the water in the flask represent? What did the water in the beaker represent?

   _____

   _____

   _____

3. Based on your results, is distillation a useful method for obtaining fresh water from salt water? Why or why not?

   _____

   _____

   _____

4. **Think About It** Imagine building a desalination plant that uses the method of distillation to produce water for a city. What difficulties might you encounter in using this process on such a large scale?

   _____

   _____

   _____

   _____

Design an Experiment

How could you change the setup and procedure to recover fresh water from salt water without using the hot plate? Design an experiment to accomplish this goal. *Obtain your teacher's permission before carrying out your experiment.*

Water to Drink

2–3 periods, 1–1 1/2 blocks

Ability Levels Key

L1 Basic to Average
L2 For All Students
L3 Average to Advanced

Objectives

H.2.2.1 Identify factors that affect water quality.
H.2.2.2 Explain why drinking water is treated before being consumed.
H.2.2.3 Describe what happens to wastewater in most communities.

Key Terms

• water quality • concentration • pH
• hardness • filtration • coagulation • sewage

Local Standards

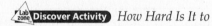

PRETEACH

Build Background Knowledge
Display a glass of water, and elicit responses on where the water came from.

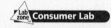 **Discover Activity** *How Hard Is It to Move Water?* **L1**

Targeted Resources

❏ **All in One** **Teaching Resources**
  L2 Reading Strategy Transparency H17: Sequencing

❏ 💿 **Presentation-Pro CD-ROM**

INSTRUCT

Water Quality Ask questions to help students identify factors that affect water quality.
Treating Drinking Water Use a diagram to sequence how water is treated and why each step is required.
Treating Wastewater Discuss where wastewater goes for treatment and how it is treated in a septic tank.

Lab zone **Consumer Lab** *Testing Water* **L2**

Targeted Resources

❏ **All in One** **Teaching Resources**
  L2 Guided Reading, pp. 130–133
  L2 Transparencies H18, H19
  L2 Lab: *Testing Water*, pp. 136–138
❏ **PHSchool.com** Web Code: cfd-3022
❏ 💿 **Student Edition on Audio CD**

ASSESS

Section Assessment Questions
🔁 Have students use their flowcharts sequencing the steps in drinking-water treatment to answer the questions.

Reteach
Draw a diagram to show how drinking water is treated and distributed.

Targeted Resources

❏ **All in One** **Teaching Resources**
  Section Summary, p. 129
  L1 Review and Reinforce, p. 134
  L3 Enrich, p. 135

Freshwater Resources · *Section Summary*

Water to Drink

Guide for Reading

■ What factors affect water quality?

■ Why is drinking water often treated before people drink it?

■ What happens to wastewater in most communities?

Water quality is a measurement of those substances in water other than water molecules. **Some substances, such as iron, can affect the taste or color of water but are harmless unless present at very high levels. Other substances, such as certain chemicals and microorganisms, can be harmful to health.** In the United States, the Environmental Protection Agency (EPA) is responsible for developing water-quality standards. These standards set concentration limits for certain substances. A **concentration** is the amount of one substance in a certain volume of another substance.

The pH level of water also affects its quality. The **pH** of water is a measurement of how acidic or basic the water is, on a scale of 0 to 14. Pure water has a pH of 7—it is neutral, meaning that it is neither an acid nor a base.

The combined level of two minerals, calcium and magnesium, in a sample of water is referred to as the **hardness** of that sample. Hard water contains high levels of calcium and magnesium. Soft water, on the other hand, contains lower levels of calcium and magnesium.

How can you be sure that the quality of water is good? **Water from both public and private supplies often needs some treatment to ensure that it is clean and safe to drink.** The first step in treating water from a lake is usually filtration. **Filtration** is the process of passing water through a series of screens that allow the water through, but not larger, solid particles.

In the second step, a chemical such as alum is added to cause sticky globs, called flocs, to form. Other particles in the water stick to the flocs in a process called **coagulation**. The heavy clumps sink to the bottom in the settling basins. The water is then filtered again.

What happens after used water goes down the drain? The wastewater and the different kinds of wastes in it are called **sewage. Two ways that communities handle sewage are septic systems and wastewater treatment plants.** Most communities treat their wastewater to make it safe to return to the environment.

Freshwater Resources • *Guided Reading and Study*

Water to Drink

This section describes sources of drinking water, how drinking water is treated to make it safe, and how water is distributed to homes and businesses. The section also describes how wastewater is treated so that it can be returned safely to the environment.

Use Target Reading Skills

As you read, make a flowchart that shows the steps of drinking-water treatment.

Drinking-Water Treatment

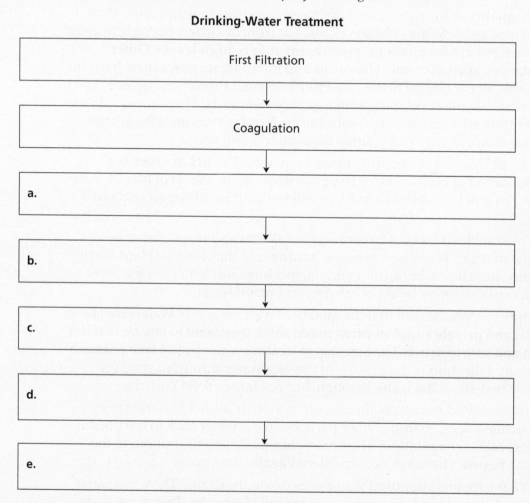

First Filtration

↓

Coagulation

↓

a.

↓

b.

↓

c.

↓

d.

↓

e.

Water Quality

1. Circle the letter of each choice that is an important source of drinking water in the United States.

   a. reservoirs   **b.** rivers
   c. oceans   **d.** lakes

2. Most people in rural areas of the United States get their drinking water from

   _____.

3. How do large communities maintain public water supplies?

   _____

   _____

Freshwater Resources · *Guided Reading and Study*

4. A measurement of those substances in water other than water molecules is referred to as _____.

5. Is the following sentence true or false? The pH of water is a measurement of how acidic or basic the water is. _____

6. Is the following sentence true or false? The higher the pH, the more acidic the water. _____

7. How can acidic water cause problems?

   _____

   _____

8. The combined level of calcium and magnesium in water is referred to as

   _____.

9. What is the main problem with hard water for most people?

   _____

   _____

10. What does the coliform count measure?

    _____

    _____

11. Is the following sentence true or false? A high coliform count may indicate that the water contains more than one kind of disease-causing organism.

    _____

12. The amount of one substance in a certain volume of another substance is called

    _____.

13. Is the following sentence true or false? EPA water-quality standards allow drinking water to contain only water molecules. _____

Treating Drinking Water

14. Add arrows to the drawing to show the direction in which water moves through a water treatment plant.

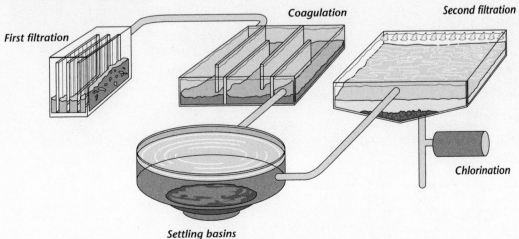

First filtration

Coagulation

Second filtration

Chlorination

Settling basins

Freshwater Resources • *Guided Reading and Study*

Water to Drink *(continued)*

15. When alum is added to water, sticky globs, or _____, form.

Match the step in the water treatment process with its description.

Step	Description
____ 16. filtration	a. Water is treated to create flocs.
____ 17. coagulation	b. Water is treated to kill microorganisms.
____ 18. chlorination	c. Water is passed through screens to remove objects.

19. Circle the letter of the choice that shows the correct sequence that water follows after it has been treated.

 a. Small pipes, central pumping station, water mains
 b. Central pumping station, water mains, small pipes
 c. Water mains, small pipes, central pumping station
 d. Central pumping station, small pipes, water mains

20. What causes the water to move through a community's system of underground water pipes?

_____

_____

_____

Freshwater Resources • *Guided Reading and Study*

Treating Wastewater

21. Sewage is carried away from many homes by

_____.

22. Complete the table.

Wastewater Terms

Term	What It Means
a.	Wastewater and the different kinds of wastes that it contains
b.	Deposits of fine solids that settle out from wastewater in a septic system
c.	Treated wastewater that you cannot drink

23. An underground tank containing bacteria that treat wastewater is called a(n) _____.

24. The area of ground in a septic system that the water filters through is called a(n) _____.

Freshwater Resources

Freshwater Resources ▪ *Review and Reinforce*

Water to Drink

Understanding Main Ideas

Complete the flowchart by filling in the spaces with the names of the steps.

Drinking-Water Treatment

1. _____ Fish, leaves, and trash removed.

2. _____ Alum is added to form flocs.

3. _____ Water and flocs sink.

4. _____ Water trickles through sand or gravel.

5. _____ Chlorine is added to kill organisms.

6. _____ Bubbling air through the water reduces unpleasant odors and taste.

7. _____ Minerals are added to soften the water.

Building Vocabulary

Match each term with its definition by writing the letter of the correct definition on the line beside the term in the left column.

_____ 8. filtration

_____ 9. concentration

_____ 10. pH

_____ 11. hardness

_____ 12. water quality

_____ 13. sewage

_____ 14. coagulation

a. a measurement of how acidic or basic a substance is

b. wastewater and the different kinds of wastes in it

c. forming of heavy clumps

d. the toal amount of calcium and magnesium in water

e. process of passing water through a series of screens that allow the water to pass, but not solid particles

f. the amount of one substance in a certain volume of another substance

g. the measurement of substances in water other than water molecules

The Path of Water Through a City

The figure below shows in a general way the path of water through a city.
Study the figure, and then answer the questions below.

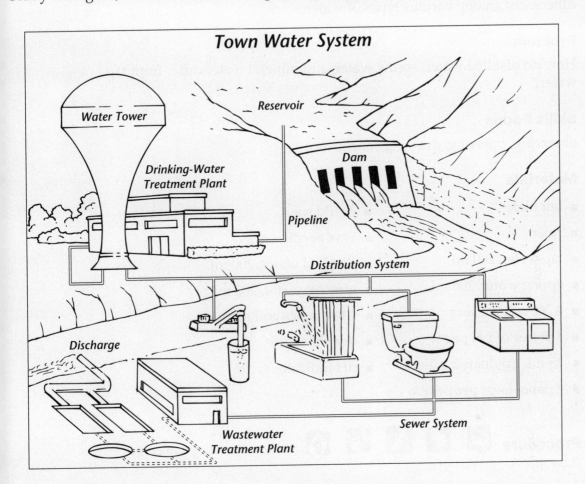

Answer the following questions on a separate sheet of paper.

1. What is this city's source of water?
2. What happens to the water before it is distributed to homes?
3. What is the purpose of the water tower?
4. What happens to the water before it is discharged into the river?

Freshwater Resources ▪ *Consumer Lab*

Testing Water

How does the bottled water sold in supermarkets differ from the water that comes out of your kitchen faucet? In this lab, you will discover some differences among various types of water.

Problem

How do distilled water, spring water, and mineral water differ from tap water?

Skills Focus

observing, inferring, drawing conclusions

Materials

- hot plate
- ruler
- tap water, 200 mL
- spring water, 200 mL
- 4 200-mL beakers
- 4 pieces of pH paper
- 25-mL graduated cylinder
- 4 paper cups per person
- liquid soap
- wax pencil
- distilled water, 200 mL
- mineral water, 200 mL
- 4 test tubes and stoppers
- test tube rack
- pH indicator chart

Procedure 🦺 🧤 🧪 🧹 🔥 *Review the safety symbols in Appendix A.*

1. Use the data table on the next page to record your results.
2. Label the beakers A, B, C, and D. Pour 100 mL of tap water into beaker A. Pour 100 mL of the other water samples into the correct beaker (refer to the data table).
3. Heat each water sample on a hot plate until about 20 mL remains. Do not allow the water to boil completely away. **CAUTION:** *Do not touch the hot plate or beakers.*
4. After the water samples have cooled, look for solids that make the water cloudy. Rank the samples from 1 to 4, where 1 has the fewest visible solids and 4 has the most visible solids. Record your rankings in the data table.

Name _____ Date _____ Class _____

Freshwater Resources • *Consumer Lab*

5. Label four test tubes A, B, C, and D. Pour 10 mL of each water sample from the source bottle into the correct test tube.

6. Dip a piece of pH paper into test tube A to measure its acidity. Match the color of the pH paper to a number on the pH indicator chart. Record the pH (0–14) in your data table.

7. Repeat Step 6 for the other samples.

8. Add two drops of liquid soap to test tube A. Put a stopper in the test tube and shake it 30 times. With the ruler, measure the height of the soapsuds in the test tube. Record your measurement in your data table.

9. Repeat Step 8 for the other samples.

10. Label the four cups A, B, C, and D. Write your name on each cup.

11. Pour a little tap water into cup A directly from the original source bottle. Taste the tap water. In your data table, describe the taste using one or more of these words: *salty, flat, bitter, metallic, refreshing, tasteless.*
CAUTION: *Do not conduct the taste test in a lab room. Use a clean cup for each sample and discard it after use.*

12. Repeat Step 11 with the other samples.

Data Table

Water Sample	Visible Solids (1–4)	pH (0–14)	Soapsud Height (cm)	Taste
A – Tap water				
B – Distilled water				
C – Spring water				
D – Mineral water				

Freshwater Resources • *Consumer Lab*

Testing Water *(continued)*

Analyze and Conclude

Write an answer for each question. If you need more space, use the back of this sheet.

1. Review your data table. Compare each of the bottled water samples to the tap water sample. What similarities and differences did you detect?

   _____

   _____

   _____

2. Rank the samples from the one with the fewest soapsuds to the one with the most. Compare this ranking to the one for visible solids. What pattern do you see? What do both of these tests have to do with the hardness of water?

   _____

   _____

   _____

3. What other information about the water samples might you need before deciding which one to drink regularly? Explain.

   _____

   _____

   _____

4. Based on your results, which sample would you most want to use for (a) drinking, (b) boiling in a kettle, and (c) washing laundry? Which sample would you least want to use for each purpose? Explain.

   _____

   _____

   _____

5. **Think About It** Create a brochure to educate consumers about water quality. Include information about acidity, hardness, and other factors that can affect the appearance, taste, and safety of drinking water.

More to Explore

Conduct a survey to find out what percentage of people buy bottled mineral water, distilled water, and spring water. Why do they buy each type of water, and how do they use it in their homes?

Freshwater Pollution

🕐 *2–3 periods, 1–1 1/2 blocks*

Ability Levels Key
L1 Basic to Average
L2 For All Students
L3 Average to Advanced

Objectives

H.2.3.1 Explain one way that sources of pollution are classified.

H.2.3.2 Identify three sources of water pollution.

H.2.3.3 Describe the two parts of the solution to water pollution.

Key Terms

• water pollution • pollutant • point source
• nonpoint source • acid rain • pesticide

Local Standards

PRETEACH

Build Background Knowledge
Invite students to define water pollution and name possible things that pollute water.

 **Discover Activity** *Will the Pollution Reach Your Wells?* **L1**

Targeted Resources

❑ **All in One Teaching Resources**
  L2 Reading Strategy Transparency H20: Outlining
❑ 💿 **Presentation-Pro CD-ROM**

INSTRUCT

What Is Pollution? Use a table to classify sources of pollution as point or nonpoint.

Human Wastes Discuss how water becomes contaminated with human and animal wastes.

Industrial Wastes Use photographs to examine sources of water pollution from industrial wastes.

Chemical Runoff Consider how chemical runoff from farms and roads gets into water sources.

Water Pollution Solutions Explain and give examples of the two parts to solving water pollution.

Targeted Resources

❑ **All in One Teaching Resources**
  L2 Guided Reading, pp. 141–144
  L2 Transparencies H21, H22
❑ **www.SciLinks.org** Web Code: scn-0823
❑ 💿 **Student Edition on Audio CD**

ASSESS

Section Assessment Questions
🔊 Have students use their outlines of the section to answer the questions.

Reteach
Brainstorm examples of water pollution, and classify them according to source and type.

Targeted Resources

❑ **All in One Teaching Resources**
Section Summary, p. 140
  L1 Review and Reinforce, p. 145
  L3 Enrich, p. 146

Freshwater Pollution

Guide for Reading

- What is one way that sources of pollution are classified?

- What are four sources of water pollution?

- What are the two parts of the solution to water pollution?

The addition of any substance that has a negative effect on water or the living things that depend on water is called **water pollution.** Water pollution can affect surface water, groundwater, and even precipitation. The substances that cause water pollution are called **pollutants.** Types of pollutants include disease-causing organisms, pesticides and fertilizers, industrial chemicals, metals, radioactive wastes, and petroleum products.

Sources of polution are classified, in part, on how they enter a body of water. A **point source** is a specific source of pollution that can be identified, such as a leaking pipe. A **nonpoint source** is a widely spread source of pollution that can't be tied to a specific point of origin, such as runoff from a highway. **The three major sources of water pollution are human wastes, industrial wastes, and chemical runoff.**

Dumping human wastes into drinking water can spread disease because human wastes contain disease-causing organisms. Water treatment usually kills bacteria. During heavy rains and floods, sewage from sanitary sewers can pollute the drinking water. In rural areas, livestock wastes that run off into water supplies can also be a problem.

Water pollution from factories and mines is a more common problem than sewage in most areas. Some factories release toxic chemicals directly into nearby waters. Smoke and exhaust from power plants, factories, and vehicles release chemicals into the atmosphere. The result is rain or other forms of precipitation that are more acidic than normal, called **acid rain.** Warm water from factories can also act as a pollutant by changing the temperature of streams or ponds into which it is discharged.

Agricultural chemicals that can enter surface water in runoff from fields include fertilizers and pesticides. **Pesticides** are chemicals intended to kill insects and other organisms that damage crops. When pesticides are washed from fields by rain or irrigation, they can harm other organisms. Runoff from roads is another source of pollution. Gasoline, oil, and salt in road runoff pollute rivers, lakes, and groundwater. **Solving pollution problems involves cleaning up existing problems as well as preventing new ones.**

Many pollutants are eventually removed from bodies of fresh water through natural cleaning processes. Living things in lakes, streams, and wetlands filter out and break down waste materials. Plant roots filter larger particles from water, and certain bacteria break down toxic chemicals in rivers and lakes. The rock and sand of an aquifer naturally filter and purify groundwater.

Freshwater Pollution

This section describes ways that fresh water can become polluted. The section also describes how freshwater pollution can be cleaned up and how it can be prevented.

Use Target Reading Skills

As you read, make an outline about freshwater pollution.

Freshwater Pollution

I.   What is pollution?
    A. Point and nonpoint sources
    B.
 	
II.
    A.
    B.
 	
III.
    A.
    B.
    C.
 	
IV.
    A.
    B.
 	
V.
    A.
    B.

What Is Pollution?

1. The addition of any substance that has a negative effect on water or the living things that depend on water is called _____.

2. Circle the letter of each sentence that is true about water pollution.

    a. It can affect surface water.

    b. It cannot affect groundwater.

    c. It results from human activities.

    d. It does not result from natural causes.

3. The substances that cause pollution are called

    _____.

4. Is the following sentence true or false? It is safe to bathe or swim in polluted water as long as you do not drink it.

    _____

5. What are some types of pollutants found in water?

    _____

    _____

Freshwater Resources • *Guided Reading and Study*

Freshwater Pollution *(continued)*

6. List the four major sources of water pollution.

a. _____   b. _____

c. _____   d. _____

7. What is the difference between a point source and a nonpoint source of water pollution?

_____

_____

_____

Human Wastes

8. How can a flood cause polluted surface water?

_____

_____

_____

9. Is the following sentence true or false? Disposing of human waste is a problem only in big cities. _____

Industrial Wastes

10. Complete the concept map.

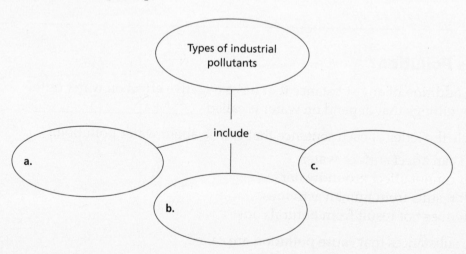

11. Circle the letter of each sentence that is true about toxic chemical wastes from industry.

a. Few industrial processes involve toxic chemicals.
b. Some toxic wastes are side effects of manufacturing and mining.
c. Chemical pollution from factories is now controlled by law.
d. Factories no longer release toxic chemicals directly into rivers and lakes.

12. Rain that is more acidic than normal is called _____.

Freshwater Resources • *Guided Reading and Study*

13. Circle the letter of each sentence that describes an outcome of acid rain.

    a. Fish die off.

    b. Groundwater is polluted with oil and gasoline.

    c. Stone buildings and statues are eaten away.

    d. Lake water becomes acidic.

14. How could warm water act as a pollutant?

_____

_____

_____

_____

Chemical Runoff

15. Is the following sentence true or false? Fertilizers in runoff are a point source of pollution. _____

16. Chemicals intended to kill insects and other organisms that damage crops are called _____.

17. List three pollutants that are found in runoff from roads.

    a. _____   b. _____

    c. _____

18. Is the following sentence true or false? Road runoff is a nonpoint source of pollution. _____

Freshwater Resources

Freshwater Resources · *Guided Reading and Study*

Freshwater Pollution *(continued)*

Water Pollution Solutions

19. Circle the letter of each sentence that describes a way that polluted fresh water is cleaned naturally.

   a. Runoff waters from farm fields dilute the pollution in rivers and lakes.
   b. Plants absorb metals and chemicals from lake and pond water.
   c. Bacteria eat toxic chemicals and oil spills.
   d. Sand and rock layers filter groundwater as it flows down through them.

20. Is the following sentence true or false? Most pollutants are not very difficult to remove. _____

21. Is the following sentence true or false? It is often easier to avoid causing pollution in the first place than it is to clean it up. _____

22. Describe some ways that industry and agriculture can help lessen pollution.

_____

_____

_____

_____

Freshwater Pollution

Understanding Main Ideas

Fill in the spaces in the table below.

Freshwater Pollutants

Pollutant	Major Source of Pollution	Point or Nonpoint Source
Sewage leaking from pipe	Human Waste	1. _____
Toxic wastes leaking from barrels	2. _____	Point source
Salt sprinkled on roads	Runoff from roads	3. _____
Chemicals from factory dumped into a river	Industrial waste	4. _____
Fertilizer in runoff	5. _____	Nonpoint source

Answer the following on a separate sheet of paper.

6. How can water pollution be cleaned up naturally?

7. Explain how runoff from farms can affect ponds and streams.

Building Vocabulary

Fill in the space to complete each statement.

8. Chemicals intended to kill insects and other organisms that damage crops are called _____.

9. The addition of any substance that has a negative effect on water or the living things that depend on water is called _____.

10. Rain and other forms of precipitation that are more acidic than normal are called _____.

Freshwater Resources • *Enrich*

Location, Location

Homeowners in rural areas sometimes discover that it matters a great deal where they dig a well. Remember, a well provides the home with groundwater for drinking and other household purposes. Study the figure below of two houses on a hill. Then answer the questions that follow.

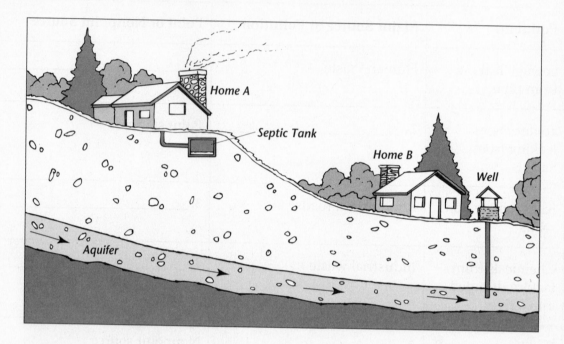

Answer the following questions on a separate sheet of paper.

1. What is the purpose of the septic tank near Home A?
2. What happens to the water that flows into the septic tank?
3. What is the source of Home B's drinking water?
4. If a coliform count were done on the water from the well of Home B, how would you predict that it would compare to the EPA's standard? Explain your answer.
5. How could the pollution problem shown in this situation be solved?

Droughts and Floods

 1–2 periods, 1/2–1 blocks

Ability Levels Key
L1 Basic to Average
L2 For All Students
L3 Average to Advanced

Objectives

H.2.4.1 Explain what a drought is.
H.2.4.2 State what a flood is and explain how the dangers of floods can be reduced.

Key Terms

• drought • flash flood • levee

Local Standards

PRETEACH

Build Background Knowledge

Ask students why conservation practices are needed during periods of low precipitation.

 **Discover Activity** *How Does Dryness Affect Soil?* **L1**

Targeted Resources

❑ **All in One** **Teaching Resources**
   L2 Reading Strategy Transparency
H23: Comparing and Contrasting
❑ 🔘 **Presentation-Pro CD-ROM**

INSTRUCT

Droughts Define a drought, its effects, and how to prepare for one.
Floods Examine the causes and effects of floods.
Flood Precautions Analyze ways of reducing the dangers of floods, including warnings and actions by individuals.

Targeted Resources

❑ **All in One** **Teaching Resources**
   L2 Guided Reading, pp. 149–150
   L2 Transparencies H24, H25
❑ **PHSchool.com** Web Code: cfd-3024
❑ 🔘 **Student Edition on Audio CD**

ASSESS

Section Assessment Questions

🕐 Have students use their graphic organizers comparing and contrasting droughts and floods to answer the questions.

Reteach

Sketch an outline of the section, and ask students to fill in the details of each subheading.

Targeted Resources

❑ **All in One** **Teaching Resources**
Section Summary, p. 148
L1 Review and Reinforce, p. 151
L3 Enrich, p. 152

Freshwater Resources

Freshwater Resources · *Section Summary*

Droughts and Floods

Guide for Reading

- What is a drought?

- What is a flood, and how can the dangers of floods be reduced?

Water shortages can be triggered by human activities, such as overuse of an aquifer. However, natural processes also can cause areas to receive too little water—or conversely, too much water. A certain area might receive, on average, plenty of rainfall to meet its water needs. But if the area experiences a long period of scarce rainfall, a condition know as **drought** might occur. A drought reduces the supplies of groundwater and surface water. Without precipitation to recharge the aquifer, the amount of groundwater in the aquifer decreases.

Droughts are weather-related events. **They are usually caused by dry weather systems that remain in one place for weeks or months at a time.** Droughts can be difficult to predict. However, people can prepare for droughts in several ways. In general, practicing water conservation and soil conservation ensures that when droughts do occur, the effects will be as mild as possible.

Natural processes also can cause areas to receive too much water. All floods occur when the volume of water in a river increases so much that the river overflows its channel. Unexpected floods, called flash floods, are the most dangerous of all because the water rises very rapidly, and people have little time to reach safe ground. A **flash flood** is a sudden, violent flood that occurs within a few hours, or even a few minutes, of a storm.

Using different types of technology, scientists can often issue flood warnings. **Advance warnings help reduce flood damage and loss of life.** Weather satellites supply information that scientists can use to predict flooding. The goal is to issue warnings in time for people to prepare and evacuate if necessary.

For as long as people have lived near rivers, they have tried to control floods. **Building dams is one method of flood control.** There is a natural defense against floods—sediments. As a river overflows, it slows down, depositing its heavier sediments along the river channel. Over time, these deposits build up into long ridges called **levees**. Levees that form naturally help keep the river inside its banks. People sometimes strengthen natural levees with sandbags or stone and concrete to provide further protection against floods.

Droughts and Floods

Use Target Reading Skills

Comparing and Contrasting

Feature	Droughts	Floods
Cause	Scarce rain fall	a. _____
Possible to predict?	b. _____	c. _____
Preparation	d. _____	e. _____
Major effects	f. _____	g. _____

Droughts

1. Fill in the following flowchart.

```
┌─────────────────────────────────────────────┐
│     lack of rainfall                         │
└─────────────────────────────────────────────┘
                      │
                      ▼
┌─────────────────────────────────────────────┐
│  reduces a. _____ and b. _____ │
└─────────────────────────────────────────────┘
                      │
                      ▼
┌─────────────────────────────────────────────┐
│  water in c. _____ decreases     │
└─────────────────────────────────────────────┘
```

2. What are the effects of long-term drought?

_____

_____

3. How can droughts be predicted?

_____

_____

Freshwater Resources • *Guided Reading and Study*

Droughts and Floods *(continued)*

Floods

4. When does a flood occur?

   _____

   _____

5. Is the following sentence true or false? Floods are the most dangerous weather-related events in the United States. _____

6. A sudden, violent flood that occurs within a few hours, or even minutes, of a storm is called a(n) _____.

7. Complete the concept map.

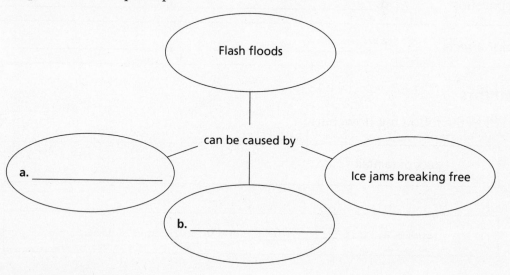

Flood Precautions

8. How can dams help control floods?

   _____

   _____

9. Long ridges of sediments along the channel of a river are called

   _____.

10. Why do scientists try to predict floods?

    _____

    _____

11. What should you do in the event of a flood?

    _____

    _____

    _____

Freshwater Resources ▪ *Review and Reinforce*

Droughts and Floods

Understanding Main Ideas
Answer each of the questions below.

1. What changes might occur in an aquifer because of lack of precipitation?
   _____

2. Lack of precipitation could produce a _____, reducing the
   amount of _____ in the aquifer.

3. Explain how a drought might result in a famine.
   _____
   _____

4. What can be done to prepare for droughts?
   _____
   _____

5. How might melting snow contribute to flooding?
   _____

6. How do weather satellites help scientists predict flooding?
   _____
   _____

7. What are two ways floods can be controlled?
   _____
   _____

8. What leads to most flash floods?
   _____

9. Why do forecasters try to predict flood heights at different points along a river?

10. What is the first rule of flood safety?

11. In addition to high water, what are some other flood hazards?

Building Vocabulary
Fill in the blanks with the correct terms.

12. A sudden violent flood that occurs within a few hours, or even minutes, of a storm
    is a _____.

13. A long period of scarce rainfall is called a _____

14. _____ are naturally formed, heavy sediment deposits along a
    river.

Freshwater Resources · *Enrich*

Where Do Floods Occur?

Not all parts of the United States are equally at risk of floods. Do you know what the risk is in your part of the country? The map below shows recent serious floods that occurred in the United States. These are floods that caused deaths or damage in excess of $500,000.

Recent Serious Floods in the United States

☐ *Deaths*

● *Damage > $500,000*

Alaska   *Hawaii*   *Puerto Rico*

Answer the following questions on a separate sheet of paper.

1. How many serious floods has your state had recently?

2. Which part of the country appears to be least affected by serious floods? Why do you think this is so?

3. Which state has had the largest amount of damage caused by floods?

4. Why are some states more greatly affected by serious floods than others?

5. How does the number of recent serious floods in your state compare with the numbers in other states? Would you classify the risk of serious floods in your state as low, medium, or high?

Water Power

 *1–2 periods, 1/2–1 blocks*

Ability Levels Key
L1 Basic to Average
L2 For All Students
L3 Average to Advanced

Objectives

H.2.5.1 Explain how the energy of moving water can be used to produce electricity.

H.2.5.2 Identify some advantages and disadvantages of hydroelectric power plants.

Key Terms

• kinetic energy • potential energy
• hydroelectric power

Local Standards

PRETEACH

Build Background Knowledge

Show a picture of Niagara Falls or water flowing over a dam, and ask students to describe the force of the water.

Discover Activity *Can Water Do Work?* **L1**

Targeted Resources

☐ **All in One Teaching Resources**
  L2 Reading Strategy Transparency H26: Asking Questions

☐ ◉ **Presentation-Pro CD-ROM**

INSTRUCT

Energy and Moving Water Explain how moving water can be used to produce electricity in terms of how energy changes form.

Hydroelectric Power Plants Compare the advantages of hydroelectric power with other ways of generating electricity, and identify disadvantages of hydroelectric power.

Targeted Resources

☐ **All in One Teaching Resources**
  L2 Guided Reading, pp. 155–157
  L2 Transparency H27

☐ **PHSchool.com** Web Code: cfp-3025

☐ ◉ **Student Edition on Audio CD**

ASSESS

Section Assessment Questions

⟳ Have students use their questions and answers about water power to answer the questions.

Reteach

Draw a diagram of a hydroelectric power plant, and ask students to describe the steps.

Targeted Resources

☐ **All in One Teaching Resources**
  Section Summary, p. 154
  L1 Review and Reinforce, p. 158
  L3 Enrich, p. 159

Freshwater Resources

Freshwater Resources • *Section Summary*

Water Power

Guide for Reading

- How can the energy of moving water be used to produce electricity?

- What are some advantages and disadvantages of hydroelectric power plants?

The energy of moving water is a source of electrical power in many parts of the world. **Hydroelectric power** is electricity produced by the kinetic energy of water moving over a waterfall or through a dam. **Kinetic energy** is the form of energy that an object has when it is moving.

To generate hydroelectric power, engineers build a dam across a river. Water backs up behind the dam, floods the valley, and creates a reservoir. Water stored behind a dam has potential energy. **Potential energy** is energy that is stored and waiting to be used. Potential energy is changed to kinetic energy when the water behind the dam is released.

Hydroelectric power plants capture the kinetic energy of moving water and change it into electrical energy. The water moving through the dam turns the blades of a turbine in a hydroelectric power plant, producing mechanical energy. That energy turns a magnet inside wire coils, producing electric energy.

In some ways, hydroelectric power is an ideal way to produce electricity. **Hydroelectric power is clean, safe, and efficient. Although building a dam is expensive, the water is free and is naturally renewed by the water cycle.** Unlike power plants that burn coal or oil, hydroelectric plants do not contribute to air pollution.

Hydroelectric plants do have limitations, however. Dams affect all living things in the area around them. **Flooding the land behind a dam can change wildlife habitats, as well as farms and towns. In addition, the dam is a barrier across the river.** Some organisms cannot survive the change. Also, sediment deposits build up behind a dam instead of being carried downstream to enrich the flood plain near the river's mouth. A large dam can flood hundreds or thousands of square kilometers, covering towns and valleys with water. Many people may have to relocate when such a dam is built.

Hydroelectric power is the least expensive and least polluting large-scale energy source. Besides electricity, dams can supply water for irrigation and help in flood control.

Freshwater Resources ▪ *Guided Reading and Study*

Water Power

This section describes how water moving over a waterfall or dam can be used to generate electricity. The section also identifies some of the benefits and drawbacks of building dams.

Use Target Reading Skills

Preview the red headings in your textbook. In the graphic organizer, ask a how *or* what *question for each heading. As you read, answer your questions.*

Water Power

Question	Answer
How are energy and moving water related?	Hydroelectric power . . .

Energy and Moving Water

1. Electricity produced by water moving over a waterfall or dam is called _____.

2. Complete the Venn diagram by labeling each circle with the type of energy it represents.

a. _____   b. _____

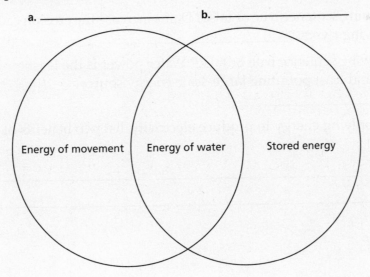

Energy of movement   Energy of water   Stored energy

Freshwater Resources

Freshwater Resources · *Guided Reading and Study*

Water Power *(continued)*

Hydroelectric Power Plants

Match the part of a hydroelectric power plant with the way it converts energy.

	Part		How It Converts Energy
_____	3.	penstock	a. Converts mechanical energy to electrical energy
_____	4.	turbine	b. Converts kinetic energy to mechanical energy
_____	5.	generator	c. Converts potential energy to kinetic energy

6. Circle the letter of each sentence that is true about hydroelectric power.
   a. It is clean.
   b. It is efficient.
   c. It is safe.
   d. It causes air pollution.

7. Is the following sentence true or false? Hydroelectric power can be generated by any source of moving water. _____

8. Circle the letter of each sentence that describes how dams affect the environment.
   a. Dams destroy wildlife habitats.
   b. Dams prevent fish from swimming upstream.
   c. Dams increase fish populations.
   d. Dams enrich farmlands downstream.

9. Is the following sentence true or false? Dams increase the erosion caused by fast-moving rivers. _____

10. Is the following sentence true or false? Water power is the least expensive and least polluting large-scale energy source.

   _____

11. Besides supplying energy to produce electricity, list two benefits of dams.

   a. _____

   b. _____

Freshwater Resources ▪ *Guided Reading and Study*

12. What are the pros and cons of building small dams to supply power to local areas?

_____

_____

_____

_____

_____

Name _____ Date _____ Class _____

Water Power

Understanding Main Ideas

On a separate sheet of paper, classify each label on the figure below as either an advantage or a disadvantage of hydroelectric power. Then write a sentence that explains each of the labels.

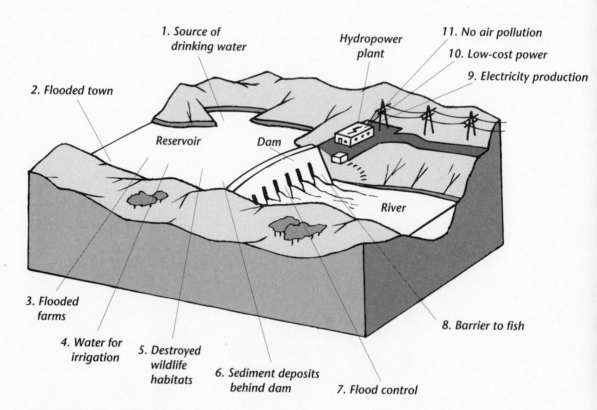

1. Source of drinking water

11. No air pollution

Hydropower plant

10. Low-cost power

9. Electricity production

2. Flooded town

Reservoir

Dam

River

3. Flooded farms

8. Barrier to fish

4. Water for irrigation

5. Destroyed wildlife habitats

6. Sediment deposits behind dam

7. Flood control

Building Vocabulary

Classify each of the following descriptions of energy by writing either potential or kinetic in the blank beside it.

_____ **12.** The form of energy of a moving object

_____ **13.** The form of energy that water behind a dam has

_____ **14.** The form of energy that is stored and waiting to be used

_____ **15.** The form of energy that flowing water has

Hydroelectric Dams: A Case Study

A hydroelectric dam provides benefits to an area, but it often has disadvantages as well. The Aswan High Dam in Egypt is one of the world's most important hydroelectric dams. Read the case study below to find out about the consequences of building this dam.

The Aswan Dam

The Aswan High Dam spans the Nile River in southern Egypt, far from where the river empties into the Mediterranean Sea. The dam opened in 1964 with great expectations that it would serve the people of Egypt well. Building this new dam required flooding farms and towns to create the reservoir, Lake Nasser, behind it. About 80,000 people in Egypt and neighboring Sudan had to relocate. Lake Nasser has since provided the water to irrigate 405,000 hectares of land that was formerly desert. Because this water is available year-round, farmers can raise crops three times a year instead of only once a year.

The Aswan High Dam also supplies the energy needed to produce electricity in hydroelectric power plants. These power plants supply about one third of Egypt's electrical power. The Egyptian capital, Cairo, far to the north, depends on this electricity for its homes and industries.

The dam has stopped the floods that used to cover much of the Nile Valley every year. Although the floods often caused problems for local residents, the floods enriched the soil of the valley by depositing silt. The floods also washed away salts in the soil. To make up for the benefits of floods, farmers now have to treat the land with costly fertilizers. The industries that make the fertilizers use a large share of the electricity produced by the hydropower plants.

Finally, silt is building up behind the dam. Much of that silt used to be deposited at the river's mouth on the Mediterranean Sea. Without that deposition, the sea is creeping inland. The habitats for many kinds of fish have been destroyed because of the changes at the mouth of the river. As a result, thousands of people have lost jobs in the fishing industry.

Answer the following on a separate sheet of paper.

1. What are the benefits that the Aswan High Dam has provided?
2. What problems has the dam caused?
3. In your opinion, do the benefits of the dam outweigh the problems? Give reasons for your answer.

Freshwater Resources

Freshwater Resources ▪ *Key Terms*

Key Terms

Solve the clues with key terms from Chapter 3. Then put the numbered letters in order to reveal the message.

Clues

Key Terms

1. Combined level of calcium and magnesium in water

$\underset{1}{\underline{\quad}}\ \underline{\quad}\ \underline{\quad}\ \underline{\quad}\ \underline{\quad}\ \underset{2}{\underline{\quad}}\ \underline{\quad}\ \underline{\quad}$

2. Sticky globs created during water treatment

$\underline{\quad}\ \underline{\quad}\ \underset{3}{\underline{\quad}}\ \underline{\quad}\ \underline{\quad}\ \underline{\quad}$

3. Chemical intended to kill insects or other pests

$\underset{4}{\underline{\quad}}\ \underline{\quad}\ \underline{\quad}\ \underline{\quad}\ \underline{\quad}\ \underset{5}{\underline{\quad}}\ \underline{\quad}\ \underline{\quad}\ \underline{\quad}$

4. Amount of one substance in a certain volume of another

$\underline{\quad}\ \underset{6}{\underline{\quad}}\ \underset{7}{\underline{\quad}}\ \underline{\quad}\ \underline{\quad}\ \underline{\quad}\ \underline{\quad}\ \underline{\quad}\ \underline{\quad}\ \underline{\quad}\ \underline{\quad}\ \underline{\quad}$

5. Type of underground tank that contains bacteria for treating wastewater

$\underset{8}{\underline{\quad}}\ \underset{9}{\underline{\quad}}\ \underline{\quad}\ \underline{\quad}\ \underline{\quad}\ \underline{\quad}$

6. Using a resource wisely

$\underline{\quad}\ \underline{\quad}\ \underline{\quad}\ \underline{\quad}\ \underline{\quad}\ \underset{10}{\underline{\quad}}\ \underset{11}{\underline{\quad}}\ \underline{\quad}\ \underline{\quad}\ \underline{\quad}\ \underline{\quad}$

7. Sediments that settle out during waste water treatment

$\underline{\quad}\ \underline{\quad}\ \underline{\quad}\ \underline{\quad}\ \underline{\quad}\ \underset{12}{\underline{\quad}}$

8. Water containing human wastes

$\underline{\quad}\ \underline{\quad}\ \underset{13}{\underline{\quad}}\ \underset{14}{\underline{\quad}}\ \underline{\quad}\ \underline{\quad}$

9. Process of passing water through screens to remove objects

$\underline{\quad}\ \underline{\quad}\ \underline{\quad}\ \underset{15}{\underline{\quad}}\ \underline{\quad}\ \underline{\quad}\ \underline{\quad}\ \underline{\quad}\ \underline{\quad}$

10. Process of removing salt from water

$\underline{\quad}\ \underset{16}{\underline{\quad}}\ \underline{\quad}\ \underline{\quad}\ \underline{\quad}\ \underline{\quad}\ \underline{\quad}\ \underline{\quad}\ \underline{\quad}\ \underline{\quad}\ \underline{\quad}$

11. Water shortage due to long periods of low precipitation

$\underline{\quad}\ \underset{17}{\underline{\quad}}\ \underline{\quad}\ \underline{\quad}\ \underline{\quad}\ \underline{\quad}\ \underline{\quad}$

Hidden Message

$\underset{1}{\underline{\quad}}\ \underset{2}{\underline{\quad}}\ \underset{3}{\underline{\quad}}\ \underset{4}{\underline{\quad}}\quad \underset{5}{\underline{\quad}}\ \underset{6}{\underline{\quad}}\ \underset{7}{\underline{\quad}}\ \underset{8}{\underline{\quad}}\ \underset{9}{\underline{\quad}}\ \underset{10}{\underline{\quad}}\ \underset{11}{\underline{\quad}}\ \underset{12}{\underline{\quad}}$

$\underset{13}{\underline{\quad}}\ \underset{14}{\underline{\quad}}\ \underset{15}{\underline{\quad}}\ \underset{16}{\underline{\quad}}\ \underset{17}{\underline{\quad}}$

Connecting Concepts

Develop a concept map that uses the key concepts and key terms from this chapter. Keep in mind the big idea of this chapter. The concept map shown is one way to organize the information in this chapter. You may use an extra sheet of paper.

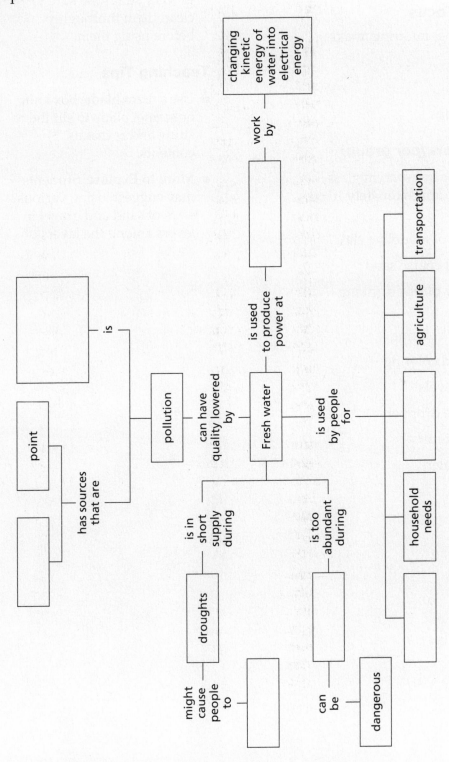

Pollution of a Water Supply

Key Concept

Pollutants can travel through the groundwater in an aquifer.

Skills Focus

observing, inferring, making models

Time

40 minutes

Materials (per group)

plastic or transparent glass loaf pan, approximately 10 cm × 20 cm

2 blocks of modeling clay

2 cups of coarse sand

14 heavy plastic drinking straws

red food coloring

blue food coloring

paper towels

medicine droppers

watering can

metric ruler

Advanced Preparation

- Collect clear plastic loaf pans used as packaging by grocery stores. Be sure to clean them thoroughly before using them.

Teaching Tips

- Use a razor blade, box knife, or scalpel blade to slit the straw and reveal its contents.

- **More to Explore** Students may suggest using various sizes of sand and gravel in layers among the layers of clay.

Freshwater Resources ▪ *Laboratory Investigation*

Pollution of a Water Supply

Pre-Lab Discussion

Many communities get their water from sources deep in the ground. This groundwater seeps slowly through the pores of sediment and rock layers. The rate of movement depends largely on the slope of the rock layers and the permeability of the rock.

People bring groundwater to the surface in wells. If water is pumped out too fast, a well can go dry. The quality of groundwater is also a concern. Many pollutants that contaminate surface water also contaminate groundwater.

In this investigation, you will create a model of a well system and add pollutants. You will study the spread of the pollutants and their effect on the water supply.

1. What are three sources of groundwater pollution?

_____

_____

_____

2. What is the difference between point sources and nonpoint sources of water pollution? Give an example of each.

_____

_____

_____

_____

Problem

How does groundwater pollution affect a community's water supply?

Materials (per group)

plastic or transparent glass loaf pan, approximately 10 cm × 20 cm

2 blocks of modeling clay

2 cups of coarse sand

14 heavy plastic drinking straws

red food coloring

blue food coloring

paper towels

medicine dropper

watering can

metric ruler

Name _____ Date _____ Class _____

Freshwater Resources · *Laboratory Investigation*

Pollution of a Water Supply *(continued)*

Safety 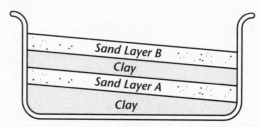 *Review the safety guidelines in the front of your lab book.*

To prevent slips or falls, immediately wipe up any water spilled on the floor. Handle glass objects carefully. If they break, tell the teacher. Do not pick up broken glass. Wear safety goggles and an apron at all times.

Procedure

1. Cover the bottom of the pan with a layer of modeling clay to a depth of 1–2 cm. Build it up at one end to create a slope. See Figure 1. Press the clay tightly against the bottom and sides of the pan.

Sand Layer B

Clay

Sand Layer A

Clay

Figure 1

2. Cover the clay with sand. The sand layer should be about 1–2 cm thick and follow the slope of the clay. Lightly sprinkle the sand with water, using the watering can. This is sand layer A.

3. Place a thin layer of modeling clay (about 1 cm thick) on top of the sand, following the slope of the layers below. Press the clay tightly against the sides of the pan.

4. Finally, cover the clay with about 1 cm of sand, following the slope of the layers below. Lightly sprinkle the sand with water. This is sand layer B. Your final model should resemble Figure 1.

5. Hold your finger over the top of a drinking straw. Insert the straw on one side of the model about 5 cm from the highest spot. See Figure 2. The end of the straw should just go into the bottom layer of clay. Withdraw the straw. A slight twist will help remove it. The clay and sand should come out with the straw, leaving a hole.

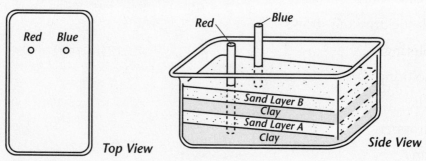

Red   Blue

Red   Blue

Top View

Sand Layer B

Clay

Sand Layer A

Clay

Side View

Figure 2

6. Carefully insert another straw in the same hole to about the same depth. Put five or six drops of red food coloring in the straw. Do not drip the food coloring on the surface of the sand. Remove the straw. Rinse the plastic dropper.

7. Using the same method as in Step 5, insert a third straw in the other side of the pan, but this time just until it touches the **top** layer of clay. Withdraw the straw. Again, the clay and sand should come out with the straw.

8. Carefully insert another straw in the same hole. Put five or six drops of blue food coloring in this straw. Remove the straw carefully.

9. The food coloring represents pollutants that have been introduced into a shallow well (blue) and a deep well (red).

10. Lightly, but thoroughly, sprinkle the surface of the sand with water. This process simulates rainfall. Wait a few minutes for the water to soak into the layers.

11. Insert another straw to the bottom of the pan, uphill or downhill from a well. See Figure 3. Remove it and lay it on a paper towel. Record the sample distance from the original well in the Data Table, and label it *uphill* or *downhill*.

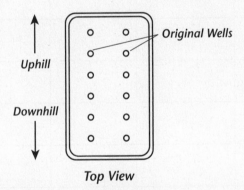

Top View

Figure 3

12. Predict the color of the sand from each sand layer the straw passed through. Record your predictions in the table. Ask your teacher to cut the side of the straw. **CAUTION:** *Do not cut the straw yourself.* Examine the contents of the core, and record your observations in the table. Note any color, how strong the color is, and in which sand layer the color appears.

13. Using the method in Steps 11 and 12, take ten core samples uphill and downhill in a straight line from both wells. See Figure 3. Record your predictions and your observations.

Freshwater Resources · *Laboratory Investigation*

Pollution of a Water Supply *(continued)*

Observations
Data Table

Core Sample	Distance From Well (Indicate Uphill or Downhill)		Color			
			Sand Layer A		Sand Layer B	
	Red Well	Blue Well	Prediction	Actual	Prediction	Actual
1						
2						
3						
4						
5						
6						
7						
8						
9						
10						

1. In which direction do the pollutants travel faster? Why?

_____

_____

_____

_____

Freshwater Resources ▪ *Laboratory Investigation*

2. In which sand layer do the pollutants travel faster? Why?

_____

_____

_____

_____

Analyze and Conclude

1. What does the modeling clay represent?

_____

2. Did you find any red coloring in sand layer B? Why or why not?

_____

_____

3. Did you find any blue coloring in sand layer A? Why or why not?

_____

_____

4. Which sand layer is harder to pollute from the surface? Why?

_____

5. Which sand layer is harder to purify if it does become contaminated? Why?

_____

Critical Thinking and Applications

1. How could wastes buried in soil eventually pollute the groundwater?

_____

_____

_____

2. How does the pollution of groundwater differ from the pollution of surface water?

_____

_____

_____

_____

Freshwater Resources • *Laboratory Investigation*

Pollution of a Water Supply *(continued)*

3. Do you agree that water in deep wells is less likely to be polluted than water in shallow wells? Give a reason for your answer.

_____

_____

_____

_____

More to Explore

New Problem How do different kinds of sediments affect the movement of pollutants?

Possible Materials Consider which materials you can use from the previous part of this lab. Choose additional materials to represent different sediments.

Safety Wipe up spills immediately. Handle glass objects carefully. Be sure to wear your safety goggles and apron.

Procedure Develop a procedure to solve the problem. Write your procedure in your notebook. Have the teacher approve your procedure before you carry out the investigation.

Observations In your notebook, make a data table similar to the one in the previous part of this lab in which to record your data and observations.

Analyze and Conclude Do certain types of materials act as filters for pollutants? Describe the evidence for your answer.

_____

_____

_____

_____

_____

_____

Hard or Soft Water?

Students are presented with the problem of determining the hardness of two water samples, labeled only as A and B. To solve this problem, students will apply the concepts they have learned about the factors that affect water quality.

Expected Outcome

Students may use any of the materials they are given to test the two water samples—distilled water (soft water) and mineral water (hard water). Only one test, however—the soapsuds test—will indicate which is the hard water sample and which is the soft water sample. In the soapsuds test, the distilled water should make more soapsuds than the mineral water.

Content Assessed

This activity assesses students' understanding of factors that affect water quality, including the hardness of water.

Skills Assessed

designing experiments, observing, drawing conclusions

Materials

Provide students with test tubes and stoppers that fit tightly so they can add liquid soap to water and shake the mixture to make soapsuds to test for hardness.

Obtain narrow-range pH paper (6–8), which can detect subtle differences better than regular pH paper.

Provide thermometers that students can use to measure the temperature of the water samples.

Put the two types of water in pitchers or plastic bottles, and then place the water at a central location in the classroom. Label the distilled water A and the mineral water B.

Advance Preparation

- Purchase distilled water in jugs from a grocery store. You can also purchase mineral water, as long as it is noncarbonated.

- A good alternative to commercial mineral water is well water.

Time

30 minutes

Safety

- Caution students to be careful when handling the glass test tubes and to inform you immediately if there is any breakage.

- Tell students that they are not allowed to taste either of the water samples.

Monitoring the Task

- Allow students to consider the materials and decide for themselves which test or tests they will carry out. Do not make any suggestions that they should use only the soapsuds test.

- If students use soap in a test, advise them to fill the test tubes only about half full of water and to add only about 0.5 mL of soap.

Freshwater Resources ▪ *Performance Assessment* **Scoring Rubric**

Hard or Soft Water?

In assessing students' performance, use the following rubric.

	4	3	2	1
Identifying the Two Types of Water	The student correctly identifies water A as soft water and water B as hard water, using only the results of the soapsuds test.	The student correctly identifies water A as soft water and water B as hard water after carrying out two different tests.	The student correctly identifies water A as soft water and water B as hard water after carrying out three or more different tests.	The student incorrectly identifies the two types of water and does not use the soapsuds test.
Concept Understanding	The student demonstrates a mastery of the concepts related to factors that affect water quality, including hardness.	The student demonstrates an adequate understanding of the concepts related to factors that affect water quality, including hardness.	The student demonstrates only a partial understanding of the concepts related to factors that affect water quality, including hardness.	The student demonstrates little or no understanding of the concepts related to factors that affect water quality.

Freshwater Resources · *Performance Assessment*

Hard or Soft Water?

Problem

Suppose that you are planning to open a laundromat and you're considering two different locations. You hope to find a place that has soft water. You've obtained a sample of water from each location. How can you test the water samples to find out which sample is softer?

Materials

water sample A

water sample B

thermometer

2 test tubes with stoppers

liquid soap

2 pieces of pH paper

pH indicator chart

Devise a Plan

1. Study the materials provided. Think of how you could use these materials to test the two water samples for hardness.
2. Write a description of the test or tests that could help you determine which water sample is softer.
3. Conduct your tests and record your results.

Analyze and Conclude

Answer the items below on a separate sheet of paper.

1. Which tests did you carry out, and what were the results of each?
2. How would you describe the hardness of the water sample in Bottle A? How did you determine this?
3. How would you describe the hardness of the water sample in Bottle B? How did you determine this?
4. Which water sample would be better for a laundromat? Explain your answer.
5. What determines the hardness of water?

Freshwater Resources

Multiple Choice
Write the letter of the correct answer on the line at the left.

_____ 1. The amount of one substance in a certain volume of another substance is called a
   a. drought.
   b. concentration.
   c. coagulation.
   d. leach field.

_____ 2. A high coliform count is an indicator that the water may contain
   a. high levels of minerals.
   b. high pH levels.
   c. great kinetic energy.
   d. large numbers of disease-causing organisms.

_____ 3. What is added to drinking water to kill bacteria and other organisms?
   a. sand
   b. alum
   c. chlorine
   d. dissolved solids

_____ 4. Wastewater and the different kinds of waste in it are called
   a. sludge.
   b. floc.
   c. sewage.
   d. hardness.

_____ 5. A condition in which an area gets less precipitation than normal for a few years is a
   a. drought.
   b. pollutant.
   c. floc.
   d. demand.

_____ 6. Using a resource wisely so that it will not be used up is called
   a. filtration.
   b. conservation.
   c. distillation.
   d. coagulation.

_____ 7. The result of sulfur and nitrogen reacting with water in the atmosphere is
   a. sludge.
   b. desalination.
   c. acid rain.
   d. potential energy.

_____ 8. Chemicals intended to kill insects and other organisms that damage crops are called
   a. pesticides.
   b. aquifers.
   c. fertilizers.
   d. flocs.

_____ 9. Which of the following can break down toxic chemicals in rivers and lakes?
   a. septic tanks
   b. sludge
   c. acid rain
   d. bacteria

_____ 10. A hydroelectric power plant changes the energy of moving water into
   a. electrical energy
   b. industrial wastes
   c. reservoirs
   d. kinetic energy

Freshwater Resources · *Chapter Test*

Completion

Fill in the line to complete each statement.

11. In a process called _____, particles in water clump together onto flocs.

12. When water is carried into fields in open irrigation ditches, much of it is lost to _____.

13. Any substance that causes water pollution is called a _____.

14. The process of obtaining fresh water from salt water is called _____.

15. The kind of energy that an object has when it is moving is called _____ energy.

True or False

If the statement is true, write true. *If it is false, change the underlined word or words to make the statement true.*

_____ 16. <u>Water quality</u> is a measure of the substances in water besides water molecules.

_____ 17. A water shortage occurs when there is too great a <u>supply</u> in an area.

_____ 18. Oil that washes off a road into a stream is an example of a <u>nonpoint source</u> of pollution.

_____ 19. Because of sewage pollution, people should boil water for drinking and cooking after a <u>drought</u>.

_____ 20. Water stored behind a dam has <u>kinetic</u> energy.

Freshwater Resources • *Chapter Test (continued)*

Using Science Skills

Use the illustration below to answer the questions that follow.

21. Observing What is occurring in the illustration that could affect a drinking-water supply?

_____

_____

_____

Chemical Factory

River

22. Classifying Is this an example of a point source of pollution or a nonpoint source? Explain.

_____

_____

_____

_____

23. Drawing Conclusions What could the company do to stop the harm being done to the water in the river?

_____

_____

Essay

Write an answer for each of the following.

24. What is the purpose of drinking-water treatment? Describe a typical treatment process at a city plant.

_____

_____

_____

_____

_____

25. How do fertilizers in agricultural runoff affect lakes and ponds?

_____

_____

_____

_____

_____

Freshwater Resources ▪ *Chapter Test*

Using Science Skills

Use the flow chart below to answer the following questions. If you need more space, use the back of this sheet.

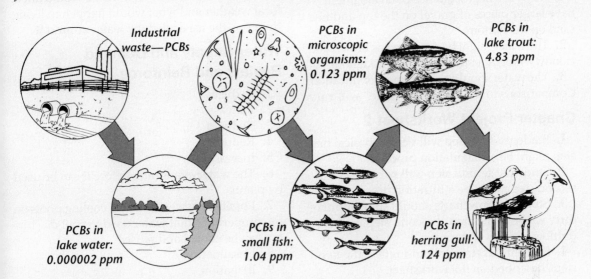

Industrial waste—PCBs

PCBs in microscopic organisms: 0.123 ppm

PCBs in lake trout: 4.83 ppm

PCBs in lake water: 0.000002 ppm

PCBs in small fish: 1.04 ppm

PCBs in herring gull: 124 ppm

26. Interpreting Data PCBs are a type of industrial pollutant. Refer to the flowchart and describe how the concentration of PCBs changes. Explain why this change occurs.

_____

_____

27. Relating Cause and Effect Explain how humans could be affected by PCB pollution.

_____

_____

Essay

Write an answer for each of the following. Use the back of this sheet if you need more space.

28. Explain how a water shortage can be caused by changes in either supply or demand.

_____

_____

29. Explain what causes acid rain. How does acid rain affect wildlife?

_____

_____

30. How can moving water produce electricity?

_____

_____

Chapter Project Worksheet 1

1. The basic setup should look like the figure shown on the worksheet. The sequence of layers will vary. A typical sequence of layers might have larger pieces of gravel on the top and fine sand on the bottom.

2. The water might be described as brown and cloudy, with suspended particles throughout.

3. The water should be cleaner after filtration. Comparisons to the "cleanness scale" will vary.

Chapter Project Worksheet 2

1. Students' first step will vary. A typical first step might be a coagulation process.

2. Students' second step will vary. A typical second step might be a filtration process.

3. Students' flowcharts should show input of dirty water, a first step, a second step, and an outflow of clean water.

4. Students' sketches should reflect the two steps described on the worksheet.

Water Supply and Demand
Guided Reading and Study

Use Target Reading Skills This is one possible way to complete the graphic organizer. Accept all logical answers.

What You Know

1. I can conserve water by taking shorter showers.

2. Reducing water use helps conserve water.

3. People often use more water than they need.

What You Learned

1. Recycling and reusing water are two more ways to conserve water.

2. For every minute that I shower, I use 18 liters of water.

3. Agriculture accounts for the highest consumption of water in the United States.

1. False

2. A water shortage occurs when there is too little water, too great a demand, or both.

3. drought

4. a, b, d

5. It can be recharged by precipitation.

6. conservation

7. a, c

8. True

9. They help conserve water by reducing evaporation.

10. **a.** Reducing water use
    b. Recycling water
    c. Reusing water

11. c

12. desalination

13. The iceberg could be wrapped and tugged to the area, and the water could be piped ashore as the iceberg melted.

14. Questions include how the ice would affect local weather and what would happen to living things as the ice cooled the water around it.

Water Supply and Demand
Review and Reinforce

1. Reduces

2. Increases

3. Reduces

4. Reduces

5. Increases

6. The water evaporates before it can be used by plants

7. Possible answer: building cooling pools on the property so that water used to cool machinery can be cooled and reused.

8. Desalination

9. Irrigation

10. Conservation

Water Supply and Demand
Enrich

1. 15.5 million liters

2. 3.1 million liters

3. 20.5 million liters

4. The yearly demand is 4.4 million liters more than the yearly supply.

5. Possible answer: conservation efforts should be made to cut down on overall demand.

Getting the Salt Out
Skills Lab

For answers, see the Teacher's Edition.

Water to Drink
Guided Reading and Study

Use Target Reading Skills This is one possible way to complete the graphic organizer. Accept all logical answers.

Drinking-Water Treatment

a. Setting basins b. Second Filtration
c. Chlorination d. Aeration
e. Additional Treatment

1. a, d

2. aquifers

3. They collect, treat, and distribute water to residents.

4. water quality

5. True

6. False

7. It can dissolve lead or other metals from the pipes it passes through.
8. hardness
9. Hard water does not form suds well when mixed with soap.
10. It measures the number of *Escherichia coli* bacteria in water.
11. True
12. concentration
13. False
14. Arrows flow from first filtration to coagulation, from coagulation to setting basins, from setting basins to second filtration, and from second filtration to chlorination.
15. flocs
16. c
17. a
18. b
19. b
20. Water pressure causes the water to move through the system.
21. sanitary sewers
22. **a.** Sewage **b.** Sludge **c.** Gray water
23. septic tank
24. leach field

Water to Drink
Review and Reinforce

1. First filtration
2. Coagulation
3. Settling basins
4. Second filtration
5. Chlorination
6. Aeration
7. Additional treatment
8. e
9. f
10. a
11. d
12. g
13. b
14. c

Water to Drink
Enrich

1. A reservoir
2. It goes to the drinking water treatment plant.
3. Water storage
4. The water passes through the wastewater treatment plant.

Testing Water
Consumer Lab

For answers, see the Teacher's Edition.

Freshwater Pollution
Guided Reading and Study

Use Target Reading Skills This is one possible way to complete the graphic organizer. Accept all logical answers.
Freshwater Pollution
I. What is pollution?
  A. Point and nonpoint sources
  B. Effects of pollutants
II. Human wastes
  A. Sewage in cities
  B. Sewage in rural areas
III. Industrial wastes
  A. Chemicals
  B. Smoke and exhaust
  C. Heat pollution
IV. Chemical runoff
  A. Runoff from farms
  B. Runoff from roads
V. Water pollution solutions
  A. Cleanup
  B. Prevention

1. water pollution
2. a, c
3. pollutants
4. False
5. Types of pollutants include disease-causing organisms, toxic chemicals and metals, and radioactive substances.
6. **a.** human wastes
  b. industrial wastes
  c. agricultural chemicals **d.** runoff from roads
7. A point source has a specific point of origin that can be identified. A nonpoint source cannot be tied to a specific point of origin.
8. During a flood, sanitary sewers can overflow into storm sewers and pollute the surface water.
9. False
10. **a.** Chemicals **b.** Smoke and exhaust
  c. Heated water
11. b, c
12. acid rain
13. a, c, d
14. Warm water released into a river or pond can raise the temperature of the water enough to harm the living things there.
15. False
16. pesticides
17. **a.** gasoline **b.** oil **c.** salt
18. True
19. b, c, d
20. False

21. True

22. Ways include cooling and reusing water from factories instead of returning it to a river, and collecting runoff water from pastures and barnyards and using it for irrigation.

Freshwater Pollution
Review and Reinforce

1. Point source

2. Industrial waste

3. Nonpoint source

4. Point source

5. Agricultural waste

6. Living things in lakes, streams, and wetlands filter out and break down waste materials.

7. Runoff from farms may contain fertilizers and pesticides. The fertilizers can cause eutrophication. The pesticides can harm animals other than those they are intended to kill.

8. pesticides

9. water pollution

10. acid rain

Freshwater Pollution
Enrich

1. The septic tank treats the wastewater from the home.

2. Bacteria break down the waste. Then the water flows into the surrounding soil.

3. The source is the aquifer accessed by a well.

4. The coliform count would probably be above the EPA's standard because the water in the well has been polluted by the wastewater from Home A's septic tank.

5. Students' answers will vary. A typical answer might suggest that Home A find another way to dispose of its wastewater or that Home B use another source of water.

Droughts and Floods
Guided Reading and Study

Use Target Reading Skills This is one possible way to complete the graphic organizer. Accept all logical answers.

    a. large amounts of rainfall **b.** no **c.** yes **d.** conserve water, plant drought-resistant plants, soil conservation **e.** predicting flood heights along a river, building dams, strengthening levees **f.** reduces the supplies of groundwater and surface water **g.** downed electrical poles and wires, landslides, mudslides, washed-out roads, contaminated food and water

1. a. groundwater **b.** surface water
    c. aquifer

2. crop failure, or even famine

3. Droughts are difficult to predict, but scientists monitor soil, water conditions, and precipitation levels.

4. A flood occurs when the volume of water in a river increases so much that the river overflows its channels.

5. True

6. flash flood

7. a. Rain **b.** Dams breaking

8. Dams can help by redirecting or storing extra water.

9. levees

10. Scientists try to predict floods because advance warning can help reduce flood damage and loss of life.

11. Move to higher ground and stay away from flood waters. Evacuate the area if local authorities recommend it.

Droughts and Floods
Review and Reinforce

1. The amount of groundwater in the aquifer may decrease.

2. drought, groundwater

3. Droughts can cause crop failure, resulting in lack of food for people and animals.

4. Conserve water, plant drought-resistant plants, conserve soil

5. Melting snow becomes water that increases the height and energy of the river it enters.

6. Weather satellites supply information about snow cover so that scientists can predict how much water will run into the rivers when the snow melts.

7. Dams, levees

8. Large amounts of rain

9. To issue warnings early enough to help people prepare or evacuate if necessary

10. Move to higher ground and stay away from floodwaters.

11. Downed electrical poles and wires, landslides and mudslides, flooded and washed-out roads, and contaminated food and water

12. flash flood

13. drought

14. Levees

Droughts and Floods
Enrich

1. The number of recent serious floods will depend on the state in which students live.

2. The western part of the country appears to be least affected by serious floods. This is because this part of the country has a dry climate.

3. Nebraska has had the largest amount of damage caused by floods.

4. States near major rivers, such as Missouri, Mississippi, and Ohio, are more greatly affected by serious floods.

5. The answer will depend on the state in which students live. A state might be classified as having a low risk of serious floods if it had fewer than 5 floods. It might be classified as having a medium risk if it had 5 to 15 floods. It might be classified as having a high risk if it had more than 15 floods.

Water Power
Guided Reading and Study

Use Target Reading Skills This is one possible way to complete the graphic organizer. Accept all logical answers.
How are energy and moving water related?
Hydroelectric power is electricity produced by the kinetic energy of water moving over a waterfall or through a dam.
How does a hydroelectric power plant work?
The kinetic energy of moving water turns turbine blades, producing mechanical energy, that in turn is converted to electrical energy when the turbine turns the electromagnet on a generator.

1. hydroelectric power
2. a. Kinetic Energy   **b.** Potential Energy
3. c
4. b
5. a
6. a, b, c
7. False
8. a, b
9. False
10. True
11. a. Supplying water for irrigation
    b. Helping in flood control
12. Small dams uproot fewer people and do less harm to the environment. However, they may not produce enough power to be worth the expense of building them.

Water Power
Review and Reinforce

1. Advantage. A reservoir is a good source of drinking water.

2. Disadvantage. The people in the flooded town had to move.

3. Disadvantage. The people on the farms had to move and start new farms.

4. Advantage. The farms around the reservoir have a source of water to grow crops.

5. Disadvantage. Some wildlife would not have been able to survive the destruction of their habitats.

6. Disadvantage. The sediments will not be carried downstream to enrich the land there.

7. Advantage. The farms and towns in this area have a reduced risk of flooding.

8. Disadvantage. Fish may not be able to swim past the dam to the place where they lay their eggs.

9. Advantage. The electricity can power homes and businesses.

10. Advantage. Hydroelectric power is efficient, so the cost of electricity is low.

11. Advantage. The air around the hydropower plant will not be polluted since it does not burn coal or oil.

12. Kinetic **13.** Potential **14.** Potential
15. Kinetic

Water Power
Enrich

1. The benefits include electric power from the hydropower plants, water for irrigating desert land, water for raising three crops per year, and flood control.

2. Problems include the relocation of people in Egypt and the Sudan, the loss of silt that used to enrich the land, the buildup of salts in the land, the need for fertilizers, the creeping of the sea inland at the river's mouth, the destruction of fish habitats, and the loss of fishing jobs.

3. Students' answers will vary. A typical answer might suggest that the problems outweigh the benefits. The electricity produced by the power plant is nearly used up by companies that make the fertilizers the soil needs since the dam stopped the flooding. In addition, many jobs in the fishing industry have been lost because the silt building up behind the dam has damaged the fishery at the river's mouth.

Key Terms

1. hardness
2. flocs
3. pesticide
4. concentration
5. septic
6. conservation
7. sludge
8. sewage
9. filtration
10. desalination
11. drought
   Hidden Message: Help conserve water.

Connecting Concepts

This concept map is only one way to represent the main ideas and relationships in this chapter. Accept other logical answers from students.

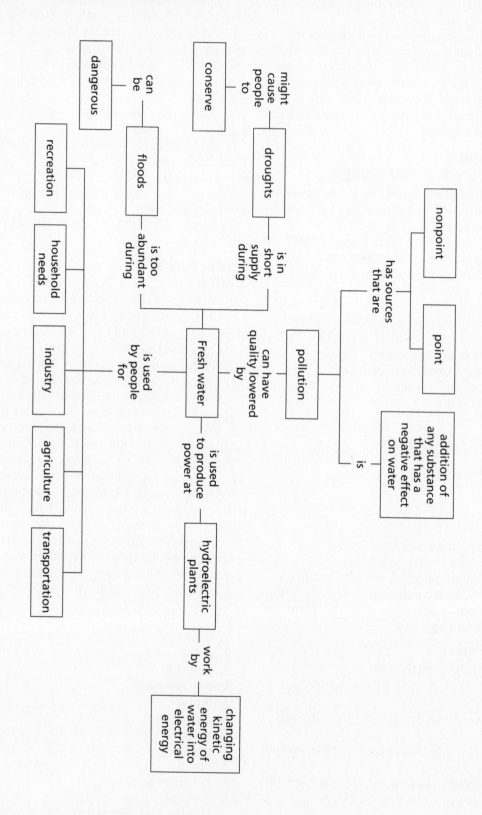

Laboratory Investigation
Pollution of a Water Supply

1. Possible answers include human wastes, industrial wastes, agricultural wastes, and run-off from roads.

2. Point sources are specific sources of pollution; industrial outfall pipe. Nonpoint sources are widely spread sources of pollution that cannot be pinpointed; runoff.

Observations

Data Table Distances uphill and downhill from the original wells will vary. Data should indicate stronger colors of pollutants downhill from the original wells, and mostly red in sand layer A and blue in sand layer B.

1. The pollutants travel faster downhill because of gravity.

2. The pollutants travel faster in sand layer B because this layer is closer to the top and absorbs most of the rain.

Analyze and Conclude

1. Rock layers that are not permeable.

2. No, because the pollutant does not rise.

3. No, because the blue coloring could not permeate the clay.

4. Sand layer A, because the layer of clay would block the flow of surface pollution.

5. Sand layer A, because it is deeper and the layer of clay would block some cleaning efforts.

Critical Thinking and Applications

1. The wastes could seep through permeable layers of soil and rock and eventually reach the groundwater.

2. Surface water is usually polluted directly by point sources, such as pipes dumping pollutants into a river. Groundwater is usually polluted by nonpoint sources, such as agricultural chemicals that seep into the ground. Groundwater pollution is also more difficult to detect than surface water pollution.

3. Answers will vary. Deep wells are more likely to be protected by impermeable rock layers that prevent pollution from seeping down to them. However, if water from deep sources does become polluted, it is harder to purify than water from more shallow wells.

More to Explore

Be sure students state the evidence from their results that justifies their answer to Analyze and Conclude. Students will likely find that the finer the sediments, the more effective they are at blocking the movement of pollutants.

Chapter Performance Assessment

1. Answers will vary, depending on the tests that students conducted. If students carried out the soapsuds test, water from Bottle A should make more soapsuds than water from Bottle B.

2. The water sample in Bottle A is soft water, because it formed heavy suds when it was mixed with soap.

3. The water in Bottle B is hard water, because it formed few suds when mixed with soap.

4. The sample from Bottle A; soft water uses less detergent to get laundry clean and, unlike hard water, it has few of the minerals that form deposits that can clog pipes and machinery.

5. The total amount of calcium and magnesium determines the hardness of water.

Chapter Test

1. b
2. d
3. c
4. c
5. a
6. b
7. c
8. a
9. d
10. a
11. coagulation
12. evaporation
13. pollutant
14. desalination
15. kinetic
16. true
17. demand
18. True
19. flood
20. potential
21. Chemicals from the factory are entering the river.

Freshwater Resources

22. It is an example of a point source because a specific source of pollution can be identified.

23. The company could stop the flow of chemicals through the pipe and dispose of them in a safe way.

24. Drinking-water treatment makes the water safe and appealing to drink. The process in such treatment include filtration, coagulation, chlorination, aeration, and the addition of fluoride and other chemicals.

25. Fertilizers in runoff provide nutrients from the growth of algae in lakes and ponds. As the algae grow, a thick scum forms on top of the water, blocking sunlight and choking the flow of water. This changes the living conditions for other living things.

26. The concentration of PCBs increases. This occurs because the flowchart shows the feeding relationships among these organisms. In such a process, the larger organisms eat a great number of the smaller organisms, consuming the PCBs of all the smaller organisms. The PCBs thus build up in the bodies of the larger organisms.

27. Humans eat trout and other large fish, just as the herring gull does. Therefore, PCBs could build up in the human body just as they have in the gull's body. Such a buildup can cause diseases such as cancer.

28. A water shortage can be caused by a decrease in supply, such as occurs during a drought, if the demand remains the same. A water shortage can be caused by an increase in demand, such as a rise in population, if the supply remains the same.

29. When power plants or factories burn coal or when cars and trucks burn gasoline, molecules of sulfur dioxide and nitrogen dioxide are released into the atmosphere. There, those gases react with water, forming sulfuric and nitric acids. The result is rain and other forms of precipitation that are more acidic than normal. This acid rain causes water in ponds and lakes to become so acidic that fish and other wildlife cannot survive.

30. Moving water can turn the blades of a turbine in a hydroelectric power plant. The shaft of the turbine is connected to a generator that contains a large magnet. When the magnet turns inside a coil of wires, electricity is produced.

Ocean Motions

Design and Build an Erosion-Proof Beach

Lab zone Chapter Project

The following steps will walk you through the Chapter Project. Use the hints and detailed directions as you guide your students through the gathering of information, presentation, and reflection.

Chapter Project Overview

Have students read the Chapter Project Overview. Review the project's rules, and hand out the Chapter Project Scoring Rubric you will use for scoring students' work. Discuss with students what will be expected of them. If you wish, divide the class into small groups to carry out the project.

Set a deadline for the project presentation and interim dates for the Check Your Progress at the end of Section 1, Section 2, and Section 4. Encourage students to copy the dates in the Project Timeline.

Distribute copies of Chapter Project Worksheet 1 to help students plan their wave tank and Chapter Project Worksheet 2 to help them plan their models to scale. Also remind students to refer to the hints in the Chapter Project Overview as they plan and carry out the project.

This project may also be done in a single large class wave tank. Each group should take turns demonstrating their method and rebuilding the beach for the next group.

Keep Students on Track— Section 1

Check that each student has planned his or her wave tank to have a sloping bottom like the ocean floor in order for waves to break naturally on the beach.

Make sure students have a plan for generating waves that are consistent in size. Explain why it is crucial to control wave height in order to assess the effectiveness of different methods of erosion control.

Make sure students have selected beach materials that are fine enough to erode in the waves.

Remind students that their plans must include a way to measure erosion so they can

test the effectiveness of erosion-control methods later in the project.

Keep Students on Track— Section 2

Encourage students to test at least one of the erosion-control methods listed in the Chapter Project Overview: groins, stabilized sand dunes, seawalls, and breakwaters. Share with students the sketch of a seawall and breakwater in the figure below if they do not think of these ideas on their own.

Make sure students are controlling all the relevant variables as they test methods of erosion control. They should be making the waves consistently and to scale and returning the beach to its original condition after each method is tested.

As an alternative to using toothpicks for keeping track of erosion, students may simply measure the distance from the water to the lighthouse after each wave or set of waves.

Encourage students to use different methods to record their erosion data, such as tables, line graphs, and to-scale drawings on graph paper.

You may wish to have students use a video camera to document the effectiveness of different methods of erosion control. However, they still should quantify erosion in order to make precise comparisons of the different methods.

Keep Students on Track— Section 4

If students build sand dunes for erosion control, urge them to stabilize the dunes with materials such as model plants, fences, or brush.

If students use groins for erosion control, make sure they have placed them perpendicular to the beach. Suggest that they experiment with different spacing and length of groins to find the best arrangement for protecting their beach. Point out how the groins increase erosion farther down the shore.

To clarify the difference between a seawall and breakwater, you might suggest that students construct and test first a seawall and then a breakwater made of the same materials. They should observe how the two different structures affect the movement of waves near shore and which works best to control erosion.

Challenge one or more students to try another method of erosion control called beach nourishment, which involves building up the beach with additional sand or soil.

Chapter Project Wrap Up

Students should demonstrate at least one method of erosion control. In their presentations, they should explain how the demonstrated method works and also its advantages over other methods.

Guide students in concluding that all of the methods of erosion control have drawbacks and that most are only temporary solutions to wave erosion.

Extensions

Students will learn more about waves and beach erosion if they vary some of the parameters of the project, such as the structure and composition of the beach and lighthouse and the way in which waves are generated. For example, students might build the lighthouse on a spit that extends out from the beach instead of building it on a featureless shoreline, or they might make waves with a fan or hair dryer instead of by moving an object up and down in the water.

Students can use their wave tank and models to simulate longshore drift by generating waves at an angle to the beach. They should note where sandbars form and be able to explain which method of erosion control works best to prevent longshore drift.

Students can make waves of different heights to simulate ocean waves on calm and stormy days. They should compare how much erosion occurs with each type of weather.

Challenge students to generate a tsunami by simulating an earthquake across the water from the beach. They should compare the erosion caused by the tsunami with the amount caused by wind-generated waves.

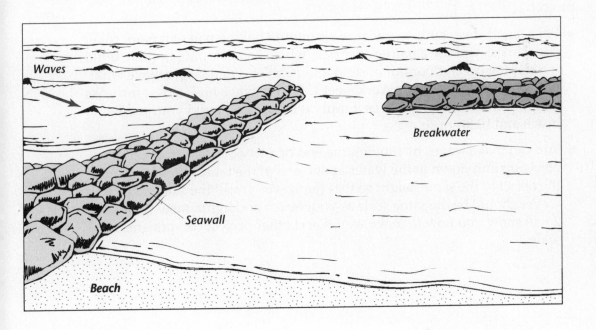

Waves

Breakwater

Seawall

Beach

Ocean Motions

⚠ **Chapter Project** **Design and Build an Erosion-Proof Beach**

As waves break on the shore, they wash away sand and deposit it elsewhere, constantly changing the shoreline. Lighthouses, homes, and many other structures are built on shorelines. Without protection, the shorelines and their structures may eventually be washed away by the action of the waves.

Project Rules

In this project, you will build a tank for making waves and then see how the waves erode a model beach and lighthouse. You will also apply at least one method of erosion control and measure how effective it is in preventing erosion on your beach. Follow these steps to complete the project successfully.

- Plan and sketch the wave tank and models, and make a list of materials.

- Build the wave tank, and practice making waves.

- Build the model beach and lighthouse.

- Apply and test methods of erosion control.

- Demonstrate and explain the best method of erosion control to the class.

Project Hints

The following hints will guide you through each of the major steps of the project.

- For a small wave tank, use a large aluminum baking pan or a paint roller pan. Unless you use a paint roller pan, which has a sloping bottom, build the sloping ocean floor out of sand and pebbles. For a larger wave tank, follow the instructions in Worksheet 1. Fill the wave tank to test for leaks and to practice making waves. Empty it before you build your model beach and lighthouse.

- You can make waves by moving the end of a wooden spoon or other object up and down in the water at one end of the tank. Each time, raise the object to the same height so that the waves are all the same size. Your waves should be the same scale as your beach and lighthouse. Worksheet 2 will show you how to make waves and other project components to scale.

Ocean Motions · *Chapter Project*

- Your model beach should be able to hold its shape until the waves start to erode it. It should also be made to scale. Use fine sand and silt and very small pebbles. Try to use a variety of materials and shapes to make your beach realistic. Variation in materials and shape may also give you ideas for controlling erosion later in the project.

- Your model lighthouse should be built to scale and also should be similar to real lighthouses in ways that affect its ability to hold up to erosion. Look at pictures of lighthouses for ideas on size, shape, and construction materials. For example, use "mortar" of modeling clay to hold blocks together, and bury its base deep in the sand. Also, place your lighthouse close to the shore, just like a real lighthouse.

- To control erosion, choose from among groins, sand dunes that have been stabilized with plants or other materials, seawalls, and breakwaters. If any of these methods are unfamiliar to you, do some research to learn about them.

- To test which method of erosion control works best, measure how much erosion occurs with a given number of waves of the same height, both before and after you apply the method. One way to measure erosion is to stick toothpicks in the beach at regular intervals, starting with one row very close to the water and backed up by one or more additional rows a few centimeters apart. Put a small piece of masking tape on each toothpick so that you can number the toothpicks and keep track of them as they fall.

- Always return the beach to its original condition and make the waves in the same way for each test.

- Demonstrate the best method to the class. In addition to showing how your method prevents erosion, also explain how it works and why other methods were less effective.

Project Timeline

Task	Due Date
1. Complete design of model beach and list of materials	_____
2. Construct model shoreline and lighthouse	_____
3. Test effects of wave erosion on model	_____
4. Test method of erosion control	_____
5. Test improved method of erosion control	_____
6. Present model to class	_____

Ocean Motions · *Chapter Project*   **Worksheet 1**

Making a Large Wave Tank

Follow the instructions below to make a large wave tank.

Materials

two large rectangular cardboard box tops, such as those from copier-paper boxes, or underbed storage boxes

large sheet of clear plastic

waterproof tape, such as adhesive or electrical tape

scissors

silt, sand, and small pebbles

Procedure

1. Cut one of the short ends from each box or box top, and then tape the two boxes or tops together to form one long, shallow tank.

2. Cut a small observation window a few centimeters across in one of the short sides of the tank.

3. Completely line the tank, including the small window, with a single, large sheet of clear plastic.

4. Tape the plastic securely in place with waterproof tape.

5. Use silt, sand, and pebbles to build a sloping ocean floor on one long side of the tank.

6. Fill the tank with water to test it for leaks. Repair if necessary.

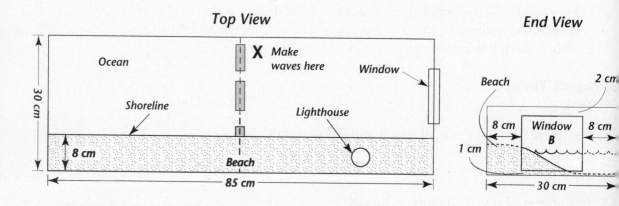

Measurements based on two copier-paper box tops

Working to Scale

For a model to best represent the real world, it should be made to scale. This means that all of the parts of the model are the correct size relative to one another. Usually models are smaller than the real objects they represent. For example, a model might have a scale of 1 centimeter to 1 meter, meaning that 1 centimeter in the model represents 1 meter in the real world. A 40-meter stretch of beach would be represented by a 40-centimeter stretch of beach in this model.

   Below is a list of items that might be found on a real beach. For each item, estimate its size in meters. Then calculate how large a scale model of that item would be in centimeters, using a scale of 1 centimeter to 1 meter.

Items	Estimated Size (in meters)	Size of Model (in centimeters)
lighthouse		
adult human		
child		
bush		
sea gull		
beach pail		
beach umbrella		
lifeguard stand		
beach towel		
fence		

Waves, like other project components, should be made to scale. In the ocean, most waves are about 2 to 5 meters high. Again using a scale of 1 centimeter to 1 meter, how high should the waves in your wave tank be? _____

Ocean Motions ▪ *Chapter Project* **Scoring Rubric**

Lab zone™ Chapter Project — Design and Build an Erosion-Proof Beach

In evaluating how well you complete the Chapter Project, your teacher will judge your work in three categories. In each, a score of 4 is the best rating.

	4	3	2	1
Planning Models and Materials	Makes highly detailed plans of models and a complete list of appropriate materials.	Makes somewhat detailed plans of models and a nearly complete list of appropriate materials.	Makes partial plans of models and an incomplete list of appropriate materials.	Makes inadequate plans of models and lists few if any appropriate materials.
Building Models and Testing Erosion-Control Methods	Builds highly accurate models, tests three or more erosion-control methods, and collects and records complete erosion data.	Builds somewhat accurate models, tests two or more erosion-control methods, and collects and records nearly complete erosion data.	Builds inaccurate but workable models, tests one or more erosion-control methods, and collects and records some erosion data.	Builds unworkable models, fails to test adequately an erosion-control method, and collects and records little if any erosion data.
Presenting the Results	Demonstrates very effective control of erosion and explains accurately and convincingly why the selected method was chosen.	Demonstrates good control of erosion and explains clearly why the selected method was chosen.	Demonstrates some control of erosion and explains adequately why the selected method was chosen.	Demonstrates little if any control of erosion and does not explain adequately why the selected method was chosen.

Wave Action

 2–3 periods, 1–1 1/2 blocks

Ability Levels Key
L1 Basic to Average
L2 For All Students
L3 Average to Advanced

Objectives

H.3.1.1 Explain how waves form.
H.3.1.2 Describe how waves change near the shore.
H.3.1.3 Explain how waves affect shorelines and beaches.

Key Terms

- wave • wavelength • frequency
- wave height • tsunami • longshore drift
- rip current • groin

Local Standards

PRETEACH

Build Background Knowledge
Recall experiences about waves at the beach.

 *How Do Waves Change a Beach?* **L1**

Targeted Resources

- ☐ **All in One Teaching Resources**
  L2 Reading Strategy Transparency H29: Using Prior Knowledge
- ☐ ⊙ **Presentation-Pro CD-ROM**

INSTRUCT

What Is a Wave? Explain how wind causes waves.
How Waves Change Near Shore Describe why and how a wave changes near shore.
How Waves Affect the Shore Use the longshore drift diagram to explain how waves affect the shore.
Waves and Beach Erosion Explain how waves can cause beach erosion.

Targeted Resources

- ☐ **All in One Teaching Resources**
  L2 Guided Reading, pp. 193–196
  L2 Transparencies H30, H31, H32
- ☐ **www.SciLinks.org** Web Code: cfp-3031
- ☐ ⊙ **Student Edition on Audio CD**

ASSESS

Section Assessment Questions
↻ Have students use their completed Using Prior Knowledge graphic organizers to answer the questions.

Reteach
Create a labeled drawing of a wave.

Targeted Resources

- ☐ **All in One Teaching Resources**
  Section Summary, p. 192
  L1 Review and Reinforce, p. 197
  L3 Enrich, p. 198

Ocean Motions

Ocean Motions · *Section Summary*

Wave Action

Guide for Reading

■ How does a wave form?

■ How do waves change near the shore?

■ How do waves affect shorelines and beaches?

Waves are important forces that reshape beaches and coastlines. A **wave** is the movement of energy through a body of water. **Most waves form when winds blowing across the water's surface transmit their energy to the water.** The stronger the wind, the longer it blows. The greater the distance over which it blows, the bigger the waves. Individual water particles in waves move up and down as the wave passes, but they do not move closer to shore. Only the energy of the wave moves toward shore.

The highest point of a wave is the **crest.** The lowest point is the trough. The distance between crests is the **wavelength.** The distance from the crest to the trough is the **wave height.** Wave height is a measure of a wave's energy. The number of waves that pass a point in a certain amount of time is their **frequency.** Waves that are frequent, or close together, have short wavelengths.

As waves enter the shallow water near shore, they begin to touch the ocean floor and slow down. **Near shore, the wave height increases and the wavelength decreases.** The energy of the breaking wave causes the water to push up on the beach, but the force of gravity quickly pulls it back to sea.

Some waves are not caused by wind but by earthquakes on the ocean floor. These waves are called **tsunamis.** Tsunamis usually are much higher and stronger than waves caused by wind. They are most common in the Pacific Ocean.

As waves come in to shore, water washes up the beach at an angle, carrying sand grains with it. The water and sand then run straight back down the beach. This movement of sand along the beach is called **longshore drift.** As the waves slow down, they deposit the sand they are carrying on a shallow, underwater ridge called a sandbar. If water breaks through the sandbar, it may create a **rip current**. This is a rush of water that flows out from the shore through a narrow opening.

Waves shape a beach by eroding the shore in some places and building it up in others. People have developed ways to reduce wave erosion. One method is to build a **groin,** a wall of rocks or concrete built outward from the shore. A groin interrupts the process of longshore drift. There are also natural methods of protecting the shore. Dunes, or hills of windblown sand, and barrier beaches, which lie just offshore, are two natural formations that help protect the shoreline from erosion.

Wave Action

This section explains how waves form and how they change near shore. The section also describes how waves affect the shore and how wave erosion can be reduced.

Use Target Reading Skills

Before you read the section, write what you know about waves. As you read, write what you learn.

What You Know
1. There are waves in the ocean.
2.

What You Learned
1.
2.

What Is a Wave?

1. The movement of energy through a body of water is a(n) _____.

2. How do most waves form?

   _____

   _____

3. Is the following sentence true or false? Waves start in the open ocean.

   _____

Ocean Motions • *Guided Reading and Study*

Wave Action *(continued)*

4. Circle the letter of each choice that determines the size of a wave.

   a. Strength of the wind

   b. How long the wind blows

   c. How far the wind blows

   d. Amount of water the wave carries

5. Is the following sentence true or false? Water is moved toward shore by a wave. _____

6. Circle the letter of the sentence that describes what happens to water particles near the surface when a wave passes by.

   a. The water particles move toward shore.

   b. The water particles move in circles.

   c. The water particles move randomly.

   d. The water particles move little if at all.

7. Circle the letter of the sentence that describes what happens to water particles in deep water when a wave passes by.

   a. The water particles move away from shore.

   b. The water particles move in large circles.

   c. The water particles move randomly.

   d. The water particles move little if at all.

How Waves Change Near Shore

Match the term with its definition.

	Term		Definition
____	8. wavelength	**a.**	Horizontal distance between crests
____	9. frequency	**b.**	Vertical distance from crest to trough
____	10. wave height	**c.**	Number of waves that pass a point in a certain amount of time

Name _____ Date _____ Class _____

Ocean Motions ▪ *Guided Reading and Study*

11. Label a crest and a trough in the drawing of waves.

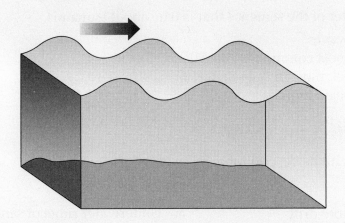

12. Is the following sentence true or false? The energy of a wave depends mainly on its wavelength. _____

13. As a wave approaches shore, what happens to wave height and wavelength?

_____

_____

14. How is surf formed?

_____

_____

_____

15. Water that moves up the beach in a wave flows back out to sea due to

_____.

Ocean Motions ▪ *Guided Reading and Study*

Wave Action *(continued)*

16. Circle the letter of the sentence that is true about tsunamis.

    a. They are waves.

    b. They are most common in the Atlantic Ocean.

    c. They are felt most in deep water.

    d. They cause earthquakes.

How Waves Affect the Shore

Match the term with its description.

	Term		Description
_____	**17.** longshore drift	**a.**	Underwater ridge of sand
_____	**18.** sandbar	**b.**	Movement of sand along a beach
_____	**19.** rip current	**c.**	Rapid rush of water out to sea

Waves and Beach Erosion

20. How do waves shape a beach?

_____

_____

21. A wall of rocks or concrete built outward from a beach to stop longshore drift is called a(n) _____.

22. Hills of wind-blown sand covered with plants are called

_____.

Name _____ Date _____ Class _____

Wave Action

Understanding Main Ideas

Fill in the spaces in the drawing below.

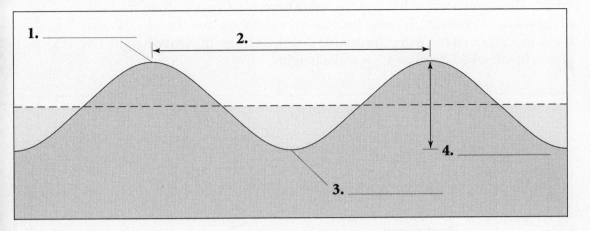

1. _____

2. _____

3. _____

4. _____

Answer the following questions on a separate sheet of paper.

5. How does a wave change when it enters shallow water near shore?

6. When does longshore drift occur?

7. How do waves change a beach?

8. What are three ways to prevent beach erosion?

Building Vocabulary

Match each term with its definition by writing the letter of the correct definition on the line beside the term.

_____ 9. wave

_____ 10. frequency

_____ 11. longshore drift

_____ 12. sandbar

_____ 13. rip current

_____ 14. groin

_____ 15. tsunami

_____ 16. wavelength

a. the distance between crests

b. the movement of energy through water

c. a long, low ridge of sand deposited offshore as waves go back out to sea

d. the number of waves that pass a point in a given amount of time

e. a giant wave caused by an earthquake on the ocean floor

f. a wall of rocks or concrete built outward from a beach to prevent erosion

g. a rush of water that flows out from the shore through a narrow opening

h. the movement of sand down a beach

Ocean Motions · *Enrich*

How Far From Shore Do Waves Break?

In Section 1 you learned that when waves move into shallow water, the troughs begin to drag along the bottom. This creates friction and causes the troughs to slow down. However, the crests continue moving at the same speed. This results in the front of the wave becoming steeper than the back of the wave. Eventually, the crest topples over and the wave "breaks." Waves break in water that has a depth equal to about 1.3 times the wave height. Or, waves break when depth = 1.3 × wave height.

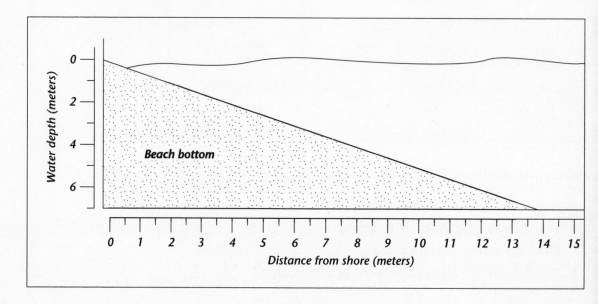

Answer the following questions on a separate sheet of paper.

1. If a wave has a wave height of 5 meters, in what depth of water would it begin to break?

2. In what depth of water would a wave begin to break if it had a wave height of 3 meters?

3. According to the diagram, how far from shore would a wave break if it had a wave height of 3 meters?

4. How high must a wave be to break in water that is 7.8 meters deep?

5. If the wind picked up and caused an increase in wave height, would waves break farther from shore or closer to shore? Why?

Tides

🕐 *1–2 periods, 1/2–1 block*

Ability Levels Key
L1 Basic to Average
L2 For All Students
L3 Average to Advanced

Objectives

H.3.2.1 Explain what causes tides.

H.3.2.2 Explain what affects the height of tides.

H.3.2.3 Describe how tides are a source of energy.

Key Terms

• tides • spring tide • neap tide

Local Standards

PRETEACH

Build Background Knowledge
Share observations of tides.

 **Discover Activity** *When Is High Tide?* **L1**

Targeted Resources

❏ **All in One** Teaching Resources
  L2 Reading Strategy Transparency H33: Previewing Visuals
❏ 💿 **Presentation-Pro CD-ROM**

INSTRUCT

What Causes Tides? Compare the formation of tides to a figure skater being held by her skates as she spins.
Energy From Tides Describe the energy transformations that occur when tides are used as a source of power.

Targeted Resources

❏ **All in One** Teaching Resources
  L2 Guided Reading, pp. 201–203
  L2 Transparency H34
❏ **PHSchool.com** Web Code: cfd-3032
❏ 💿 **Student Edition on Audio CD**

ASSESS

Section Assessment Questions
↻ Have students use their Previewing Visuals graphic organizers to help them answer the questions.

Reteach
Diagram the positions of the sun, Earth, and moon during spring tide and neap tide.

Targeted Resources

❏ **All in One** Teaching Resources
  Section Summary, p. 200
  L1 Review and Reinforce, p. 204
  L3 Enrich, p. 205

Ocean Motions

Ocean Motions · *Section Summary*

Tides

Guide for Reading

■ What causes tides?

■ What affects the heights of tides?

■ How are tides a source of energy?

The daily rise and fall of Earth's waters on its coastlines are called **tides.** As the tide comes in, the level of the water on the shore gradually rises. At the highest point, it is called high tide. Then the water gradually goes back out again. At the lowest point, it is called low tide.

Tides are caused by the interaction of Earth, the moon, and the sun. The gravity of the moon pulls on Earth's waters, creating a bulge of water on the side of Earth closest to the moon. A tidal bulge forms on the opposite side of Earth as well. As points on Earth's surface rotate through the tidal bulges, they experience high tide. The points between the tidal bulges experience low tide. Because Earth rotates on its axis every 24 hours, there are two high tides and two low tides each day. The high tides are about 12 hours and 25 minutes apart.

Changes in the positions of Earth, the moon, and the sun affect the heights of the tides during a month. Twice a month, during the new and full phases of the moon, Earth, the moon, and the sun are positioned in a straight line. When that happens, the sun's gravity adds to the moon's pull on Earth's waters. This arrangement causes the greatest range between high and low tide and is called **spring tide.** During the first and third quarters of the moon, the moon and the sun are at right angles to each other. When that happens, the sun's gravity works against the moon's pull on Earth's waters. This arrangement causes a tide with the least difference between low and high tide and is called **neap tide.**

Although many factors affect tides, scientists can predict quite precisely when they will occur in a given location. The schedule of tides is often published in the local newspaper. It is important to sailors, people who fish, and others who depend on or live by the sea.

The movement of huge amounts of water between high and low tide is a source of potential energy—energy that is stored and can be used. Engineers have designed tidal power plants that capture some of this energy. As the water flows back out to sea, it powers generators that produce electricity. Only in a few places in the world, however, is the difference between high and low tide great enough to generate power on a large scale.

Tides

This section explains what causes tides and describes the daily and monthly cycles of tides. The section also explains how energy in tides can be harnessed.

Use Target Reading Skills

Before you read, look at Figure 11. Then write two questions that you have about the diagram. As you read, answer your questions.

Spring and Neap Tides

Q. When do spring tides occur?
A.
Q.
A.

What Causes Tides?

1. The daily rise and fall of Earth's water on its coastlines are called
   _____.

2. What is the difference between high tide and low tide?
   _____
   _____
   _____

3. At which two points are tidal bulges occurring when Earth and the moon are in the positions shown in the drawing?
   _____
   _____
   _____
   _____

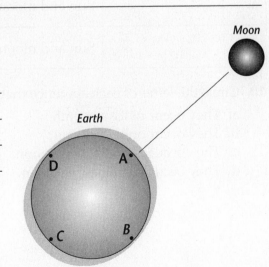

Moon

Earth

Ocean Motions • *Guided Reading and Study*

Tides *(continued)*

4. Explain why a tidal bulge occurs on the side of Earth opposite the moon.

_____

_____

_____

_____

5. Circle the letter of each sentence that is true about high tides.
   a. They occur twice a day.
   b. They occur later in the west.
   c. They occur six hours apart.
   d. They occur more often than low tides.

6. Is the following sentence true or false? High tides occur about twelve and a half hours apart. _____

7. What factors affect the height of the tide in any particular location?

_____

_____

8. Is the following sentence true or false? The sun's gravity affects Earth's tides. _____

9. Complete the compare/contrast table with the following terms: least, greatest, neap tide, spring tide.

Monthly Tide Cycle		
Type of Tide	**Position of Sun and Moon**	**Difference Between High and Low Tides**
a.	Sun and moon in straight line	b.
c.	Sun and moon at right angles	d.

10. Circle the letter of each sentence that is true about spring tides.
    a. They occur twice a month.
    b. They occur only in spring.
    c. They occur during a new moon.
    d. They occur during a full moon.

Ocean Motions • *Guided Reading and Study*

11. Who needs to know the times and heights of tides?

_____

_____

_____

Energy From Tides

12. Is the following sentence true or false? The energy stored in tides is potential energy. _____

13. Describe how a tidal power plant captures tidal energy.

_____

_____

_____

_____

14. Circle the letter of the sentence that is true about tidal energy.

   a. It is clean.

   b. It is nonrenewable.

   c. It can be used on any coast.

   d. It cannot be harnessed.

Ocean Motions · *Review and Reinforce*

Tides

Understanding Main Ideas

Study the diagram and then complete the following statements.

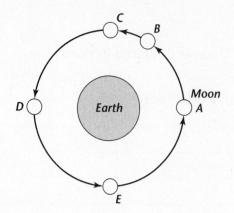

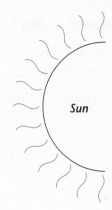

1. The greatest difference between high and low tide occurs when the moon is in positions _____ and _____.

2. A neap tide occurs when the moon is in position _____ or _____.

3. When the moon is in position D, Earth experiences a _____ tide.

4. When the moon is in position E, high tides are _____ than when the moon is in position A.

5. Earth experiences a _____ tide when the moon is in position A.

6. When the moon is in position B, the difference between high and low tides is _____ than when the moon is in position C.

Building Vocabulary

Match each term with its definition by writing the letter of the correct definition on the line beside the term.

_____ 7. neap tide

_____ 8. high tide

_____ 9. spring tide

_____ 10. low tide

a. tide with the greatest difference between high and low tide

b. tide in which water reaches its lowest point on the beach each day

c. tide with the least difference between high and low tide

d. tide in which water reaches its highest point on the beach each day

Name _____ Date _____ Class _____

What Affects the Heights of Tides?

Just how large high tides are at a given place and time depends on many factors. One factor that influences the height of tides is the shape of the moon's orbit. As you can see in the figure below, the moon's path around Earth is not a perfect circle. Rather, its path has a more oval shape, closer to Earth at some points and farther at others. Because of this, the distance between Earth and the moon ranges from 357,000 kilometers to 408,000 kilometers. This difference is greater than the distance from New York City to Los Angeles. When the moon is closest to Earth, tides are unusually high because the moon's pull is stronger when it is closer to Earth. These tides are called **perigee tides.** When the moon is farthest away from Earth, tides are unusually low. These tides are called **apogee tides.**

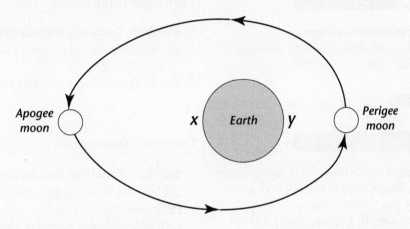

1. Would the daily high tides at points *x* and *y* be higher during a perigee moon or an apogee moon? Explain.

   _____

   _____

   _____

2. Compare and contrast perigee tides and spring tides.

   _____

   _____

   _____

3. Like the moon's orbit, Earth's orbit is not a perfect circle, but an oval. How do you think this might affect Earth's tides?

   _____

   _____

   _____

Ocean Water Chemistry

 2–3 periods, 1–1 1/2 blocks

Objectives

H.3.3.1 Describe the salinity of ocean water.

H.3.3.2 Explain how the temperature and gas content of ocean water vary.

H.3.3.3 Describe how conditions in the ocean change with depth.

Key Terms

• salinity • submersible

Local Standards

PRETEACH

Build Background Knowledge

Compare and contrast the freezing of ocean water and fresh water.

 *Will the Eggs Sink or Float?* **L1**

Targeted Resources

❑ **All in One** **Teaching Resources**
 L2 Reading Strategy Transparency H35: Asking Questions

❑ ◉ **Presentation-Pro CD-ROM**

INSTRUCT

The Salty Ocean Describe salts in ocean water.
Other Ocean Properties Summarize the distribution of gas in ocean water.
Changes With Depth Explain how pressure changes with depth.

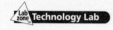 *Investigating Changes in Density* **L2**

Targeted Resources

❑ **All in One** **Teaching Resources**
 L2 Guided Reading, pp. 208–210
 L2 Transparency H36
 Lab: *Investigating Changes in Density*, pp. 213–215

❑ 📼 **Lab Activity Video/DVD**
 Technology Lab: *Investigating Changes in Density*

❑ **www.SciLinks.org** Web Code: scn-0833

❑ ◉ **Student Edition on Audio CD**

ASSESS

Section Assessment Questions

↺ Have students use their Asking Questions graphic organizers to help them answer the questions.

Reteach

Describe how salinity, temperature, and gases in the ocean vary.

Targeted Resources

❑ **All in One** **Teaching Resources**
 Section Summary, p. 207
 L1 Review and Reinforce, p. 211
 L3 Enrich, p. 212

Ocean Motions • *Section Summary*

Ocean Water Chemistry

Guide for Reading

- How salty is ocean water?

- How do the temperature and gas content of ocean water vary?

- How do conditions in the ocean change with depth?

Ocean water contains dissolved salts. The salt that is most common in ocean water is sodium chloride, also known as table salt. Ocean water also contains smaller amounts of magnesium, calcium, potassium, and several other substances.

The total amount of dissolved salts in a sample of water is the **salinity** of that sample. **On average, one kilogram of ocean water contains about 35 grams of salts—that is, 35 parts per thousand.** Salinity is lower near the surface, where precipitation and melting ice add fresh water to the ocean. It is also lower near the mouths of large rivers that empty large amounts of fresh water into the ocean. Salinity is higher where evaporation is high, such as in hot, dry climates. It is also higher near the poles, where surface water freezes into ice and leaves the salt behind.

The dissolved salts in ocean water give it different properties from those of fresh water. Ocean water is more dense than fresh water. Because of its greater density, ocean water has more buoyancy than fresh water. This means that it lifts, or buoys up, less dense objects floating in it.

Like temperatures on land, temperatures at the surface of the ocean vary with location and the seasons. Gases in ocean water vary as well. Two gases found in ocean water that are necessary for living things are oxygen and carbon dioxide.

The surface of the ocean absorbs energy from the sun and heats up. Because warm water is less dense than cold water, the warm water stays on the surface. Surface water is warmest near the equator and becomes colder as you travel away from the equator. Since cold water can hold more dissolved oxygen than warm water, there is more oxygen in polar waters than in tropical waters.

If you could travel from the surface of the ocean to the ocean floor, you would pass through a vertical section of the ocean called the water column. Conditions change greatly as you travel down through the water column. **Temperature decreases as you descend through the ocean.** It drops to about 4°C at 1 kilometer below the surface. Below that, the temperature stays at about 3.5°C throughout most of the ocean. **Pressure increases continuously with depth in the ocean.** This is an obstacle to underwater exploration. A diver can descend safely to only about 40 meters. To go deeper, scientists must use a **submersible,** an underwater vehicle built of strong materials that resist water pressure.

Ocean Water Chemistry

This section describes the saltiness of ocean water and the gases that ocean water contains. The section also describes how temperature, pressure, and other properties of ocean water change as you go deeper in the ocean.

Use Target Reading Skills

Preview the red headings in your textbook. In the graphic organizer, ask a how *or* what *question for each heading. As you read, answer your questions.*

Ocean Water Chemistry

Question	Answer
How salty is the ocean?	One kilogram of ocean water has . . .

The Salty Ocean

1. The total amount of dissolved salts in water is called _____.

2. Label the two parts of the circle graph.

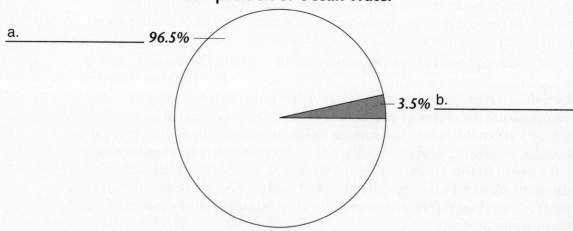

Composition of Ocean Water

a. _____ 96.5%

3.5% b. _____

Ocean Motions • *Guided Reading and Study*

3. Circle the letter of each place in the ocean where salinity is likely to be relatively low.
   a. Near melting ice
   b. Near the mouth of a large river
   c. Where the climate is hot and dry
   d. Near the poles

4. Circle the letter of the sentence that is true about the effect of salinity on ocean water.
   a. Salinity increases the freezing point of ocean water.
   b. Salinity decreases the density of ocean water.
   c. Salinity decreases the mass of ocean water.
   d. Salinity increases the buoyancy of ocean water.

Other Ocean Properties

5. List two gases found in ocean water that are necessary for living things.

   a. _____ b. _____

6. Is the following sentence true or false? There is more oxygen in seawater than in air. _____

7. Why does warm water stay at the surface of the ocean?

   _____

   _____

8. Is the following sentence true or false? Warm water contains more dissolved oxygen than does cold water. _____

Ocean Motions • *Guided Reading and Study*

Ocean Water Chemistry *(continued)*

Changes with Depth

9. A vertical section of the ocean is called the _____.

10. Complete the compare/contrast table.

Depth of Ocean Zones	
Zone	**Depth**
a.	Extends from about 1 kilometer below the surface to the ocean floor
b.	Extends from the surface to about 200 meters below
c.	Extends from about 200 meters below the surface to about 1 kilometer below the surface

11. Circle the letter of each sentence that is true about temperature in the ocean.
    a. Temperature decreases as depth increases.
    b. Temperature is highest in the transition zone.
    c. Temperature drops quickly in the surface zone.
    d. Temperature is lowest in the deep zone.

12. Is the following sentence true or false? Below the surface zone, the salinity of ocean water remains fairly constant. _____

13. Circle the letter of each sentence that is true about pressure in the ocean.
    a. Pressure is the weight of the water above pressing down.
    b. Pressure rises continuously as depth increases.
    c. Pressure on the ocean floor is twice as great as pressure at sea level.
    d. A diver can safely withstand pressure at 1 kilometer below sea level.

14. An underwater vehicle built to resist pressure is called a(n)
    _____.

Ocean Water Chemistry

Understanding Main Ideas

Fill in the spaces in the table below.

The Water Column

Depth Zone	Depth Range	Average Temperature (°C)
Surface	1. _____	2. _____
3. _____	4. _____	4°C–10°C
5. _____	1 km to ocean floor	6. _____

Answer the following questions in the spaces provided or on the back of this sheet.

7. What is the average salinity of ocean water?

_____

8. Name three factors that affect how salty the ocean is.

_____

9. Which is more dense, ocean water or fresh water?

_____

10. What is the most abundant salt in seawater?

_____

11. Why is there more oxygen at the surface of the ocean than in deeper layers?

_____

_____

12. What prevents scuba divers from going deeper than about 40 meters below the surface?

_____

_____

Building Vocabulary

Fill in the space to complete each sentence.

13. A _____ is an underwater vehicle built of strong materials to resist pressure.

14. The total amount of dissolved salts in ocean water is called _____.

15. A vertical section of the ocean from the surface to the ocean floor is referred to as the _____.

Ocean Motions · *Enrich*

The Composition of Ocean Water

On average, one kilogram of ocean water contains about 35 grams of salts. That is, salts make up about 3.5 percent of the mass of ocean water. Although sodium chloride is the most abundant and familiar salt in seawater, many other salts are also dissolved in seawater. The table below lists the salts that a scientist recovered by evaporating a 100-gram sample of ocean water. The second column of the table lists the mass of each salt recovered.

Major Salts From a Sample of Ocean Water

Salts	Mass (g of salt recovered from 100 g of ocean water)	Number of Degrees on Circle Graph	Percentage of Total Salts
Sodium chloride	2.72		
Magnesium chloride	0.38		
Magnesium sulfate	0.17		
Calcium sulfate	0.13		
Potassium sulfate	0.08		
Calcium carbonate	0.01		
Magnesium bromide	0.01		

Follow these steps to complete the table and make a circle graph. To review how to make a circle graph, see the Skills Handbook at the back of your textbook.

1. Use this equation to fill in the third column of the table.

$$\frac{\text{mass of salt}}{\text{total mass of salts (3.5 g)}} = \frac{x}{\text{total number of degrees in circle (360)}}$$

2. Use this equation to fill in the fourth column of the table.

$$\text{Percentage of total salts} = \frac{\text{number of degrees on circle graph}}{360} \times 100\%$$

3. Use a protractor and the data in the table to make a circle graph showing the percentage of each salt recovered from the sample of ocean water. Label each section of the graph.

Name _____ Date _____ Class _____

Investigating Changes in Density

Problem

Can you design and build an instrument that can detect differences in density?

Materials

thumbtacks	graduated cylinder, 250 mL
thermometer	ice
table salt	balance
fine-point permanent marker	water
metric ruler	hot plate
unsharpened pencil with eraser	spoon
	various other materials provided by your teacher

Procedure   *Review the safety guidelines in Appendix A.*

PART 1 Research and Investigate

1. One way to measure the density of a liquid is with a tool called a hydrometer. You can make a simple hydrometer using an unsharpened wooden pencil.

2. Starting at the unsharpened end of a pencil, use a permanent marker to make marks every 2 mm along the side of the pencil. Make longer marks for every whole centimeter. Continue making marks until you have marked off 5 cm.

3. Label each of the long marks, starting at the unsharpened end of the pencil.

4. Insert 3 thumbtacks as weights into the eraser end of the pencil. **CAUTION:** *Be careful not to cut yourself on the sharp points of the thumbtacks.*

5. Fill the graduated cylinder with 250 ml of water at room temperature. Place the pencil in the water, eraser end down.

6. Add or remove thumbtacks and adjust their placement until the pencil floats upright, with about 2 cm sticking up above the surface of the water.

7. In your notebook, record the temperature of the water. Next to that number, record the reading on the pencil hydrometer at the surface of the water.

8. Fill the graduated cylinder with cold water. Place the pencil hydrometer into the water, eraser end down. Then repeat Step 7.

Ocean Motions • *Technology Lab*

Investigating Changes in Density *(continued)*

PART 2 Design and Build

9. Using what you learned in Part 1, design and build a hydrometer that can detect density differences among different samples of water. Your hydrometer should

   - be able to measure density differences between hot water and cold water.

   - be able to measure density differences between salt water and fresh water.

   - be constructed of materials approved by your teacher.

10. Sketch your design in your notebook, and make a list of the materials you will need. Write a plan for how you will construct your hydrometer. After you have received your teacher's approval for your design, build your hydrometer.

PART 3 Evaluate and Redesign

11. Test your hydrometer by using it to measure the density of water at different temperatures. Then test samples of water that have different salinities. Create a data table in which to record your results.

12. Based on your tests, decide how you could improve the design of your hydrometer. For example, how could you change your design so that your hydrometer is able to detect smaller differences in density? Obtain your teacher's approval, then make the necessary changes, and test how it functions.

Data Table

Manipulated Variable: _____	
Condition Tested	**Hydrometer Reading**

Ocean Motions · *Technology Lab*

Analyze and Conclude

Write an answer for each question in the spaces provided.

1. Explain why cold water is more dense than hot water. Explain why salt
   water is more dense than fresh water.

   _____

   _____

2. How well did the pencil hydrometer you built in Part 1 work? What
   problems did you encounter with the hydrometer?

   _____

   _____

3. How did you incorporate what you learned in Part 1 into your
   hydrometer design in Part 2? For example, how did your hydrometer
   address the problems you encountered in Part 1?

   _____

   _____

4. In Part 3, how well did your hydrometer perform when you measured
   water samples of different densities? How did you redesign your
   hydrometer to improve its function?

   _____

   _____

5. What limitations such as buoyancy, materials, time, costs, or other
   factors place on the design and function of your hydrometer? Describe
   how you adapted your design to work within these limitations.

   _____

   _____

   _____

Communicate

Create an informative poster that describes how your hydrometer works.
Include illustrations of your hydrometer and any important background
information on density.

Currents and Climate

 3–4 periods, 1–2 blocks

Objectives

H.3.4.1 Identify what causes surface currents and explain how surface currents affect climate.

H.3.4.2 Identify the causes of deep currents and describe the effects that the currents have.

H.3.4.3 Describe how upwelling affects the distribution of nutrients in the ocean.

Key Terms
• current • Coriolis effect • climate
• El Niño • upwelling

Local Standards

PRETEACH

Build Background Knowledge
Explain how a message in a bottle might get to a faraway location.

Discover Activity *Which Is More Dense?* **L1**

Targeted Resources

☐ **All in One** **Teaching Resources**
   L2 Reading Strategy Transparency H37: Relating Cause and Effect
☐ **⊙** **Presentation-Pro CD-ROM**

INSTRUCT

Surface Currents Explain how the Coriolis effect changes ocean currents.
Deep Currents Compare surface currents and deep currents.
Upwelling Explain the process by which deep ocean water is brought to the surface.

Skills Lab *Modeling Ocean Currents* **L2**

Targeted Resources

☐ **All in One** **Teaching Resources**
   L2 Guided Reading, pp. 218–221
   L2 Transparencies H38, H39, H40
   L2 Lab: *Modeling Ocean Currents*, pp. 224–225
☐ **Lab Activity Video/DVD**
   Skills Lab: *Modeling Ocean Currents*
☐ www.SciLinks.org Web Code: scn-0834
☐ **⊙** **Student Edition on Audio CD**

ASSESS

Section Assessment Questions
⟳ Have students use their Relating Cause and Effect graphic organizers to help them answer the questions.

Reteach
Define important terms related to currents.

Targeted Resources

☐ **All in One** **Teaching Resources**
   Section Summary, p. 217
   L1 Review and Reinforce, p. 222
   L3 Enrich, p. 223

Currents and Climate

Guide for Reading

- What causes surface currents, and how do they affect climate?

- What causes deep currents, and what effects do they have?

- How does upwelling affect the distribution of nutrients in the ocean?

Currents are large streams of moving water that flow through the oceans. Unlike waves, currents carry water great distances. Some currents move water at the surface of the ocean. Other currents move water deep below the surface.

Surface currents, which affect water to a depth of several hundred meters, are driven mainly by winds. Therefore, surface currents follow the major wind patterns of the globe, moving in a circular pattern in the five major ocean basins. The **Coriolis effect,** which is the effect of Earth's rotation on the direction of winds and currents, is the reason for this circular pattern. The Coriolis effect causes currents to curve to the right in the Northern Hemisphere and to the left in the Southern Hemisphere. The largest, most powerful surface current in the North Atlantic Ocean is the Gulf Stream.

Climate is the pattern of temperature and precipitation typical of an area over a long period of time. Currents affect climate by moving cold and warm water around the globe. **A surface current warms or cools the air above it, influencing the climate of the land near the coast.**

Deep currents are caused by differences in density of ocean water. Density, in turn, depends on temperature and salinity. When ice forms near the poles, the salinity of the remaining liquid water increases. This cold, salty water is dense and sinks, flowing along the ocean floor as a deep current. **Deep currents move and mix water around the world. They carry cold water from the poles toward the equator.** They flow much more slowly than surface currents.

Another type of water movement is **upwelling.** This is the upward movement of cold water from the ocean depths to replace warm surface water moved away by winds. **Upwelling brings up tiny ocean organisms, minerals, and other nutrients from the deeper layers of the water. Without this motion, the surface waters of the open ocean would be very scarce in nutrients.** Areas of upwelling usually attract huge schools of fish that feed on these nutrients.

El Niño is an abnormal climate event that occurs every 2 to 7 years in the Pacific Ocean. An unusual pattern of winds in the western Pacific pushes a vast sheet of water eastward toward the South American coast. This prevents upwelling off the western coast of South America and causes unusual weather patterns around the world. El Niño can cause rainstorms, floods, and mudslides in some areas and droughts in others.

Currents and Climate

This section describes surface and deep ocean currents and explains how they affect climate.

Use Target Reading Skills

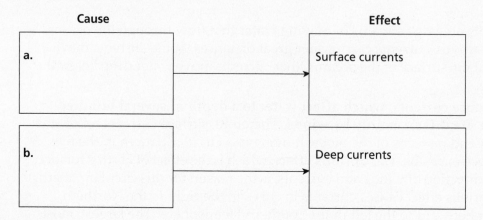

Introduction

1. A large stream of moving water that flows through the oceans is a(n) _____.

2. Is the following sentence true or false? Currents carry water great distances. _____

Surface Currents

3. Circle the letter of each sentence that is true about surface currents.

    a. They affect water down to 1 kilometer.

    b. They are driven mainly by winds.

    c. They move in circular patterns.

    d. They occur only in the Pacific Ocean.

Ocean Motions • *Guided Reading and Study*

4. The effect of Earth's rotation on the direction of winds and currents is called the _____.

5. Is the following sentence true or false? In the Northern Hemisphere, surface currents curve to the left. _____

6. The largest and most powerful surface current in the North Atlantic Ocean is the _____.

7. Circle the letter of the sentence that is true about the Gulf Stream.

   a. It is caused by strong winds from the north.
   b. It carries more water than the Mississippi River.
   c. It is a cold-water current.
   d. It curves westward due to the Coriolis effect.

8. Is the following sentence true or false? In the Southern Hemisphere, surface currents curve to the left. _____

9. The pattern of temperature and precipitation typical of an area over a long period of time is called _____.

10. An abnormal climate event that occurs every 2 to 7 years in the Pacific Ocean is called _____.

11. How does El Niño begin?

    _____

    _____

    _____

    _____

12. Circle the letter of each sentence that is true about El Niño.

    a. It can prevent upwelling.
    b. It can affect weather worldwide.
    c. It is fully understood.
    d. Its impact can be reduced.

Ocean Motions • *Guided Reading and Study*

Currents and Climate *(continued)*

Deep Currents

13. How does the Gulf Stream influence the climate along the western coast of Norway?

_____

_____

_____

14. How do cold-water currents affect weather on land near a coast?

_____

_____

15. Deep currents are caused by differences in _____.

16. The density of water depends on its _____ and its _____.

17. Why does water get denser as it moves toward the poles?

_____

_____

_____

18. Is the following sentence true or false? Deep ocean currents move and mix water around the world. _____

Name _____ Date _____ Class _____

Upwelling

19. The upward movement of cold water from the ocean depths is referred
    to as _____.

20. Is the following sentence true or false? Upwelling is caused by tides.
    _____

21. Label the wind, warm surface water, and the area of upwelling in the
    diagram below.

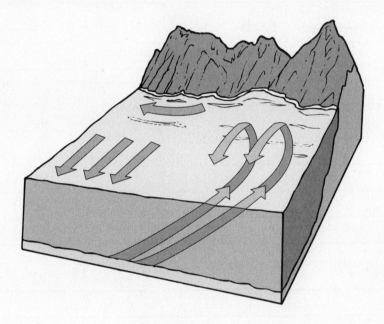

22. Why are upwelling zones usually home to enormous schools of fish?

    _____

    _____

    _____

Ocean Motions · *Review and Reinforce*

Currents and Climate

Understanding Main Ideas

Fill in the spaces in the table below.

Comparing Currents

Type of Current	Cause	Possible Temperatures
1. _____	Winds	2. _____
Deep	3. _____	4. _____

Answer each of the following questions in the spaces provided.

5. How do surface currents affect climate?

   _____

   _____

   _____

   _____

6. Why does upwelling attract huge numbers of fish?

   _____

   _____

   _____

Building Vocabulary

Fill in the space to complete each statement.

7. _____ are large streams of moving water that flow through the oceans.

8. The effect of Earth's rotation on the direction of winds and currents is called the _____.

9. _____ is the pattern of temperature and precipitation typical of an area over a long period of time.

10. _____ is an abnormal climate event that occurs every 2 to 7 years in the Pacific Ocean.

Ocean Motions ▪ *Enrich*

The Sargasso Sea

The Sargasso Sea is an oval-shaped region in the North Atlantic Ocean. The Sargasso Sea gets its name from the Portuguese word for seaweed. This is because brown seaweed covers most of its surface.

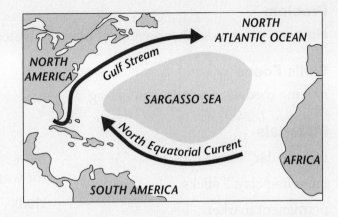

The Sargasso Sea was first described by Christopher Columbus in 1492. He was afraid that rocks might lie hidden below the seaweed and damage his ships. However, it was also the seaweed that encouraged Columbus to continue on his voyage. Because seaweed usually grows close to shore, he thought land must be near. Since Columbus' time, many legends about the Sargasso Sea have spread. The seaweed covering its surface was believed to be so thick that no ship could escape from it. Early writers described ancient ghost ships, rotting away as they remained trapped forever in the seaweed.

The legends about the Sargasso Sea are simply that. The seaweed is not thick enough to interfere with the movement of ships. Still, the Sargasso Sea has several unusual features. Its waters are exceptionally clear, allowing light to penetrate as deep as 1 kilometer. In addition, the waters of the Sargasso Sea are very calm, warm, and salty.

The unusual features of the Sargasso Sea result in part from its great depth, which averages almost 5 kilometers. The sea's location plays a role as well. It is surrounded by fast-moving currents—the Gulf Stream and the North Equatorial Current—that keep its waters from mixing with the rest of the Atlantic Ocean. The Sargasso Sea also lies in a region where temperatures are very warm. Precipitation is low and evaporation is high in this region.

Answer the following questions on a separate sheet of paper.

1. Why do you think early navigators tried to avoid the Sargasso Sea?
2. How do the waters of the Sargasso Sea differ from the waters of the rest of the North Atlantic?
3. What keeps the waters of the Sargasso Sea from mixing with the rest of the Atlantic Ocean?
4. Suggest an explanation for the high salinity of the Sargasso Sea.

Ocean Motions

Ocean Motions ▪ *Skills Lab*

Modeling Ocean Currents

Problem

How can you model the movement of ocean water due to surface currents?

Skills Focus

making models, observing, inferring

Materials

rectangular baking tray

modeling clay, 3 sticks

permanent marker

newspaper

construction paper, blue and red

jointed drinking straws, one per student

light-reflecting rheoscopic fluid, 400 mL (or water and food coloring)

chalk

ruler

hole puncher

Procedure

Review the safety guidelines in Appendix A.

1. Cover your work area with newspaper. Place the baking tray on top of the newspaper.
2. Using the map as a guide, draw a chalk outline of the eastern coast of North and South America on the left side of the tray. Draw the outline of the west coast of Europe and Africa on the right side of the tray.
3. Use modeling clay to create the continents, roughly following the chalk outlines you have drawn. Build the continents to a depth of about 3 cm. Press the clay tightly to the pan to form a watertight seal.
4. Fill the ocean area of your model with rheoscopic fluid (or water and food coloring) to a depth of 1 cm.
5. Place 10 blue paper punches in the ocean area marked with a 1 on the map. Place 10 red punches in the area marked with a 2.
6. Select a drinking straw and bend it at the joint. Write your initials on the short end of the straw with the marker.

Ocean Motions • *Skills Lab*

7. With a partner, simulate the pattern of winds that blow in this region of the world. One partner should position his or her straw across the westernmost bulge of Africa and blow toward the west (see arrow on map). The other partner should position his or her straw across the northern end of South America and blow toward the northeast (see arrow on map). Make sure that the straws are bent and that the short ends are parallel to the ocean surface. Both partners should begin blowing gently through the straws at the same time. Try to blow as continuously as possible for one to two minutes.

8. Observe the motion of the fluid and paper punches over the surface of the ocean. Notice what happens when the fluid and punches flow around landmasses.

MAP

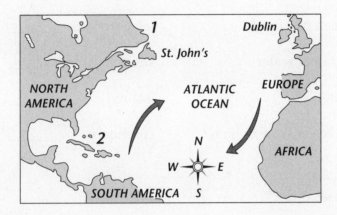

Analyze and Conclude

Write your answers on a separate sheet of paper.

1. Draw the map in your text that shows the pattern of ocean currents that was produced in your model. Use red arrows to show the flow of warm water moving north from the equator. Use blue arrows to show the flow of cold water southward from the polar regions.

2. Use the map in your text to add names to the currents you drew on your map. Which currents are warm-water currents? Which are cold-water currents?

3. Based on what you observed with your model, describe the relationship between winds and surface currents in the ocean.

4. Dublin, Ireland, is located at the same latitude as St. John's in Newfoundland, Canada. However, when it's 8°C in Dublin in January, it's usually below 0°C in St. John's. Use your knowledge of ocean currents to explain why the climate in Dublin is different from the climate in St. John's.

5. **Think About It** Suppose you wanted to sail to Europe from the East Coast of the United States. Write a dialogue you might have with a crew member in which you discuss two natural factors that could help speed up the trip.

Design an Experiment

Design an investigation in which you simulate an upwelling off the coast of Africa. (*Hint:* You may use a model similar to the one used in this investigation.) *Obtain your teacher's permission before carrying out your investigation.*

Key Terms

Use the clues to help you unscramble the key terms from the chapter. Then put the numbered letters in order to find the answer to the riddle.

Clues   **Key Terms**

1. Structure that reduces erosion   rongi   _ _ _ _ _
                                                            1

2. Highest point of a wave   tecsr   _ _ _ _ _
                                                              2

3. Ridge of sand near shore   nasdrab   _ _ _ _ _ _ _
                                                              3

4. Distance between two crests   telegawvnh   _ _ _ _ _ _ _ _ _ _
                                                                4

5. Daily rise and fall of water   sdeit   _ _ _ _ _
                                                              5

6. Saltiness of water   lstainyi   _ _ _ _ _ _ _ _
                                                                    6

7. Number of waves passing by in a   curenqefy   _ _ _ _ _ _ _ _ _
given time   7

Riddle: What causes tides?

Answer: _ _ _ _ _ _ _
             1 2 3 4 5 6 7

Connecting Concepts

Develop a concept map that uses the key concepts and key terms from this chapter. Keep in mind the big idea of this chapter. The concept map shown is one way to organize how the information in this chapter is related. You may use an extra sheet of paper.

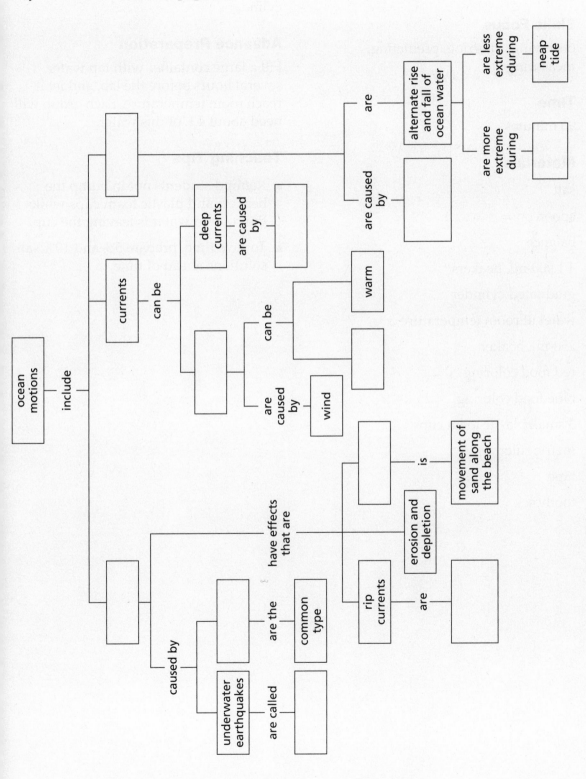

Ocean Motions

Density and Salinity

Key Concept

Water of different densities, caused by different salinities, forms layers.

Skills Focus

observing, inferring, predicting, measuring

Time

90 minutes

Materials

salt

spoon

balance

4 1,000-mL beakers

graduated cylinder

water at room temperature

250-mL beaker

red food coloring

blue food coloring

3 small plastic foam cups

metric ruler

tape

toothpick

Alternative Materials

You can use large jars instead of beakers and measuring cups instead of graduated cylinders.

Advance Preparation

Fill a large container with tap water several hours before the lab, and let it reach room temperature. Each group will need about 4 L of this water.

Teaching Tips

- Remind students not to bump the beakers and plastic foam cups while the colored water is leaving the cup.

- To save time, prepare 5% and 10% salt solutions ahead of time.

Name _____ Date _____ Class _____

Density and Salinity

Pre-Lab Discussion

The average salinity of ocean water is 35 parts of salt per thousand parts of water. Ocean salt comes from minerals on land, which dissolve into water that flows over them. Dissolved salts affect water density, and density affects the way ocean waters move and form layers. By studying the salinity of water, oceanographers learn about ocean layers and currents.

In this investigation, you will model ocean water of different salinities and use the models to determine how ocean waters form layers.

1. Define salinity.

_____

_____

2. What causes differences in the salinity of ocean water in different areas?

_____

_____

_____

Problem

How do differences in salinity create layers in ocean water?

Materials (*per group*)

salt	red food coloring
spoon	blue food coloring
balance	3 small plastic foam cups
4 1,000-mL beakers	metric ruler
graduated cylinder	tape
water at room temperature	toothpick
250-mL beaker	

Safety   *Review the safety guidelines in the front of your lab book.*
To prevent slips and falls, immediately wipe up any water spilled on the floor. Handle glass objects carefully. If they break, tell your teacher. Do not pick up broken glass.

Ocean Motions · *Laboratory Investigation*

Density and Salinity (*continued*)

Procedure

1. Make a 5% salt solution: Measure 50 g of salt, and pour it into a 1,000-mL beaker. Add 950 mL of water to the beaker. Stir until all of the salt dissolves.

2. Make a 10% salt solution: Measure 10 g of salt, and pour it into the 250-mL beaker. Add 90 mL of water to the beaker. Stir until all of the salt dissolves. Add enough blue food coloring to make the water deep blue.

3. Fill a second 1,000-mL beaker with 400 mL of water.

4. Pour 10 mL of the 5% salt solution into a plastic foam cup. Add enough red food coloring to make the water deep red. Tape the cup inside the beaker of water so that the bottom of the cup is just below the water level. See Figure 1.

Figure 1

5. Holding the plastic foam cup steady, use a toothpick to poke a small hole near the bottom of the cup.

6. Be careful not to bump the beaker. Observe what happens to the colored water. Record your observations in the Data Table. Sketch and color what you observe.

7. Fill the third 1,000-mL beaker with 5% salt solution to within 10 cm of the top.

8. Pour 10 mL of the blue 10% salt solution into the second plastic foam cup. As before, tape the cup inside the beaker so that the bottom of the cup is just below the water level.

9. Repeat Steps 5 and 6.

10. As a control, fill the fourth 1,000-mL beaker with 5% salt solution to within 10 cm of the top. Pour 10 mL of tap water into the third plastic foam cup. Add blue food coloring to the tap water until the tap water is the same color as the 10% salt solution in Step 2. Tape the cup to the inside of the beaker as before. Repeat Steps 5 and 6.

Name _____ Date _____ Class _____

Ocean Motions • *Laboratory Investigation*

Observations

Data Table

	Observations	Sketch
5% red salt solution in tap water		
10% blue salt solution in 5% salt solution		
Blue tap water in 5% salt solution		

Analyze and Conclude

1. Which water was the least dense? The most dense? Explain your reasoning.

   _____

   _____

   _____

2. How does the amount of salt dissolved in water affect its density? Give the evidence that supports your answer.

   _____

   _____

   _____

Ocean Motions • *Laboratory Investigation*

Density and Salinity *(continued)*

3. In the ocean, where would you expect to find water with the greatest salinity? Give a reason for your answer.

_____

_____

_____

Critical Thinking and Applications

1. Predict how the following kinds of water would form layers: (1) warm, slightly salty water; (2) cold, slightly salty water; (3) cold, very salty water; (4) warm rainwater. List them in order, starting with the deepest layer. Give a reason for your answer.

_____

_____

_____

_____

_____

2. Why was it important that all the water in the experiment was the same temperature?

_____

_____

_____

3. Would you expect the salinity to be high or low in the ocean off the coast of a hot, dry area? Give a reason for your answer.

_____

_____

_____

More to Explore

What would happen if you added red 5% salt solution and blue 10% salt solution from two cups at the same time to a container of tap water? Develop a hypothesis for this problem. Then write a procedure you would follow to test your hypothesis. Have the teacher approve your procedure before you carry it out. Remember to wear your safety goggles and apron.

Making Salinity Currents

Students are presented with the problem of creating a model for currents caused by differences in salinity, using the materials provided. To solve this problem, students will apply the concepts they have learned about salinity, density, and currents.

Expected Outcome

Students should devise a setup that allows them to add a small amount of colored salty water to a larger amount of uncolored fresh water. The most likely setup would include a large amount of fresh water in an aquarium or wide-mouthed jar and a small amount of colored salty water in a cup. Then students will slowly dribble the salty water into the fresh water on one side of the aquarium or jar. They should observe the colored salty water sink and spread out along the bottom of the aquarium or jar.

Content Assessed

This activity assesses students' understanding of salinity, density, and currents.

Skills Assessed

developing hypotheses, designing experiments, observing, drawing conclusions

Materials

Provide students with aquariums or wide-mouthed glass jars, beakers or cups, and stirring rods.

Place pitchers of water and containers of table salt and food coloring at a central location or on a few tables around the classroom. Advise students to use as much water and salt as they need for their setups.

Advance Preparation

- Gather several containers, such as pitchers or large plastic milk jugs, to hold the water used in the activity.

- Fill the containers with water the day before students do this activity so that all of the water will be at room temperature.

Time

30 minutes

Safety

Caution students that they will be working with glass jars that are breakable. Instruct them to wear safety goggles and to handle the jars with care. Tell them that if glass does break, they should not touch the broken pieces. Caution students to wipe up any spilled water immediately.

Monitoring the Task

- Review students' hypotheses and setup sketches before they try out their plans.

- Urge students to stir the water in the cup thoroughly after adding salt.

- Make sure students add the colored salty water to the aquarium or jar very slowly so that they can observe how the salty water moves through the fresh water.

- Provide a place for students to dispose of the water they have used.

Ocean Motions

Ocean Motions • *Performance Assessment*   **Scoring Rubric**

Making Salinity Currents

In assessing students' performance, use the following rubric.

	4	3	2	1
Planning and Constructing the Model	The student's sketch shows that the setup constructed would cause currents in the water due to differences in salinity.	The student's sketch shows that the setup constructed is flawed but might yield the expected outcome.	The student's sketch shows that an attempt was made to construct a model but the setup would not yield the expected outcome.	The student's sketch shows that little or no attempt was made to construct a model.
Concept Understanding	The student demonstrates a mastery of the concepts that underlie the model, including salinity, density, and currents.	The student demonstrates an understanding of the concepts that underlie the model, including salinity, density, and currents.	The student demonstrates a partial understanding of the concepts that underlie the model, including salinity, density, and currents.	The student demonstrates little or no understanding of the concepts that underlie the model, including salinity, density, and currents.

Name _____ Date _____ Class _____

Making Salinity Currents

Problem

How can you model ocean currents caused by differences in salinity?

Suggested Materials

aquarium or wide-mouthed glass jar

water

cup

stirring rod

table salt

food coloring

Devise a Plan

1. Study the materials provided, and think of a way they could be used to make a model of currents caused by differences in salinity. (*Hint:* Consider the relationship between salinity and density.) Formulate a hypothesis about how you could make such a model. Write your hypothesis on another sheet of paper.
2. Make a sketch of the setup you plan to use.
3. Experiment with your setup to practice using the materials to make a model of currents caused by differences in salinity.

Analyze and Conclude

On a separate sheet of paper, respond to the items that follow.

1. Make a flowchart of your model with arrows and labels to show what changes occurred in the model.
2. Describe the currents that flowed in your model. Explain why they moved as they did.
3. How do you think your currents would have been different if you had used saltier water or salt water that was ice-cold?
4. Where in the ocean would you expect to find currents caused by differences in salinity?
5. What is the relationship between salinity and density?

Ocean Motions

Multiple Choice

Write the letter of the correct answer on the line at the left.

_____ 1. When a wave passes by, water particles move
   a. toward shore in a straight line.
   b. in a circular motion.
   c. slowly toward the bottom of the ocean.
   d. in the opposite direction.

_____ 2. The strength of a wave depends mainly on its
   a. wavelength.
   b. frequency.
   c. wave height.
   d. trough.

_____ 3. Tsunamis are most common in the
   a. Indian Ocean.
   b. Atlantic Ocean.
   c. Pacific Ocean.
   d. Arctic Ocean.

_____ 4. The total number of high tides that occur each day in most places is
   a. four.
   b. two.
   c. one.
   d. five.

_____ 5. A spring tide occurs when
   a. the moon and sun are at right angles to each other.
   b. it is spring in the Southern Hemisphere.
   c. it is spring in the Northern Hemisphere.
   d. the moon, sun, and Earth are in a straight line.

_____ 6. Low tides occur about every
   a. 6 hours and 15 minutes.
   b. 12 hours and 25 minutes.
   c. 24 hours.
   d. 2 weeks.

_____ 7. Two gases found in ocean water that are necessary for living things are
   a. oxygen and carbon dioxide.
   b. oxygen and helium.
   c. carbon dioxide and hydrogen.
   d. hydrogen and helium.

_____ 8. As you go deeper in the ocean, all of the following decrease EXCEPT
   a. temperature.
   b. light.
   c. the number of algae.
   d. pressure.

_____ 9. Both surface currents and waves are caused mainly by
   a. differences in the density of water.
   b. the Coriolis effect.
   c. winds.
   d. the moon's gravity.

_____ 10. In the Northern Hemisphere, ocean currents curve to the right because of
- **a.** longshore drift.
- **b.** the Coriolis effect.
- **c.** the moon's gravity.
- **d.** earthquakes on the ocean floor.

Completion

Fill in the line to complete each statement.

11. The horizontal distance between crests of waves is the _____.

12. _____ is the force that causes tides.

13. Oxygen in ocean water comes from the atmosphere and _____.

14. The density of seawater depends on its temperature and _____.

15. The largest and most powerful surface current in the North Atlantic Ocean is the

_____.

True or False

If the statement is true, write true. *If it is false, change the underlined word or words to make the statement true.*

_____ **16.** The farther apart waves are, the greater their <u>wavelength</u>.

_____ **17.** A <u>rip current</u> is caused by an earthquake on the ocean floor.

_____ **18.** The most common salt in ocean water is <u>calcium sulfate</u>.

_____ **19.** Deep currents are caused by differences in <u>pressure</u>.

_____ **20.** Surface currents usually flow <u>more</u> quickly than deep currents.

Essay

Write an answer for each of the following.

21. How do waves change as they near the shore? Explain your answer.

_____

_____

_____

_____

_____

Ocean Motions (continued)

22. Why are large numbers of fish often found in zones of upwelling?

_____

_____

_____

Using Science Skills

Use the figure below to answer the following questions. Write your answers in the spaces provided.

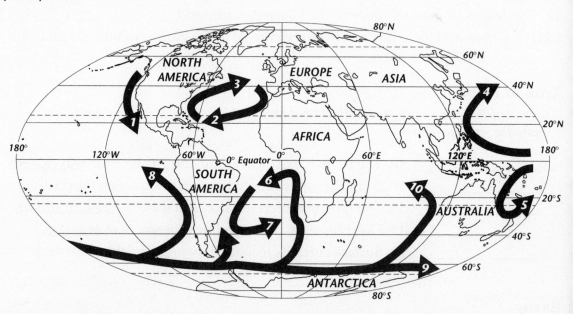

23. Classifying Identify which of the ocean currents in the figure are cold currents and which are warm currents. Explain the reasoning for your choices.

_____

24. Comparing and Contrasting How are ocean currents in the Northern and Southern Hemispheres alike? How are they different?

_____

_____

_____

25. Predicting Along the very southern coast of South America, winds blow from west to east. Based on the figure above, predict what the climate is like along the southwest coast of South America. Explain your answer.

_____

_____

_____

Name _____ Date _____ Class _____

Ocean Motions • *Chapter Test*

Using Science Skills: Making a Graph

Pressure at the surface of the ocean is about 10 units, and it increases about 100 units for every 1,000 meters you go below the surface. Use this information to answer the questions below and to complete the graph.

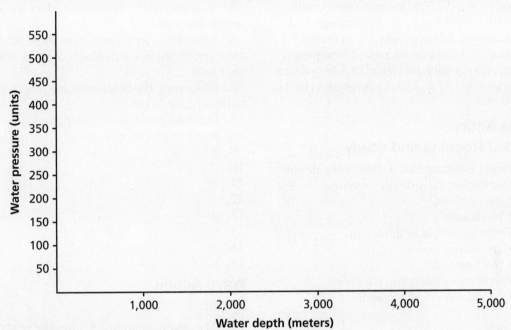

26. What is the water pressure at the following depths?

    a. 1,000 m _____

    b. 2,000 m _____

    c. 3,000 m _____

    d. 4,000 m _____

    e. 5,000 m _____

27. Plot the values from Question 26 on the graph.

28. Based on the graph, how would you describe the relationship between ocean depth and water pressure?

_____

_____

Essay

Write an answer for each of the following on a separate sheet of paper.

29. In what ways is the ocean at a depth of 1,000 meters different from the ocean at the surface in the same location?

30. Do you think that you would float more easily in the middle of the Atlantic Ocean or the Arctic Ocean? Explain your answer.

Chapter Project Worksheet 2

Answers will vary. Possible estimated sizes are 20 m (lighthouse), 2 m (adult human), 1.3 m (child), 1.5 m (bush), 0.4 (sea gull), 0.2 m (beach pail), 2.3 m (beach umbrella), 3 m (lifeguard stand), 1.6 m × 0.6 (beach towel), 1.5 m (fence). Corresponding model sizes would be 20 cm (lighthouse), 2 cm (adult human), 1.3 cm (child), 1.5 cm (bush), 0.4 cm (sea gull), 0.2 cm (beach pail), 2.3 cm (beach umbrella), 3 cm (lifeguard stand), 1.6 cm × 0.6 cm (beach towel), 1.5 cm (fence). Waves could be 2 to 5 cm high.

Wave Action
Guided Reading and Study

Use Target Reading Skills This is one possible way to complete the graphic organizer. Accept all logical answers.

What You Know
1. There are waves in the ocean.
2. Wind causes waves.

What You Learned
1. Waves move energy to the shore.
2. Earthquakes cause tsunamis.

1. wave
2. Most waves form when winds blowing across the water's surface transmit their energy to the water.
3. true
4. a, b, c
5. false
6. b
7. d
8. a
9. c
10. b
11. Students should label the top point of a wave *crest* and the lowest point on a wave *trough*.
12. false
13. Near shore, wave height increases and wavelength decreases.
14. When a wave reaches a certain height, the crest of the wave topples and breaks onto the shore, forming surf.
15. gravity
16. a
17. b
18. a
19. c
20. Waves erode the shore in some places and build it up in others.
21. groin
22. dunes

Wave Action Review and Reinforce

1. crest
2. wavelength
3. trough
4. wave height
5. Its wave height increases, and its wavelength decreases.
6. When the waves come in to shore at an angle, resulting in a movement of sand along the beach
7. By eroding the beach in some places and building it up in others
8. Building groins, stabilizing sand dunes, and protecting barrier beaches
9. b
10. d
11. h
12. c
13. g
14. f
15. e
16. a

Wave Action
Enrich

1. At a depth equal to 1.3 times the wave height, or 6.5 meters
2. At a depth of 3.9 meters
3. Where the depth was 3.9 meters, which is about 8 meters from shore
4. 6 meters high
5. Higher waves break farther from shore because as waves get higher, the water depth in which they will break becomes deeper.

Tides
Guided Reading and Study

Use Target Reading Skills This is one possible way to complete the graphic organizer. Accept all logical answers.

Spring and Neap Tides
Q: When do spring tides occur?
A: During the full and new moons
Q: What is a neap tide?
A: A smaller tide that happens at the first- and third-quarter moons

1. tides
2. High tide is when the water reaches its highest point; low tide is when the water reaches its lowest point.
3. Tidal bulges are occurring at points A and C.
4. Water on the side of Earth opposite the moon is pulled less strongly by the moon than the rest of the planet is, so this water is "left behind" to form a bulge.

5. a, b
6. true
7. Factors include landforms such as capes, peninsulas, and islands, and the basins at the mouths of rivers.
8. true
9. a. Spring tide
   b. Greatest
   c. Neap tide
   d. Least
10. a, c, d
11. Sailors, marine scientists, people who fish, and others who live along a coast need to know about tides.
12. true
13. The energy of tide water moving back to sea powers generators that produce electricity.
14. a

Tides
Review and Reinforce

1. A and D
2. C or E
3. spring
4. lower
5. spring
6. greater
7. c
8. d
9. a
10. b

Tides
Enrich

1. The daily high tides at points x and y would be higher during a perigee moon because the moon's pull is stronger when it is closer to Earth.

2. Both perigee and spring tides are tides with an unusually large range between high and low tide. Perigee tides occur twice a month when the moon's orbit passes closest to Earth. Spring tides occur twice a month when the moon, the sun, and Earth are in a straight line.

3. Students may say that when Earth is closest to the sun, the sun's influence on tides would be greater. As a result, there would be more difference between spring and neap tides. Similarly, when Earth is farthest from the sun, the sun's influence on tides would be less, and there would be less difference between spring and neap tides.

Ocean Water Chemistry
Guided Reading and Study

Use Target Reading Skills This is one possible way to complete the graphic organizer. Accept all logical answers.

How salty is the ocean? One kilogram of ocean water contains about 35 grams of salts. That is, ocean water has an average salt concentration of 35 parts per thousand.

How does temperature vary in the surface ocean? In general, temperature is higher near the equator and lower near the poles.

How do temperature and pressure change with depth? As you descend, temperature decreases and pressure increases.

1. salinity
2. a. Water b. Dissolved salts
3. a, b
4. d
5. a. oxygen b. carbon dioxide
6. false
7. Warm water stays at the surface because it is less dense than cold water.
8. false
9. water column
10. a. Deep zone b. Surface zone
    c. Transition zone
11. a, d
12. true
13. a, b
14. submersible

Ocean Water Chemistry
Review and Reinforce

1. surface to about 200 m
2. 17.5°C or 10°C–17.5°C
3. Transition
4. bottom of surface zone to about 1 km
5. Deep
6. 3.5°C
7. 35 g of salt per kg of ocean water
8. Answers may vary. Possible answers include precipitation, rivers, evaporation, and freezing.
9. Ocean water, because it contains salt
10. Sodium chloride
11. Because that is where the ocean meets the atmosphere and where algae live
12. The pressure of the water
13. submersible
14. salinity
15. water column

Ocean Water Chemistry
Enrich

1. Sodium chloride: 280°; magnesium chloride: 39°; magnesium sulfate: 17°; calcium sulfate: 13°; potassium sulfate: 8.2°; calcium carbonate: 1.0°; magnesium bromide: 1.0°

2. Sodium chloride: 78%; magnesium chloride: 11%; magnesium sulfate: 4.7%; calcium sulfate: 3.6%; potassium sulfate: 2.3%; calcium carbonate: 0.28%; magnesium bromide: 0.28%

3. Students' graphs should show the correct percentages for each salt as given above, with each section of the graph clearly labeled with the name of the salt.

Investigating Changes in Density
Technology Lab

For answers, see the Teacher's Edition.

Currents and Climate
Guided Reading and Study

Use Target Reading Skills This is one possible way to complete the graphic organizer. Accept all logical answers.
a. Winds
b. Differences in ocean water density

1. current
2. true
3. b, c
4. Coriolis effect
5. false
6. Gulf Stream
7. b
8. true
9. climate
10. El Niño
11. El Niño begins when an unusual pattern of winds over the western Pacific Ocean causes a vast sheet of warm water to move eastward toward the South American coast.
12. a, b, d
13. The warm waters of the Gulf Stream bring the western coast of Norway a fairly mild climate for its northern location.
14. They bring cool, dry weather to land near a coast.
15. density
16. temperature; salinity
17. It gets denser because its temperature decreases and its salinity increases.
18. true
19. upwelling
20. false
21. Students should label "wind" occurring along the front of the mountains, "warm surface water" flowing out from the mountains, and "upwelling" occurring on the right side of the diagram above the water.

22. Upwelling zones have so many fish because upwelling brings up nutrients from the deeper layers of the water.

Currents and Climate
Review and Reinforce

1. Surface
2. Warm or cold
3. Density differences
4. Cold
5. By moving warm or cold water around the globe, warming or cooling the air above
6. Because it increases the supply of nutrients by bringing up tiny ocean organisms, minerals, and other materials from the deeper layers of the water
7. Currents
8. Coriolis effect
9. Climate
10. El Niño

Currents and Climate
Enrich

1. Early navigators tried to avoid the Sargasso Sea because of legends that its blanket of seaweed could trap ships. Its usually weak winds also made it difficult for sailing ships to cross.
2. The waters of the Sargasso Sea are clearer, calmer, warmer, and saltier than the waters of the rest of the North Atlantic.
3. The Sargasso Sea is surrounded by fast-moving currents that keep its waters from mixing with the rest of the Atlantic Ocean.
4. The Sargasso Sea is so salty because it lies in a region where precipitation is low and the sun is hot, leading to high evaporation.

Modeling Ocean Currents
Skills Lab

For answers, see the Teacher's Edition.

Key Terms

1. groin
2. crest
3. sandbar
4. wavelength
5. tides
6. salinity
7. frequency
Answer: gravity

Connecting Concepts

This concept map is only one way to represent the main ideas and relationships in this chapter. Accept other logical answers from students.

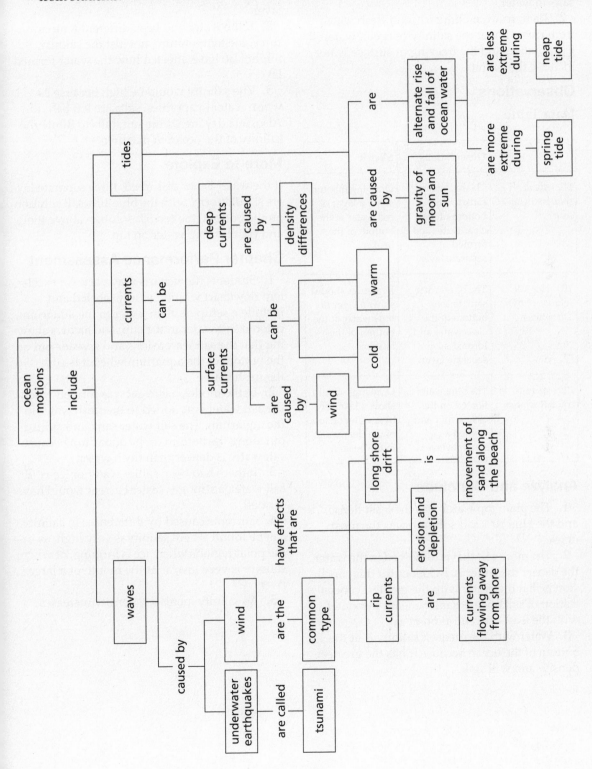

Ocean Motions

Laboratory Investigation

Density and Salinity

Pre-Lab Discussion

1. Salinity is the total amount of dissolved salts in water.

2. Rain, snow, melting ice, and fresh water from rivers lower the salinity of ocean water. Evaporation and the freezing of surface water increase the salinity.

Observations

Data Table

	Observations	Sketch
5% red salt solution in tap water	The red water sank to the bottom of the clear water and formed a separate layer.	Drawings should show a layer of red water at the bottom of the beaker.
10% blue salt solution in 5% salt solution	The blue water sank to the bottom of the clear water and formed a separate layer.	Drawings should show a layer of blue water at the bottom of the beaker.
Blue tap water in 5% salt solution	The blue water floated on the clear water and formed a separate layer.	Drawings should show a layer of blue water on top of the clear water in the beaker.

Analyze and Conclude

1. The plain tap water was the least dense, and the blue 10% salt solution was the most dense.

2. The more salt that is dissolved in the water, the denser the water is. Evidence for this conclusion is that the water with the greatest concentration of salt always sank beneath the water with the least concentration of salt.

3. Water with the greatest salinity is at the bottom of the ocean because it has the greatest density and will sink.

Critical Thinking and Applications

1. From bottom to top: 3, 2, 1, 4. As water's temperature decreases and its salinity increases, it becomes more dense and sinks. Rainwater is fresh water and therefore would form the top layer.

2. If the water had been different temperatures, the temperature, not just the salinity, might also have affected how the water formed layers.

3. The salinity would be high because as warm water evaporates, salts are left behind. Also, in a dry area, little rain falls to dilute the salinity of the ocean in that area.

More to Explore

If the water is not disturbed, three separate layers should form, with the blue 10% salt solution on the bottom, the red 5% solution above that, and the clear tap water on top.

Chapter Performance Assessment

1. Students' flowcharts may vary. An excellent flowchart would be fully labeled and include a setup of plain water in the aquarium, colored salt water in the cup, and arrows showing that the salt water sinks and spreads out on the bottom of the aquarium when it is added to the fresh water.

2. In the model, a current was formed when the salt water was added to the fresh water in the aquarium. The salt water sank and spread out along the bottom of the aquarium because salt water is denser than fresh water.

3. If there had been saltier water or ice-cold salt water, a stronger, faster current would have formed.

4. Currents caused by differences in salinity can be found where salinity is very high, as in the polar regions where ice is forming, or where salinity is very low, as at the mouth of a large river.

5. As salinity increases, density increases.

Chapter Test

1. b
2. c
3. c
4. b
5. d
6. b
7. a
8. d
9. c
10. b
11. wavelength
12. Gravity
13. algae
14. salinity
15. Gulf Stream
16. true
17. tsunami
18. sodium chloride
19. density
20. true
21. As the water becomes more shallow, the bottoms of the waves drag on the ocean floor and slow down. This makes the wavelength decrease. The water piles up, causing the wave height to increase.
22. Upwelling brings up tiny ocean organisms, minerals, and other materials from deeper layers of the water, increasing the supply of nutrients.
23. Cold currents: 1, 2, 6, 8, 9, 10; warm currents: 3, 4, 5, 7. Generally, ocean currents carry warm water from the tropics toward the poles or carry cold water from the poles toward the equator.

24. They are alike in that they move in circular patterns in the major ocean basins. They are different because they curve to the right in the Northern Hemisphere and to the left in the Southern Hemisphere.
25. The climate along the west coast of South America is cool and dry because a cold current flows along that coast, causing the air above it to be cool and dry.
26. a. 110 units
    b. 210 units
    c. 310 units
    d. 410 units
    e. 510 units
27. Students should plot the data from their answer to Question 26.
28. Water pressure increases steadily with increasing depth.
29. Compared with the surface of the ocean, the ocean at 1,000 meters deep is dark because no sunlight penetrates below about 200 meters. The ocean at 1,000 meters deep is an average of 13.5°C colder than the surface, as well as saltier. Because the deeper water is colder and saltier, it is also denser. The pressure at 1,000 meters deep is about 100 times that at the surface.
30. You would float more easily in the Arctic Ocean because its cold, highly saline water is denser than the warmer, less saline water of the middle of the Atlantic Ocean.

Ocean Zones

Lab zone Chapter Project ▶ At Home in the Sea

The following steps will help you implement the Chapter Project successfully. Use these suggestions and detailed instructions as you guide students through the planning, building, and presentation of their model marine habitats and organisms.

Chapter Project Overview

Before you present the project to the class, choose a suitable area for displaying the models, such as the auditorium, cafeteria, library, or a long hallway. If such an area is not available to you, arrange the classroom to provide display space without interfering with regular class activities. Measure the area and divide it so each group will have about the same amount of space for its habitat.

To introduce the project and motivate student interest, show students photographs, a video, or a CD-ROM illustrating different marine habitats with their typical organisms. Encourage students to offer comments about the environments and organisms shown and to ask questions about them, but do not preteach chapter concepts. Instead, point out to students that they can use their questions as guides for their research during the project.

Point out that this chapter deals with different habitats in the ocean. Ask: **Why do you think it would be helpful to build models of ocean habitats?** (*Students might suggest that they cannot visit the habitats in person and view them directly, so this is a good way to learn about them.*)

Have students read the project description in the text. Then distribute the Chapter Project Overview. Review and discuss the project rules to make sure students understand what is expected of them. Encourage students to ask questions and offer their comments about the project. You may also want to distribute the Chapter Project Scoring Rubric you will use in evaluating students' work.

Divide the class into groups of three or four students each. Emphasize that *every* group member shares the responsibility for creating a complete model habitat. Tell students that they may divide the tasks in various ways so long as each group member participates in all three stages—planning the model habitat, building it, and presenting it to the rest of the class. Also stress that although each group member will build his or her own model organism, *every* group member should be prepared to discuss *all* the organisms in the habitat.

Set a deadline for the presentation of the models and key interim dates. Encourage students to copy the dates in the Project Timeline.

Explain that you will assign each group a certain amount of space for its model habitat and will show them the space so they can measure it and begin planning.

Discuss possible materials with students. Explain that you will provide a variety of materials but that they may use any other materials they choose, with the only limitation being safety concerns—such as not using highly flammable materials or glue that produces toxic fumes. Encourage students to be creative in their choice and use of materials and to try to make their model habitats and organisms as realistic as they can.

As students begin to choose habitats to model, monitor their choices to avoid repetition and encourage variety.

Keep Students on Track— Section 2

Assemble the class in the display area, and have each group identify the habitat it has chosen. Ask students for their ideas about arranging the habitats in a logical order—for example, from the highest part of the intertidal zone at one end of the area to the deep zone at the other end. Assign a space to each group, and let students measure and record the dimensions.

As you review each group's labeled habitat sketch, evaluate how well students understand the habitats' physical features, including the water depth, the slope and configuration of the ocean floor in that area, and the amount of sunlight the area receives. Use prompting questions to draw students' attention to any errors or omissions and to elicit their own corrections.

Keep Students on Track—Section 3

Make sure the organism each group member has chosen is appropriate for the group's habitat and can be shown to scale with the other organisms. Distribute Chapter Project Worksheet 1 for students to record the information they research about their chosen organisms. Point out that the worksheet includes spaces for the organism's predators (animals that eat the organism) and prey (animals, plants, or other organisms that the organism eats). Tell students that when they set up their habitats, they could show its food web by connecting the organisms with colored yarn.

Distribute Chapter Project Worksheet 2 to give students practice in making a model organism. Provide various materials, such as fabric, marking pens, glue, beads, and sequins.

Review each group's final plans for the habitat model and selection of materials. As students build their models, meet with them regularly to discuss their progress and any problems they may be encountering.

Establish a plan for the presentations at the conclusion of the chapter, allowing 10–15 minutes for each group. If the class arranged the habitats in a logical order, assign group presentations in that order.

Chapter Project Wrap Up

Remind students that when they give their presentations, all members of the group should participate in describing both the habitat and the organisms, focusing on the specific adaptations for survival in that habitat. Work with groups individually as needed to help students prepare for the presentation.

Provide class time for the presentations. As each group presents its habitat and organisms, encourage the other groups to ask questions and offer comments. Make sure you provide all students with positive feedback.

Extensions

When all presentations have been completed, ask students whether other groups' models gave them any ideas for improving their own models. If time allows, let students make changes in their models.

If any groups were unable to complete food webs because some necessary organisms were missing from their habitats, encourage them to model those organisms, add them to the habitats, and indicate the food web.

Suggest that students store their models in a dry, protected area for display later on Parents' Night.

Ocean Zones

Ocean Zones • *Chapter Project*   **Overview**

Lab zone Chapter Project **At Home in the Sea**

What different environments are found in the ocean? What organisms live in each environment? In this project you will work in a group to build a three-dimensional model of a marine habitat. You will also make models of some organisms found in that habitat.

The project has three major parts. First, you and your partners will plan the models. You will draw a sketch of the habitat your group has chosen and label its physical features. Each of you will choose one organism found in that habitat to research. Then you will plan a model of your organism. Second, you will build the models you have planned. You and your partners will build the model habitat together. You will make your model organism on your own and write a description of how the organism is adapted to its habitat. Finally, your group will present the models to the class.

Project Rules

■ With your partners, choose one marine habitat described in this chapter. List the habitat's physical features—the water depth, the slope of the ocean floor in that area, what the ocean floor looks like there (such as rocky or sandy), and how much sunlight the area receives. Draw a sketch of the habitat, label its features, and list the materials your group will use to build it. You will show your plan to your teacher at the end of Section 2.

■ Choose one organism, that lives in that habitat. Make sure each group member chooses a different organism. Research your organism to learn about its size, shape, color, and other physical characteristics. Draw the organism to scale. You will present your plan to your teacher at the end of Section 3.

■ Work with your partners to build the model habitat.

■ Build your model organism, and put it in the habitat. Work with your partners to show how the organisms interact with their environment and with one another.

■ Prepare a group presentation of the habitat. Be prepared to talk about every organism included in the habitat, not just your own.

Suggested Materials

Your teacher will provide a variety of materials for building the models. Try other materials, too. Use your imagination—be creative!

To make the habitat's enclosure: You could use a cardboard box cut to size or sheets of cardboard or posterboard taped together.

To shape and form the ocean floor: You could use brown paper, modeling clay, papier mâché, or plaster of paris. To add a realistic texture to the ocean floor, you could coat it with a thin layer of glue and then spread sand over it.

Ocean Zones · *Chapter Project*

To make a model organism: You could use fabric, brown or white paper (the kind that comes in rolls), construction paper, foam rubber, styrofoam, household sponges, pipe cleaners, and toothpicks. Chapter Project Worksheet 2 shows one way to make a three-dimensional model.

To represent water: Use a sheet of blue acetate or cellophane.

To show the habitat's food web: Connect the model organisms with lengths of colored yarn to show their feeding relationships.

Project Hints

- Before you and your partners choose a habitat and organisms to model, look through this chapter and other reference materials. Find illustrations and photographs of different marine habitats and the organisms that live in them. Think about how easy or difficult it will be to represent the habitats' features and the organisms' characteristics. Share your ideas with your partners.

- When you choose an organism, remember that you are supposed to build a *life-size* model. Don't choose an organism that is too large or too small to show realistically. When you and your partners plan the model organisms, check to make sure all the organisms are the right size compared with one another. For example, if your group wants to show a sea star opening and eating a clam, don't make the sea star tiny and the clam huge.

- Start with a small sample of the material you will use to make the ocean floor. Find out how easily the material can be shaped. Learn how long you can work with it before it becomes stiff or dries out. Also make sure you discover any problems you may have with it, such as cracking when it dries.

Project Timeline
Task	Due Date
1. Select marine habitat to model.	_____
2. Complete scale diagram of habitat model.	_____
3. Select and research organism to model.	_____
4. Construct habitat model.	_____
5. Construct organism model.	_____
6. Prepare written information on organism.	_____
7. Present models to class.	_____

Ocean Zones

Ocean Zones · *Chapter Project*

Marine Organism Fact Sheet

Use this fact sheet to record information about the marine organism you have chosen to model. After you complete this fact sheet, you can use it to write your explanation of how the organism is adapted to its environment.

Organism's name: _____

Habitat: _____

Where it is found in the habitat: _____

_____

Size: Length _____

Width _____

Height _____

Body parts: _____

_____

_____

Color and pattern: _____

_____

_____

Adaptations for survival: _____

_____

_____

_____

Predators: _____

_____

Prey or food source: _____

_____

Other characteristics: _____

_____

_____

_____

Making a Model Organism

Suppose you want to make a model of a fish for your group's habitat. Here is one way to make the model.

Materials

white or brown paper

pencil

scissors

light-colored fabric

straight pins

colored markers

stapler or needle and thread

cotton batting or facial tissue

glue

other materials to represent the fish's features, such as colored acetate, shiny fabric or paper, and large sequins.

Procedure

1. Make a paper pattern by drawing a fish outline on paper and cutting it out.

2. Fold the fabric to make two layers. Put the pattern on top and trace around it. Discard the pattern.

3. Pin the fabric layers together. Cut around the outline. (Keep the extra fabric for making fins later.)

4. Staple or sew the two fish pieces of fabric together along the edges. Leave the back of the tail open for now.

5. Turn the fish inside out. Stuff it with cotton batting or crumpled facial tissues. Then staple or sew the tail opening to close it.

6. Finish the model by adding fins, scales, gills, eyes, a mouth, and other features. Use the fabric scraps to make the fins. Draw the rest of the features with colored markers, or make them with other materials you choose.

Ocean Zones • *Chapter Project* **Scoring Rubric**

Lab zone Chapter Project **At Home in the Sea**

In evaluating how well you complete the Chapter Project, your teacher will judge your work in four categories. In each, a score of 4 is the best rating.

	4	3	2	1
Planning and Building Habitat Models	The marine habitat model is carefully planned and demonstrates creativity in use of materials and sophistication of detail.	The marine habitat model is adequately planned and accurately represents the habitats' features imaginatively.	The marine habitat model is loosely planned; most important habitat features are represented, but lack imagination and detail.	The marine habitat model is poorly planned and incomplete; most important habitat features are missing and/or inaccurately represented.
Creating Organism Models	The marine organism model is highly realistic and to the proper scale. The written explanation is thoroughly researched and demonstrates an excellent understanding of how the organism is adapted to its habitat.	The marine organism model includes all important features and is to scale. The written explanation is adequately researched and demonstrates a satisfactory understanding of how the organism is adapted to its habitat.	The marine organism model is missing at least one important feature and is slightly out of scale. The written explanation is partially researched and demonstrates only a limited understanding of how the organism is adapted to its habitat.	The marine organism model is missing two or more important features and is not to scale. The written explanation is inadequately researched and is incomplete and/or demonstrates little or no understanding of how the organism is adapted to its habitat.
Presenting the Models	Presentation is well-organized, complete, and demonstrates in-depth understanding of all habitat features and organism adaptations.	Presentation is fairly well-organized and demonstrates good understanding of major features and adaptations; explanations are complete but not detailed.	Presentation is fairly well-organized; explanations are incomplete unless prompted and demonstrate some confusion about features and/or adaptations.	Presentation is disorganized, incomplete, and demonstrates lack of understanding of features and adaptations.
Working Cooperatively	Takes a lead in the group's planning, building, and presentation of the models.	Actively participates in all aspects of planning, building, and presentation of the models.	Participates in most aspects of planning, building, and presentation of the models.	Participates in only a few aspects of planning, building, and presentation of the models.

Exploring the Ocean

 3–4 periods, 1–2 blocks

Objectives

H.4.1.1 Discuss the reasons that people have studied the ocean.

H.4.1.2 Identify the main sections of the ocean floor.

H.4.1.3 Describe the processes that have shaped the ocean floor.

Key Terms

• sonar • continental shelf • continental slope
• abyssal plain • mid-ocean ridge • trench
• plate • seafloor spreading

Local Standards

PRETEACH

Build Background Knowledge

Describe the ocean floor.

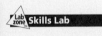 **Discover Activity** *What Can You Learn Without Seeing?* **L1**

Targeted Resources

☐ **All in One** Teaching Resources
☐ ◉ **Presentation-Pro CD-ROM**

INSTRUCT

Learning About the Ocean Compare how ancient and modern people have studied the ocean.

Features of the Ocean Floor Describe ocean floor features and compare the features to those on the continents.

Movements of the Ocean Floor Contrast plate movements.

Skills Lab *The Shape of the Ocean Floor* **L2**

Targeted Resources

☐ **All in One** Teaching Resources
   L2 Guided Reading, pp. 257–260
   L2 Transparencies, H42, H43, H44, H45
   L2 Lab: *The Shape of the Ocean Floor*, pp. 263–264
☐ 📼 **Lab Activity Video/DVD**
   Skills Lab: *The Shape of the Ocean Floor*
☐ **www.SciLinks.org** Web Code: scn-0841
☐ ◉ Student Edition on Audio CD

ASSESS

Section Assessment Questions

↻ Have students use their definitions of key terms to answer the questions.

Reteach

Diagram the ocean floor.

Targeted Resources

☐ **All in One** Teaching Resources
Section Summary, p. 256
L1 Review and Reinforce, p. 261
L3 Enrich, p. 262

Ocean Zones

Ocean Zones • *Section Summary*

Exploring the Ocean

Guide for Reading

- For what reason have people studied the ocean floor?

- What are the main sections of the ocean floor?

- What processes have shaped the ocean floor?

People have explored the ocean for thousands of years. Knowledge of the ocean has always been important to the people living along its coasts. **People have studied the ocean since ancient times because the ocean provides food and serves as a route for trade and travel. Modern scientists have studied the characteristics of the ocean's waters and the ocean floor.**

Until recently the ocean floor was unexplored, and little was known about life in the oceans. A major advance in ocean-floor mapping was **sonar,** which stands for **so**und **na**vigation and **r**anging. Sonar is a system that uses sound waves to calculate the distance to an object.

If you could travel along the ocean floor, you would see the continental shelf, the continental slope, the abyssal plain, and the mid-ocean ridge. The **continental shelf** is a gently sloping, shallow area of the ocean floor that extends outward from the edge of a continent. At a depth of about 130 meters, the slope of the ocean floor gets steeper. The steep edge of the continental shelf is called the **continental slope.** A broad area covered with thick layers of mud and silt is called the **abyssal plain.** The **mid-ocean ridge** is a continuous range of mountains that winds around Earth, much as the line of stitches winds around a baseball.

The mid-ocean ridge actually consists of two parallel chains of mountains separated by a central valley, with occasional trenches. A **trench** is a steep-sided canyon in the ocean floor. Some trenches are so deep you cannot see the bottom.

The pieces of Earth's crust, along with parts of the upper mantle, are called **plates.** Such plates move slowly on the underlying portion of the mantle. **Plate movements have shaped many of the most dramatic features of Earth, both on land and under the ocean.**

The mid-ocean ridge is located long the boundaries of plates that are moving apart, or diverging. Along the ridge, magma squeezes up through the cracks between the diverging plates. As the magma hardens along the ridge, it adds a new strip of rock to the ocean floor. Over millions of years, this process, called **seafloor spreading,** has produced the ocean floor.

Ocean Zones · *Guided Reading and Study*

Exploring the Ocean

This section describes how the ocean has been explored over the past several thousand years. The section also describes features of the ocean floor and explains how the ocean floor moves.

Use Target Reading Skills

On the lines provided, write a definition of each term in your own words.

sonar _____

_____

_____

continental shelf _____

_____

_____

abyssal plain _____

_____

_____

mid-ocean ridge _____

_____

_____

trench _____

_____

_____

plate _____

_____

_____

seafloor spreading _____

_____

_____

Ocean Zones • *Guided Reading and Study*

Exploring the Ocean *(continued)*

Learning About the Ocean

1. Circle the letter of the sentence that is true about the Phoenicians.
   a. They were one of the earliest cultures to explore the oceans.
   b. They sailed to Hawaii.
   c. They established sea routes for trade by 2000 B.C.
   d. They lived on islands in the Indian Ocean.

2. Is the following sentence true or false? Captain Cook's voyages of exploration marked the beginning of the modern science of oceanography. _____

3. Why has the deep ocean floor been explored only recently?

   _____

   _____

   _____

   _____

   _____

4. Is the following sentence true or false? To study the deep ocean floor, scientists have relied on direct methods of gathering information.

   _____

5. Circle the letter of each sentence that is true about sonar.
   a. It measures distance.
   b. It uses sound waves.
   c. It is an indirect way of gathering data.
   d. It uses X rays.

Features of the Ocean Floor

6. Circle the letter of each sentence that is true about the ocean floor.
   a. It is flat and sandy.
   b. It is rocky and uneven.
   c. It has the biggest mountains on Earth.
   d. It has deep canyons.

Name _____ Date _____ Class _____

7. Find and label each of the following ocean floor features in the drawing: continental shelf, continental slope, seamount, abyssal plain, and trench.

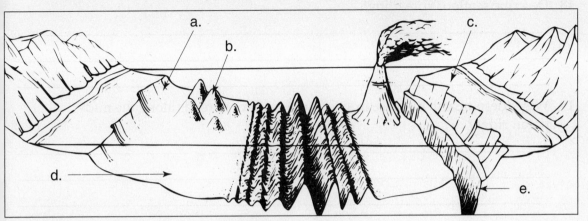

Match each feature of the ocean floor with its description.

Feature

_____ **8.** continental shelf

_____ **9.** continental slope

_____ **10.** seamount

_____ **11.** abyssal plain

_____ **12.** mid-ocean ridge

_____ **13.** trench

Description

a. Smooth and nearly flat region of the ocean floor

b. Mountain on the ocean floor that is completely under water

c. Continuous range of mountains on the ocean floor

d. Incline at the edge of the continental shelf

e. Steep-sided canyon in the ocean floor

f. Shallow area of the ocean floor extending outward from land

14. Circle the letter of each sentence that is true about the mid-ocean ridge.

    a. It passes through all of Earth's oceans.

    b. It is about 800 kilometers long.

    c. It is the longest mountain range on Earth.

    d. It is divided by a central valley.

Movements of the Ocean Floor

15. The hot liquid material inside Earth is called _____. If this material reaches the surface, it is called _____.

16. Pieces of Earth's crust, along with parts of the upper mantle, are called

    _____.

17. Circle the letter of each sentence that is true about Earth's plates.

    a. They move on the liquid of the mantle.

    b. They lie beneath the continents but not the oceans.

    c. They move several kilometers per year.

    d. Their movements create Earth's landforms.

Ocean Zones

Exploring the Ocean *(continued)*

18. Describe seafloor spreading.

_____

_____

_____

19. Why doesn't Earth increase in size as the seafloor spreads along the mid-ocean ridge?

_____

_____

_____

Ocean Zones • *Review and Reinforce*

Exploring the Ocean

Understanding Main Ideas

Answer the following questions on a separate sheet of paper.

1. What factors make it difficult to explore the ocean floor?
2. Describe the process of seafloor spreading.
3. Why doesn't Earth get larger when new rock is added to the ocean floor at the mid-ocean ridge?

Building Vocabulary

Match each letter on this diagram with one of the terms listed below. Write the letter on the line before each term. Then define each term in your own words in the spaces provided.

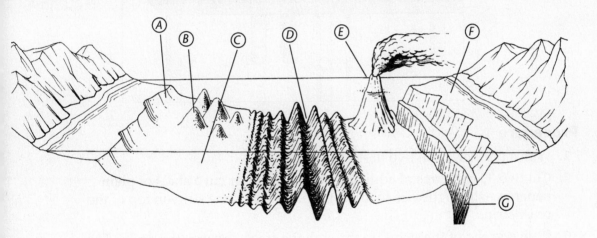

_____ 4. mid-ocean ridge _____

_____ 5. trench _____

_____ 6. continental slope _____

_____ 7. abyssal plain _____

_____ 8. seamount _____

_____ 9. continental shelf _____

_____ 10. volcanic island _____

Ocean Zones · *Enrich*

Modeling Seafloor Spreading

Materials

2 desks

2 strips of adding machine paper or plain white paper

metric ruler

red, blue, orange, and green pencils or markers

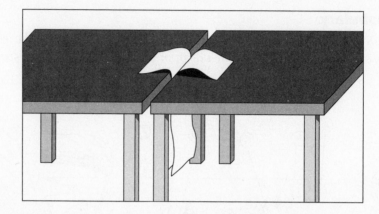

Procedure

1. With a partner, push two desks together.
2. Cut two 30-cm strips of adding machine paper or cut a sheet of plain paper in half lengthwise to make two strips. Lay one strip on top of the other strip.
3. Push one end of the strips up through the crack between the desks. The strips should stick up about 6 cm above the crack.
4. Press the ends of the strips flat against the desks. Color the ends red.
5. Push the strips another 6 cm up through the crack. Color these parts blue.
6. Repeat Step 5. Color the new parts orange.
7. Repeat Step 5 again. Color the new parts green.

Analyze and Conclude

1. In this model, what does the crack between the desks represent?
2. What does the paper represent?
3. What do the colored parts of the strips represent?
4. After Step 7, which color on the strips represents the *oldest* rock? Which color represents the *newest* rock?

The Shape of the Ocean Floor

Problem

Imagine you are an oceanographer traveling across the Atlantic along the 45° N latitude line marked on the map. You are gathering data on the depth of the ocean between Nova Scotia, Canada, and Soulac, France. How can you use data to determine the shape of the ocean floor?

Nova Scotia, Canada *Soulac, France*

Skills Focus

graphing, predicting, inferring

Materials

pencil

graph paper

Procedure

1. Draw the axes of a graph. Label the horizontal axis *Longitude*. Mark from 65° W to 0° from left to right. Label the vertical axis *Ocean Depth*. Mark 0 meters at the top of the vertical axis to represent sea level. Mark –5,000 meters at the bottom to represent the depth of 5,000 meters below sea level. Mark depths at equal intervals along the vertical axis.

2. Examine the data in the table. The numbers in the Longitude column give the ship's location at 19 points in the Atlantic Ocean. Location 1 is Nova Scotia, and Location 19 is Soulac. The numbers in the Ocean Depth column give the depth measurements recorded at each location. Plot each measurement on your graph. Remember that the depths are represented on your graph as numbers below 0, or sea level.

3. Connect the points you have plotted with a line to create a profile of the ocean floor.

Ocean Depth Sonar Data	
Longitude	Ocean Depth (m)
1. 64° W	0
2. 60° W	91
3. 55° W	132
4. 50° W	73
5. 48° W	3,512
6. 45° W	4,024
7. 40° W	3,805
8. 35° W	4,171
9. 33° W	3,439
10. 30° W	3,073
11. 28° W	1,756
12. 27° W	2,195
13. 25° W	3,146
14. 20° W	4,244
15. 15° W	4,610
16. 10° W	4,976
17. 05° W	4,317
18. 04° W	146
19. 01° W	0

Ocean Zones • *Skills Lab*

The Shape of the Ocean Floor *(continued)*

Analyze and Conclude

1. On your graph, identify and label the continental shelf and continental slope.

2. Label the abyssal plain on your graph. How would you expect the ocean floor to look there?

   _____

   _____

   _____

   _____

3. Label the mid-ocean ridge on your graph. Describe the process that is occurring there.

   _____

   _____

   _____

   _____

   _____

4. What might the feature at 10° W be? Explain.

   _____

   _____

   _____

   _____

5. **Think About It** Imagine you are traveling along the ocean floor from Nova Scotia, Canada, to Soulac, France. Describe the features you would see along your journey.

   _____

   _____

   _____

More to Explore

Use the depth measurements in the table to calculate the average depth of the Atlantic Ocean between Nova Scotia and France.

Ocean Habitats

 1–2 periods, 1/2–1 blocks

Ability Level Key
L1 Basic to Average
L2 For All Students
L3 Average to Advanced

Objectives

H.4.2.1 Identify the zones into which scientists divide the ocean.

H.4.2.2 Describe how marine organisms are classified.

Key Terms

• intertidal zone • neritic zone
• open-ocean zone • plankton • nekton
• benthos • food web

Local Standards

PRETEACH

Build Background Knowledge

Describe marine organisms.

 **Discover Activity** *How Complex Are Ocean Feeding Relationships?* **L1**

Targeted Resources

❏ **All in One Teaching Resources**
L2 Reading Strategy Transparency H46: Using Prior Knowledge

❏ **Presentation-Pro CD-ROM**

INSTRUCT

Ocean Zones and Conditions Infer conditions within ocean zones.
Life in the Ocean Describe nekton, benthos, and plankton.

Targeted Resources

❏ **All in One Teaching Resources**
L2 Guided Reading, pp. 267–269
L2 Transparencies, H47, H48, H49

❏ **PHSchool.com** Web Code: cfp-3042

❏ Student Edition on Audio CD

ASSESS

Section Assessment Questions

Have students use their using prior knowledge graphic organizers to help them answer the questions.

Reteach

Describe the three categories of ocean organisms.

Targeted Resources

❏ **All in One Teaching Resources**
Section Summary, p. 266
L1 Review and Reinforce, p. 270
L3 Enrich, p. 271

Ocean Zones

Ocean Zones · *Section Summary*

Ocean Habitats

Guide for Reading

■ Into what zones do scientists divide the ocean?

■ How are marine organisms classified?

Think of the ocean as a huge community that includes living and nonliving things. The ocean is divided into several zones. **Ocean zones include the intertidal zone, the neritic zone, and the open-ocean zone.** At the highest high tide line on land, the **intertidal zone** begins. From there, the zone stretches out to the point on the continental shelf exposed by the lowest low tide. The **neritic zone** extends from the low-tide line out to the edge of the continental shelf. Beyond the edge of the continental shelf lies the **open-ocean zone.** This zone includes the deepest, darkest part of the ocean.

On land, most organisms live on or near the surface. The ocean, on the other hand, is inhabited by organisms at every depth. **Scientists classify marine organisms according to where they live and how they move.** There are three categories of ocean organisms—plankton, nekton, and benthos. **Plankton** are tiny algae and animals that float in the water and are carried by waves and currents. Algae plankton include geometrically shaped diatoms. Animal plankton include microscopic crustaceans and some tiny fish. **Nekton** are free-swimming animals that can move throughout the water column. Squid, most fishes, and marine mammals, such as whales and seals, are nekton. **Benthos** are organisms that inhabit the ocean floor. Some benthos, like crab, sea stars, octopus, and lobsters, move from place to place. Others, like sponges and sea anemones, stay in one location.

Plankton, nekton, and benthos are all found in most marine habitats. Photosynthetic plankton are called producers. Other plankton and benthos, as well as all nekton, eat either algae or other organisms. They are called consumers. Finally, some organisms, including many benthos, break down wastes and the remains of other organisms. They are called decomposers.

All of the feeding relationships that exist in a habitat make up a **food web.** In most marine food webs, each organism depends directly or indirectly on the algae plankton. Throughout the ocean, plankton are a source of food for other organisms of all sizes. Just think—Earth's largest animal—the blue whale—feeds only on tiny plankton.

Ocean Habitats

Use Target Reading Skills

Before you read, write what you know about conditions that might determine where ocean organisms live. As you read, continue to write in what you learn.

What You Know
1. Many organisms need sunlight.
2.

What You Learned
1.
2.

Introduction

1. Is the following statement true or false? Only a few types of organisms inhabit the ocean. _____

2. Name three ocean organisms you might see during a walk on the beach.

   a. _____   b._____

   c. _____

Ocean Zones and Conditions

3. The part of the ocean that extends from the high-tide line to the low-tide line is called the _____.

Ocean Zones · *Guided Reading and Study*

Ocean Habitats *(continued)*

4. The part of the ocean that extends from the low-tide line to the edge of the continental shelf is called the _____.

5. The part of the ocean that extends beyond the edge of the continental shelf is called the _____.

6. The open-ocean zone is divided into the surface zone, the transition zone, and the _____ zone.

7. Is the following statement true or false? Physical conditions are the same in each zone of the ocean. _____

8. Where do organisms that need light for photosynthesis live?

   _____

9. What must organisms that live deep in the ocean withstand?

   _____

Life in the Ocean

10. Is the following statement true or false? Organisms inhabit every depth of the ocean. _____

11. Scientists classify marine organisms according to
    a. where they live and how they move.
    b. size and where they live.
    c. where they live and how long they live.
    d. how they move and what they eat.

12. Describe plankton.

    _____

    _____

    _____

13. Name three examples of plankton.

    _____

    _____

14. Free-swimming animals that can move throughout the water column are called _____.

15. Squid, most fishes, whales, and seals are examples of
    _____.

16. What are benthos?

    _____

    _____

Ocean Zones • *Guided Reading and Study*

17. Do benthos move from place to place or stay in one location?

_____

_____

18. Name six examples of benthos.

_____

_____

_____

19. Algae that use sunlight to produce their own food through photosynthesis are called _____.

20. What are all nekton?

   a. producers
   b. consumers
   c. decomposers
   d. benthos

21. What do decomposers eat?

_____

_____

22. Explain what a food web is.

_____

_____

_____

23. Which of the following may eat plankton?

   a. sea ducks
   b. blue whales
   c. other plankton
   d. all of the above

24. Draw a food web that shows the feeding relationships among three organisms found in the Arctic Ocean.

Ocean Habitats

Understanding Main Ideas

Answer the following questions in the spaces provided.

1. What are three ways in which the ocean's zones differ from one another?

_____

_____

2. How do scientists classify marine organisms?

_____

_____

3. Are dolphins plankton, nekton, or benthos? Explain your answer.

_____

_____

Building Vocabulary

Fill in the blanks in the diagram below.

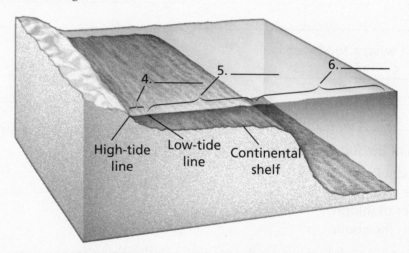

Match each term with its correct definition. Write the letter of the correct answer on the line.

____ **7.** plankton

____ **8.** nekton

____ **9.** benthos

a. organisms that inhabit the ocean floor

b. tiny algae and animals that float in the water and are carried by waves and currents

c. free-swimming animals that can move throughout the water column

Write the correct answer on the space provided.

10. What is the combination of all of the feeding relationships in a habitat called?

_____

Ocean Zones ▪ *Enrich*

A Coral Reef Food Web

The table below lists some of the feeding relationships in a coral-reef habitat. In the space below the table, draw the food web described in the table. (You may write the names of the organisms instead of drawing pictures of them.)

CORAL-REEF HABITAT

Coral-Reef Organisms	Eat . . .	Are eaten by . . .
Algae	make their own food	animal plankton, sea urchins
Animal plankton	algae	shrimp, small fish
Sea urchins	algae	
Small fish	animal plankton, shrimp	octopus, squid
Shrimp	animal plankton	small fish, octopus, squid
Octopus	small fish, crabs, shrimp	
Squid	crabs, shrimp, small fish	
Crabs	remains of dead organisms	octopus, squid
Clams	remains of dead organisms	sea stars
Sea stars	clams	

CORAL-REEF FOOD WEB

Intertidal Zone

1–2 periods, 1/2–1 blocks

Objectives
H.4.3.1 Identify the conditions that organisms in the rocky intertidal zone must tolerate.
H.4.3.2 List and describe the major types of coastal wetlands.

Key Terms
• estuary

Local Standards

PRETEACH

Build Background Knowledge
Describe the region between the tides.

 **Discover Activity** *Can Your Animal Hold On?* L1

Targeted Resources

❑ **All in One** **Teaching Resources**
   L2 Reading Strategy Transparency H50: Outlining
❑ (◉) **Presentation-Pro CD-ROM**

INSTRUCT

Rocky Shores Explain how organisms survive the intertidal zone.
Where River Meets Ocean Discuss brackish water plants.

Targeted Resources

❑ **All in One** **Teaching Resources**
   L2 Guided Reading, pp. 274–276
   L2 Transparency, H51
❑ **PHSchool.com** Web Code: cfd-3043
❑ (◉) Student Edition on Audio CD

ASSESS

Section Assessment Questions
🗘 Have students use their outlining graphic organizers to help them answer the questions.
Reteach
Describe conditions in a tidal pool.

Targeted Resources

❑ **All in One** **Teaching Resources**
   Section Summary, p. 273
   L1 Review and Reinforce, p. 277
   L3 Enrich, p. 278

Intertidal Zone

Guide for Reading

■ What conditions must organisms in the rocky intertidal zone tolerate?

■ What are the major types of coastal wetlands?

A rocky shore is one type of habitat found in the intertidal zone. You read about sandy shores, another type of intertidal zone, earlier. **Organisms that live in the rocky intertidal zone must be able to tolerate the pounding of the waves and changes in salinity and temperature. They must also withstand periods of being underwater and periods of being exposed to the air.** Animals in this zone have structures that enable them to hold onto rocks and that keep their bodies from drying out.

Other important environments along the ocean's edge are estuaries. An **estuary** is a coastal inlet or bay where fresh water from a river mixes with salty ocean water. Water that is partly salty and partly fresh is brackish.

Coastal wetlands are habitats found in and around estuaries. **Along the United States coasts, most wetlands are either mangrove forests or salt marshes.** Salt marshes have muddy soil that is rich in nutrients, and the dominant plant is cordgrass. Tide channels running through the grass break up waves, thus protecting organisms from the ocean surf.

Mangroves have arching prop roots that anchor the trees to the land. These roots break up wind and waves, thus protecting the land and the organisms that live there. The roots also trap sediment so the water is rich in nutrients.

An estuary can be polluted by harmful materials carried there by the river. These pollutants affect the organisms that live in the estuary. If the river is cleaned up, ocean tides can flush the pollutants from the estuary.

Ocean Zones • *Guided Reading and Study*

Intertidal Zone

This section describes living conditions and types of organisms found at the ocean's edge, including along rocky shores and in inlets and bays.

Use Target Reading Skills

As you read, make an outline about the intertidal zone. Use the red headings for the main topics and the blue headings for the subtopics.

Intertidal Zone

I. Rocky shores
   A. Along the rocks
   B.
 	
II. Where river meets ocean
   A.
   B.
   C.

Rocky Shores

1. List the conditions that organisms living in rocky intertidal zones must be able to tolerate.

   a. _____ b. _____

   c. _____ d. _____

2. Circle the letter of the sentence that is true about water in tide pools.

   a. The salinity of the water in a tide pool decreases if it rains.
   b. The water in a tide pool is always saltier than ocean water.
   c. Water in a tide pool cools because it is evaporating.
   d. When the water in a tide pool evaporates, all the animals trapped in it dry up and die.

3. What is the spray zone?

   _____

   _____

   _____

Ocean Zones • *Guided Reading and Study*

4. Complete the table.

Adaptations for Life in a Tide Pool	
Organism	**How it is adapted to live in a tide pool**
Barnacle	a.
Sea star	b.
Limpet	c.
Sea urchin	d.

5. Is the following sentence true or false? A stripe of black algae indicates the high-tide line in a tide pool. _____

6. The zone between the highest high-tide line and lowest low-tide line is called the _____.

7. What special conditions must organisms tolerate in the rocky intertidal zone?

_____

_____

_____

8. Depressions among the rocks that remain filled with water after the tide goes out are called _____.

9. Circle the letter of each type of organism you might see in a tide pool.

    a. sea stars
    b. sea urchins
    c. sponges
    d. blackline algae

Ocean Zones • *Guided Reading and Study*

Intertidal Zone *(continued)*

Where River Meets Ocean

10. Coastal inlets or bays where fresh water from rivers mixes with the salty ocean water are called _____.

11. Water that is partly salty and partly fresh is referred to as _____.

12. Complete the Venn diagram.

a. _____   b. _____

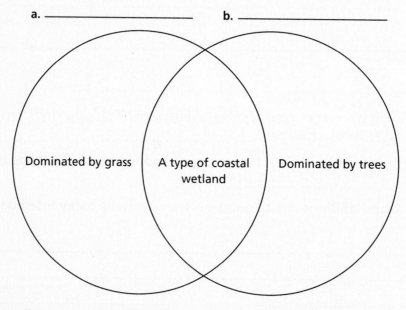

Dominated by grass   A type of coastal wetland   Dominated by trees

13. How do pollutants enter estuaries?

_____

_____

14. Describe two ways in which mangrove forests are important to the environment.

a. _____

_____

_____

_____

_____

b. _____

_____

_____

_____

_____

Intertidal Zone

Understanding Main Ideas

Answer the following questions in the spaces provided.

1. Name two types of intertidal zones.

   _____

   _____

2. What are the two boundaries of the intertidal zone? Identify three
   conditions that organisms in this zone must overcome.

   _____

   _____

   _____

3. How do pollutants from the land get into estuaries?

   _____

   _____

   _____

Building Vocabulary

Fill in the spaces in the table below.

Habitat	Description
Rocky shore	4. _____
Mangrove forest	5. _____
Salt marsh	6. _____

Write the correct term on each line to complete the sentence.

7. Two kinds of coastal wetlands are _____ and

   _____ .

8. An _____ is a coastal inlet or bay where fresh water
   from a river mixes with ocean water.

Modeling an Estuary

Materials

tap water

2 large measuring cups

1 graduated cylinder

salt

blue and yellow food coloring

stirring rod

long pencil

masking tape

clear plastic shoe box

tablespoon with flat handle

Procedure

1. Pour 500 mL tap water into each measuring cup.
2. To make "ocean water," add 90 mL of dry salt and 10 drops of blue food coloring to one cup. Stir until the salt is completely dissolved.
3. To make "river water," add 5 drops of yellow food coloring to the other cup and stir.
4. Tape the pencil to the desk so it won't roll. Rest the box on top of the pencil, with one end higher than the other end.
5. Pour the ocean water into the box. Wait until the water stops moving.
6. Hold the spoon against the inside of the box at its high end. *Slowly* pour the river water down the spoon's handle. Observe what happens to the colored water.
7. *Gently* rock the box back and forth on the pencil three times. Observe what happens to the colored water.

Analyze and Conclude

Write an answer to each of the following on a separate sheet of paper.

1. What happened to the colored water in Step 6?
2. What happened to the colored water in Step 7?
3. How does this activity model an estuary? What does the green water represent?

SECTION LESSON PLAN

Neritic Zone and Open Ocean

⏱ *2–3 periods, 1–1 1/2 blocks*

Ability Level Key
- **L1** Basic to Average
- **L2** For All Students
- **L3** Average to Advanced

Objectives

H.4.4.1 Describe the conditions in the neritic zone.

H.4.4.2 Describe the sorts of environments that support coral reefs and kelp forests.

H.4.4.3 Describe the conditions in the open ocean.

Key Terms
- atoll • bioluminescence • hydrothermal vent

Local Standards

PRETEACH

Build Background Knowledge
Describe the ocean beyond the intertidal zone.

 **Discover Activity** *How Deep Can You See?* **L1**

Targeted Resources
☐ **All in One Teaching Resources**
 L2 Reading Strategy Transparency H52: Relating Cause and Effect
☐ ⊙ **Presentation-Pro CD-ROM**

INSTRUCT

Conditions in the Neritic Zone Explain why life is abundant in the neritic zone.
Coral Reefs Describe the environment in which coral reefs grow.
Life in a Kelp Forest Learn about kelp forest habitats.
Conditions in the Open Ocean Describe conditions for life in the open ocean.

Targeted Resources
☐ **All in One Teaching Resources**
 L2 Guided Reading, pp. 281–283
 L2 Transparency H53
☐ **www.SciLinks.org** Web Code: scn-0844
☐ ⊙ Student Edition on Audio CD

ASSESS

Section Assessment Questions
↻ Have students use their Relating Cause and Effect graphic organizers to help them answer the questions.

Reteach
Diagram the ocean zones.

Targeted Resources
☐ **All in One Teaching Resources**
Section Summary, p. 280
 L1 Review and Reinforce, p. 284
 L3 Enrich, p. 285

Ocean Zones

The Neritic Zone and Open Ocean

Guide for Reading

■ What are the conditions in the neritic zone?

■ What environments support coral reefs and kelp forests?

■ What are the conditions in the open ocean?

The neritic zone is the part of the ocean that extends from the low-tide line out to the edge of the continental shelf. **The shallow water over the continental shelf receives sunlight and a steady supply of nutrients washed from the land into the ocean. The light and nutrients enable large, plantlike algae to grow.** Also, upwelling currents in many parts of the neritic zone bring more nutrients from the ocean floor to the surface.

Two habitats found in the neritic zone are coral reefs and kelp forests. **Coral reefs can form only in shallow, tropical ocean waters.** The reefs are formed by groups of tiny coral animals that produce a hard material around their soft bodies. When the animals die, the hard material is left behind. Over time, the animals' remains create a coral reef. If the sea floor is sinking there, an atoll may form. An **atoll** is a ring-shaped reef surrounding a shallow lagoon. Coral reefs can be damaged easily and do not recover quickly. **Kelp forests grow in cold neritic waters where the ocean has a rocky floor.**

The open ocean begins where the neritic zone ends, at the edge of the continental shelf. **The open ocean differs from the neritic zone in two important ways. First, only a small part of the open ocean receives sunlight. Second, the water has fewer nutrients.** As a result, the open ocean supports fewer organisms.

The surface zone is the only part of the open ocean that receives enough sunlight to support the growth of algae. Microscopic algae are the base of food webs in the open ocean. The algae are eaten by animal plankton, which in turn are eaten by many other animals.

The open ocean's deep zone is dark and cold, and fewer organisms live there. Many deep-sea fishes produce their own light to help them find food. The production of light by living things is called **bioluminescence.** Located in the deep zone are unusual habitats called hydrothermal vents. A **hydrothermal vent** is an area in which heated ocean water rises through cracks in the ocean floor. The chemical nutrients in the heated water support the unique group of organisms that are found around hydrothermal vents.

Ocean Zones • *Guided Reading and Study*

The Neritic Zone and Open Ocean

This section describes living conditions and types of organisms found in water over the continental shelf and in the open ocean.

Use Target Reading Skills

As you read, identify the conditions that affect life in the neritic zone.

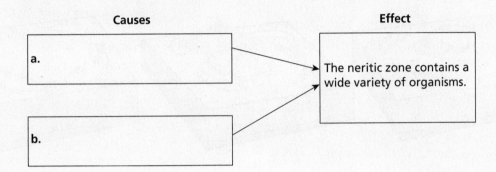

Conditions in the Neritic Zone

1. The part of the ocean that extends from the low-tide line out to the edge of the continental shelf is called the _____. The part of the ocean that extends beyond the edge of the continental shelf is called the _____.

2. Circle the letter of each sentence that helps explain why there is so much life in the neritic zone.

   a. The water is shallow.
   b. The water is high in nutrients.
   c. Large, plantlike algae grow there.
   d. Upwelling never occurs there.

3. Complete the concept map.

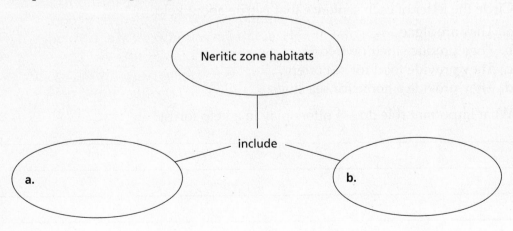

The Neritic Zone and Open Ocean *(continued)*

Coral Reefs

4. Is the following sentence true or false? A coral reef is made of living things. _____

5. Number the drawings to show the correct sequence of steps in the formation of an atoll.

_____   _____   _____

Match the type of coral reef with its description.

Type of Reef	**Description**
____ 6. atoll	**a.** Reef that is separated from land by a lagoon
____ 7. fringing reef	**b.** Ring-shaped reef that surrounds a shallow lagoon
____ 8. barrier reef	**c.** Reef that closely surrounds the edges of an island

9. Is the following sentence true or false? Reefs protect coastlines during violent storms. _____

Life in a Kelp Forest

10. Circle the letter of each sentence that is true about kelp.
    a. They are algae.
    b. They produce their own food.
    c. They provide food for sea otters.
    d. They provide a home for sea slugs.

11. What important role do sea otters play in a kelp forest?

    _____

    _____

    _____

    _____

Ocean Zones • *Guided Reading and Study*

Conditions in the Open Ocean

12. Is the following sentence true or false? The open ocean supports fewer organisms than the neritic zone. _____

13. Is the following sentence true or false? The surface zone is the only part of the open ocean that receives enough sunlight to support the growth of algae. _____

14. How is the deep zone like a desert?

_____

_____

15. The production of light by living things is called

_____.

16. An area in which heated ocean water rises through cracks in the ocean floor is a(n) _____.

17. Circle the letter of each sentence that is true about organisms around hydrothermal vents.
    a. Bacteria produce food from chemicals in the hot water.
    b. Tubeworms get their food from the bacteria inside them.
    c. Algae form the base of the food web.
    d. Giant clams feed on the algae.

Ocean Zones · *Review and Reinforce*

The Neritic Zone and Open Ocean

Understanding Main Ideas

Answer the following questions on a separate sheet of paper.

1. What two conditions account for the great variety of organisms in the neritic zone?

2. Why are there no algae living in the deep ocean?

3. What organisms form the base of the food web at a hydrothermal vent? What do these organisms use to make their own food?

Building Vocabulary

Name and describe each numbered area shown in the diagram below. Write your answers in the spaces provided.

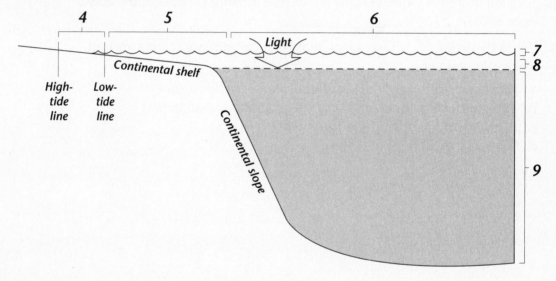

4. _____

5. _____

6. _____

7. _____

8. _____

9. _____

Ocean Zones · *Enrich*

Coral Wars

Did you know that underwater battles are being waged on coral reefs? Because space on coral reefs is limited, coral colonies compete for hard surfaces. Each coral colony, which might look like a head or branching structure, has many coral animals living in it. Each animal is like a small sac with a mouth and tentacles on top. These animals have developed ways to attack the coral animals in other colonies. The winning colony gets more space to grow and collect sunlight.

Competition among coral colonies occurs in different ways. Some colonies grow fast. These coral colonies grow over other colonies and block the sunlight that those colonies would receive. The animals in other coral colonies have weapons that can be used against their neighbors. Some coral animals have long tentacles called sweeper tentacles. Each tentacle can be several centimeters long. These tentacles contain stinging cells that can kill coral animals in neighboring colonies. Coral animals also fight with filaments, which are long, thin tubes that come from their stomachs. The filaments are used to digest coral animals in other colonies. The attacking colony then can grow into the newly opened space.

Answer the questions below on a separate sheet of paper.

1. Describe a coral animal.
2. Explain the difference between a coral animal and a coral colony.
3. Why do coral colonies compete for space?
4. How does fast growth help some coral colonies?
5. Describe two ways that coral animals attack other coral animals.

Ocean Zones

Resources From the Ocean

 3–4 period, 1–2 blocks

Ability Level Key

L1 Basic to Average
L2 For All Students
L3 Average to Advanced

Objectives

H.4.5.1 Explain how people use living resources from the ocean.

H.4.5.2 Identify some of the ocean's nonliving resources.

H.4.5.3 Identify sources of ocean pollution.

Key Terms
• aquaculture • nodule

Local Standards

PRETEACH

Build Background Knowledge
Describe familiar resources from the ocean.

 **Discover Activity** *Is It From the Ocean?* **L1**

Targeted Resources

❑ **All in One Teaching Resources**
  L2 Reading Strategy Transparency H54: Identifying Main Ideas

❑ ⊙ **Presentation-Pro CD-ROM**

INSTRUCT

Living Resources Describe living resources in the sea.

Nonliving Resources Explain why nonliving resources are extracted from the ocean.

Ocean Pollution Identify sources of ocean pollution.

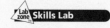 **Skills Lab** *Cleaning Up an Oil Spill* **L2**

Targeted Resources

❑ **All in One Teaching Resources**
  L2 Guided Reading, pp. 288–291
  L2 Transparency, H55
  L2 Lab: *Cleaning Up an Oil Spill*, pp. 294–296

❑ 📼 **Lab Activity Video/DVD**
  Skills Lab: *Cleaning Up an Oil Spill*

❑ **www.SciLinks.org** Web Code: scn-0845

❑ ⊙ Student Edition on Audio CD

ASSESS

Section Assessment Questions
⟲ Have students use their Identifying Main Ideas graphic organizers to help them answer the questions.

Reteach
Compare and contrast living and nonliving resources from the sea.

Targeted Resources

❑ **All in One Teaching Resources**
  Section Summary, p. 287
  L1 Review and Reinforce, p. 292
  L3 Enrich, p. 293

Ocean Zones • *Section Summary*

Resources From the Ocean

Guide for Reading

- How do people use living resources from the ocean?

- What are some nonliving ocean resources?

- What are the sources of ocean pollution?

People depend heavily on fishes and other ocean organisms for food. Ocean organisms also provide materials that are used in products such as detergents and paints. As fish and other aquatic food organisms decline, aquaculture often becomes a good option. **Aquaculture** is the farming of saltwater and freshwater organisms. Ocean organisms are also important sources of other products besides foods. Many detergents, shampoos, and cosmetics are made from a base of algae, for example. Some sediments containing parts of diatoms are used in abrasives and polishes.

In addition to living organisms, the ocean contains valuable nonliving resources. **Some nonliving ocean resources include water, fuels, and minerals.** Sediments on the continental shelves are mined for gravel, sand, shells, diamonds, and gold. Some metals are obtained when ocean water is desalinated to produce fresh water. Other metals collect in lumps called **nodules** on the ocean floor. Because they are found so far beneath the ocean's surface, these nodules have not yet been mined.

Fuels are another important ocean resource. Oil and natural gas are formed when the remains of dead organisms sink to the ocean floor. There, the remains are covered with layers of sediments. Over a long period of time, heat and pressure change the remains to oil and gas. The continental shelves have the richest deposits of oil and gas.

Although some ocean pollution is the result of natural occurrences, most pollution is related to human activities. Sewage, chemicals, and trash are dumped into the ocean. Runoff from fields and roads contains harmful chemicals. An oil spill from a damaged oil tanker or drilling platform harms marine organisms.

Nations own the ocean resources near their land, but no nation owns the open ocean or the ocean floor below it. Because the world ocean is a continuous body of water that has no boundaries, it is difficult to determine who, if anyone, should control portions of it. Nations must cooperate to manage and protect the oceans.

Ocean Zones

Resources From the Ocean

This section describes living resources, such as fish, and nonliving resources, such as fuels, that are obtained from the ocean and the ocean floor. The section also explains how the ocean becomes polluted and why Earth's oceans should be protected.

Use Target Reading Skills

As you read the section, write the main idea in the graphic organizer. Then write three supporting details.

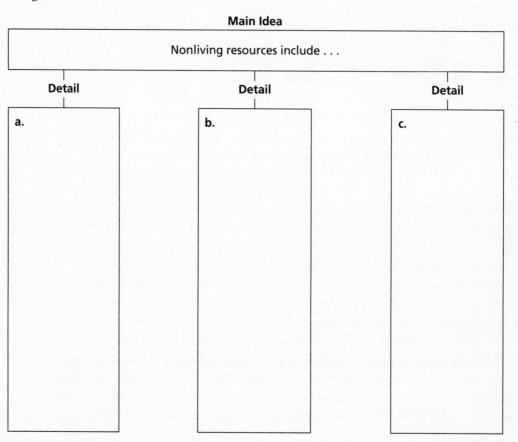

Main Idea

Nonliving resources include . . .

Detail

a.

Detail

b.

Detail

c.

Living Resources

1. Is the following sentence true or false? Foods from the ocean make up about 10 percent of the world's total food supply. _____

Ocean Zones ▪ *Guided Reading and Study*

2. List the six species of fish that make up the majority of fishes harvested for eating.

a. _____

b. _____

c. _____

d. _____

e. _____

3. Where are nearly all fishes caught?

_____

_____

_____

4. The farming of saltwater and freshwater organisms is called

_____.

Nonliving Resources

5. What are some nonliving resources from the ocean floor?

_____

_____

_____

_____

6. When metals concentrate around pieces of shell on the ocean floor, they form black lumps called _____.

7. Is the following sentence true or false? The technology to gather nodules was developed in the mid-1900s. _____

8. How is magnesium obtained from seawater?

_____

_____

_____

Ocean Zones

Ocean Zones • *Guided Reading and Study*

Resources From the Ocean *(continued)*

9. Is the following sentence true or false? Fuels on and below the ocean floor come from the remains of dead marine organisms.

   _____

10. Two fuels that are found on and below the ocean floor are

    _____ and _____.

11. Why are the richest deposits of oil and gas often located on the continental shelves?

    _____

    _____

    _____

    _____

Ocean Pollution

12. Circle the letter of each sentence that is true about ocean pollution.

    a. The ocean is so vast that it cannot become polluted.

    b. Most ocean pollution comes from the land.

    c. The ocean is a self-cleaning system.

    d. Most ocean pollution is due to natural causes.

13. Is the following sentence true or false? Some ocean pollution is the result of weather. _____

14. How can a sudden surge of fresh water from an estuary pollute the ocean?

    _____

    _____

    _____

Ocean Zones • *Guided Reading and Study*

15. List three ocean pollutants related to human activities.

a. _____   b. _____

c. _____

16. Circle the letter of the sentence that is true about oil from oil spills.

    a. It is a minor threat to ocean life.
    b. It is harmful to only a few organisms.
    c. It can destroy an animal's natural insulation.
    d. It is harmful only to animals that swallow it.

17. Describe the natural cleaning process that slowly takes place after oil spills.

_____

_____

_____

18. Why is it difficult to determine who, if anyone, should control portions of the ocean?

_____

_____

_____

19. Is the following sentence true or false? Approximately three quarters of the ocean's surface waters are owned by no nation. _____

20. Is the following sentence true or false? Ownership of the ocean floor beneath the high seas is no longer under debate. _____

Ocean Zones

Resources From the Ocean

Understanding Main Ideas

Use the table below to answer Questions 1–3.

Total Catch (in metric tons)		
Fish Species	**1970**	**1993**
Haddock	829,300	226,500
Atlantic cod	2,817,500	1,028,700
Peruvian anchovy	11,845,300	7,464,600

1. How did the catches of these three fish change in the period shown?

   _____

   _____

2. Why do you think these changes might have occurred?

   _____

   _____

3. What can be done to protect fish populations?

   _____

   _____

Answer the following questions in the spaces provided.

4. What happens to the remains of dead marine organisms to transform
   them into oil and gas?

   _____

   _____

5. Why must nations cooperate to reduce ocean pollution?

   _____

   _____

Building Vocabulary

Answer the following questions in the spaces provided.

6. What is aquaculture?

   _____

   _____

7. What are nodules?

   _____

   _____

Name _____ Date _____ Class _____

Fishing in Georges Bank

The graph below shows the amount of groundfish (cod, haddock, and flounder) caught in the Georges Bank area each year from 1960 to 1995. Use the graph to answer the questions that follow.

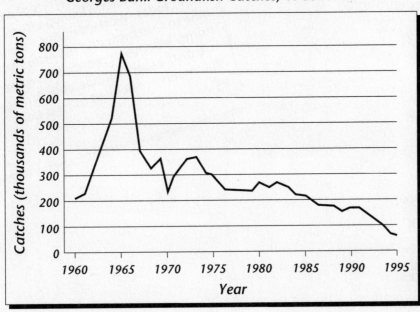

Georges Bank Groundfish Catches, 1960–1995

1. What do the numbers on the graph's vertical axis represent?
   _____

2. How many tons of groundfish were caught in 1960?
   _____

3. How many tons were caught in 1995? _____

4. How many fewer tons were caught in 1995 than in 1960?
   _____

5. When did the catch first fall below the 1960 level?
   _____

6. In late 1994, the U.S. National Marine Fisheries Service closed Georges Bank to commercial fishing. Why do you think this was done?

   _____

   _____

   _____

   _____

Name _____ Date _____ Class _____

Ocean Zones • *Skills Lab*

Cleaning Up an Oil Spill

Problem

How can an oil spill be cleaned up?

Skills Focus

making models, forming operational definitions

Materials

water

shallow pan

vegetable oil

feather

paper cup

plastic dropper

paper towels

cotton balls

wooden sticks

marking pen

graduated cylinder, 100 mL

Oil Spill in Bay

An oil tanker hit a reef yesterday, spilling thousands of barrels of crude oil into the water. Cleanup efforts will begin today. Workers must race against time to save birds and sea otters. With stormy weather forecasted, however, scientists expect considerable damage. Volunteers are needed to help clean up.

Procedure   *Review the safety guidelines in Appendix A.*

1. Place a pan on a table or desk covered with newspaper. Label one end of the pan "Beach" and the other end "Open Ocean."
2. Pour water into the pan to a depth of 2 cm.
3. Gently pour 20 mL of vegetable oil into the center of the pan. Record your observations.
4. Dip a feather and your finger into the oil. Observe how each is affected by the oil.
5. Try to wipe oil off the feather and your finger with cotton balls or paper towels. Record whether any oil is left on the feather or your skin.

Ocean Zones • *Skills Lab*

6. Now try to clean up the spill. First, using the wooden sticks, try to keep the oil from reaching the "beach." Next, gently blow across the surface of the water from the "open ocean" side to simulate wind and waves. Then use the cotton balls, paper towels, and dropper to recover as much of the oil as possible. Record your observations with each step.

7. When you are finished, dispose of the oil and used items in the paper cup. Wash your hands.

Analyze and Conclude

Write your answers in the spaces provided.

1. How successful were you in cleaning up the oil? Is the water as clean as it was at the start?

   _____

   _____

   _____

   _____

2. How well were you able to keep the oil from reaching the beach? How does this activity model the problems that actual cleanup workers encounter?

   _____

   _____

   _____

   _____

   _____

3. Describe what happened when you cleaned the feather and your finger. What might happen to fish, birds, and other animals if they were coated with oil as a result of an oil spill?

   _____

   _____

   _____

   _____

4. Predict how storms with strong winds and waves would affect the cleanup of an oil spill.

   _____

   _____

   _____

   _____

Ocean Zones

Cleaning Up an Oil Spill *(continued)*

5. **Think About It** Look at the used cleanup materials in the paper cup. What additional problems does this suggest for cleanup crews? Write instructions for procedures that cleanup crews might follow to deal with these problems.

_____

_____

_____

_____

More to Explore

One way to reduce the threat of oil spills is to transport less oil across the oceans. To make that possible, people would need to use less oil in their daily lives. Oil is used to heat homes, to produce gasoline, and to make products such as plastics and textiles. List at least three ways to reduce the amount of oil you and your family use.

_____

_____

_____

_____

_____

Ocean Zones • *Key Terms*

Key Terms

Use the clues to make a list of key terms from the chapter. Then find and circle each of the key terms in the hidden-word puzzle. The terms may be written across, down, or diagonally.

Clues

Bundle of rootlike strands that attaches algae to rocks

Device that uses sound waves to measure distance

Deep canyon in the ocean floor

Molten mixture that makes up Earth's mantle

Tiny algae and animals that float in water

Organisms that live on the bottom of the ocean

Habitat in a coastal inlet or bay where fresh and salt water mix

The practice of raising fish and other water organisms for food

Ring-shaped coral island found far from land

Mountain on the ocean floor that is completely under water

Pieces of Earth's crust along with the upper part of the mantle

Water that is partly salty and partly fresh

Free-swimming ocean animals

Key Terms

1. _____
2. _____
3. _____
4. _____
5. _____
6. _____
7. _____
8. _____
9. _____
10. _____
11. _____
12. _____
13. _____

a	c	h	o	l	d	f	a	s	t	h
d	e	s	o	n	a	r	e	f	s	r
t	r	e	n	c	h	t	n	i	h	n
a	m	a	g	m	a	o	k	e	o	b
t	w	m	e	l	t	c	c	t	m	l
o	a	o	p	l	a	n	k	t	o	n
l	l	u	v	r	l	e	n	t	v	l
l	z	n	b	e	n	t	h	o	s	l
e	s	t	u	a	r	y	h	y	d	o
a	q	u	a	c	u	l	t	u	r	e

Ocean Zones

Ocean Zones · *Connecting Concepts*

Connecting Concepts

Develop a concept map that uses the key concepts and key terms from this chapter. Keep in mind the big idea of this chapter. The concept map is one way to show how the information in this chapter is related. You may use an extra sheet of paper.

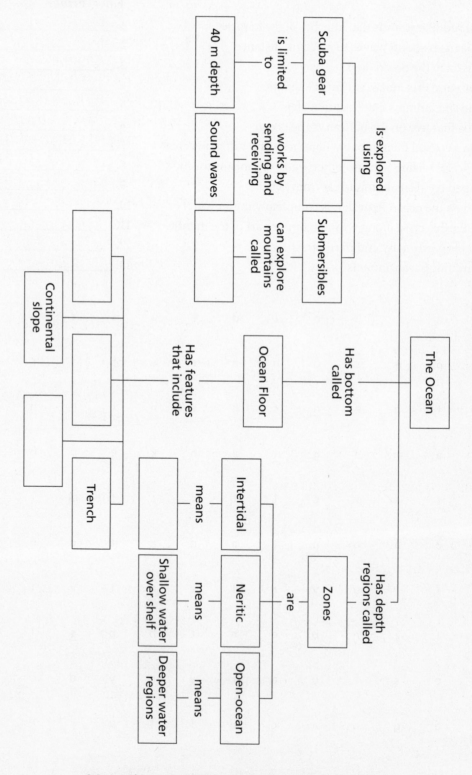

Microscopic Marine Life

Key Concept

Microorganisms are part of the ocean's food webs.

Skills Focus

observing, inferring

Time

60 minutes

Materials

prepared slides of marine plankton

compound microscope

colored pencils

Alternate Materials

If microscopes are not available, you could use a microprojector and have students sketch from the projected images. Live samples may be collected with a plankton net if you live near the ocean.

Advance Preparation

Obtain prepared slides of a variety of marine plankton, such as diatoms, dinoflagellates, foraminiferans, copepods, fish larvae, and crustacean larvae.

Teaching Tips

- Before beginning the investigation, review the parts of the microscope and its proper use. Have reference books available to help students identify the plankton they observe.

- Remind students to handle glass slides with care and to tell you if they break a slide.

- Diatoms are one-celled aquatic protists; they have delicate shells that come in many different shapes. Diatom shells are classified into two groups—those with radial symmetry and those with bilateral symmetry.

- Dinoflagellates are one-celled algae that have thick cell walls made up of thick cellulose plates that sometimes resemble helmets or suits of armor.

- Dinoflagellates have whiplike flagella located in grooves at right angles to each other.

- Foraminiferans are one-celled amebas that live inside shells. They extend pseudopods through tiny holes in their shells.

- Distinct green structures called chloroplasts will be evident in some marine plankton capable of photosynthesis, such as green algae, while some species may show only a general color.

Ocean Zones

Ocean Zones • *Laboratory Investigation*

Microscopic Marine Life

Pre-Lab Discussion

Much marine life is too small to see without a microscope. But these tiny organisms play an important role in marine habitats. They serve as food for larger organisms. At the base of all food webs are algae plankton that use sunlight to produce their own food. Their cells contain chlorophyll, a green pigment. In turn, these plankton become food for other organisms.

In this investigation, you will examine and compare microscopic organisms that live in the ocean.

1. What are plankton?

_____

_____

2. Describe the two major groups of plankton.

_____

_____

_____

Problem

What can you learn about plankton by observing them?

Materials

prepared slides of marine plankton

compound microscope

colored pencils

Safety ⚠ 🔖 *Review the safety guidelines in Appendix A of your textbook.*

Always use both hands to pick up or carry a microscope. Hold the microscope base with one hand and the microscope arm with your other hand. Handle glass slides carefully.

Procedure

1. Place a slide under the clips on the microscope stage. Adjust the mirror or lamp to shine light through the slide. **CAUTION:** *If the microscope has a mirror, do not use direct sunlight as a light source. Direct sunlight can damage your eyes.*

2. Watching the microscope from the side, use the coarse-adjustment knob to lower the low-power objective slowly until it is close to the slide. Do not let the objective touch the slide. Look into the eyepiece and raise the tube until you can see the organism. You may need to move the slide slightly to center the organism. Use the fine-adjustment knob to focus the image.

Ocean Zones • *Laboratory Investigation*

3. In Observations, record the name of the organism. Then draw and color what you see under the low-power lens. Record the magnification of the low-power lens.

4. Turn the revolving nosepiece to move the high-power objective into place. Carefully focus the image with the fine-adjustment knob. **CAUTION:** *Never focus the high-power objective with the coarse-adjustment knob. The objective could break the slide.*

5. Draw and color what you see under the high-power lens. Record the magnification of the high-power lens.

6. Repeat Steps 1–5 with each slide.

Observations

Name of organism	View under low power magnification: _____	View under high power magnification: _____
_____ _____		
_____ _____		

Ocean Zones

Name _____ Date _____ Class _____

Ocean Zones · *Laboratory Investigation*

Microscopic Marine Life *(continued)*

Name of organism	View under low power magnification: _____	View under high power magnification: _____
_____ _____		
_____ _____		
_____		
_____		

Ocean Zones • *Laboratory Investigation*

Analyze and Conclude

1. Were all the organisms you observed single-celled? If not, which ones were not?

_____

2. What similarities did you observe in the organisms?

_____

_____

_____

3. What differences did you observe in the organisms?

_____

_____

_____

Critical Thinking and Applications

1. Which of the organisms you observed produced their own food through photosynthesis? Give a reason for your answer.

_____

_____

2. Which of the organisms you observed relied on other plankton as a food source? Give a reason for your answer.

_____

_____

3. Explain how an organism can be part of the plankton at one stage of its life and part of the nekton at another stage.

_____

_____

_____

More to Explore

What do snails in an aquarium eat? Observe the activity of snails in an aquarium. Using toothpicks, scrape some green film from an aquarium glass and other surfaces. Make slides of your samples and examine them under a microscope. Wear your safety goggles. Wash up after completing the activity.

Modeling Seafloor Spreading

This activity challenges students to develop a working model of plate divergence at the mid-ocean ridge and plate convergence at a trench. To do this, students must understand and apply the concepts they have learned about how new rock is created through seafloor spreading at the mid-ocean ridge and how old rock sinks back into Earth's interior at a trench.

Expected Outcome

Students' models should use the paper strips and shoe box to represent magma welling upward at a mid-ocean ridge, the plate on each side of the mid-ocean ridge moving toward a trench, and the old rock of each plate sinking downward at each trench. Students should draw and label on the model the mid-ocean ridge, plates, and trenches. They should also indicate that the plates are moving away from the mid-ocean ridge and sinking back into Earth's interior at the trenches. An excellent model will label diverging and converging plates.

Content Assessed

This activity assesses students' understanding of the processes of seafloor spreading, plate divergence, and plate convergence that shape the ocean floor.

Skills Assessed

making models, applying concepts

Materials

Each student will need a shoe box lid or bottom that will model a section of the seafloor crust and mantle.

Each student will need two 35-cm strips of adding-machine tape or other paper cut approximately 35 cm × 10 cm.

Provide a variety of colored marking pens for students to use.

Advanced Preparation

- Prepare the shoe box lids and bottoms by cutting three parallel slits, each about 12 cm long, as shown below. The middle slit will model a mid-ocean ridge. The other two slits will model ocean trenches.

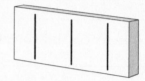

- Cut 35-cm strips of adding-machine tape or cut strips of other paper approximately 35 cm × 10 cm. For example, you can cut sheets of legal-sized paper in half lengthwise.

Time

30 minutes

Monitoring the Task

- Before distributing the student worksheet and materials, ask students to review to themselves what happens at mid-ocean ridges and deep ocean trenches.

- Hand out the worksheets and materials, and make sure students understand the instructions.

- As students sketch, encourage them to consider how they can use the materials to model the process of seafloor spreading.

- Circulate through the classroom and review students' sketches. If any students are not showing seafloor spreading correctly, use prompt questions to get them on track. For example, ask: **Which way do plates move at a mid-ocean ridge?** (*They move away from each other.*) **What happens to the plates at a trench?** (*One plate sinks under the other and back into Earth's interior.*)

- As students finish the model, you may wish to have them use the model to demonstrate seafloor spreading for you.

Ocean Zones ▪ *Performance Assessment*　　　　　　　　**Scoring Rubric**

Modeling Seafloor Spreading

In assessing students' performance, use the following rubric.

	4	3	2	1
Planning and Constructing the Model	The sketch is complete and accurate, and the model clearly demonstrates seafloor spreading, with mid-ocean ridge, plates, trenches, and other features creatively illustrated and correctly labeled.	The sketch is mostly complete and/or accurate and the model demonstrates adequately seafloor spreading, with mid-ocean ridge, plates, and trenches illustrated and correctly labeled.	The sketch is mostly complete but is inaccurate and the model has a major flaw that prevents it from clearly demonstrating seafloor spreading. Features are illustrated, but not correctly labeled.	The sketch is mostly incomplete and/or inaccurate and the model fails to demonstrate seafloor spreading. Most features are missing.
Concept Understanding	The student demonstrates a mastery of the concepts that underlie the model, including seafloor spreading and diverging and converging plates.	The student demonstrates an adequate understanding of the concepts that underlie the model, including seafloor spreading and diverging and converging plates.	The student demonstrates only a partial understanding of the concepts that underlie the model, including seafloor spreading and diverging and converging plates.	The student demonstrates little or no understanding of the concepts that underlie the model, including seafloor spreading and diverging and converging plates.

Ocean Zones

Ocean Zones · *Performance Assessment*

Modeling Seafloor Spreading (*continued*)

Problem

How can you model seafloor spreading, using the materials provided?

Materials

shoe box lid or bottom

paper strips

colored marking pens

Devise a Plan

1. On a separate sheet of paper, draw a sketch of the process of seafloor spreading. Show what happens at a mid-ocean ridge and at an ocean trench. What happens to the plates of Earth's crust at each of these places?

2. Consider your drawing and the materials you've been given. How can you use these materials to model seafloor spreading?

3. Use the materials to construct a model of seafloor spreading. Draw and label a mid-ocean ridge, two plates, and two trenches. Show how the plates are moving. Add any other labels you wish.

Analyze and Conclude

Answer the following questions on another sheet of paper.

1. What does the center slit in the shoe box represent? What do the side slits represent?

2. What do the strips of paper represent?

3. What kind of plate boundaries are demonstrated in your model?

4. Describe what happens at a mid-ocean ridge.

5. What happens at an ocean trench?

Ocean Zones

Multiple Choice

Write the letter of the correct answer on the line at the left.

_____ 1. The gently sloping, shallow ocean floor extending out from the edge of a continent is known as the
- **a.** abyssal plain.
- **b.** continental slope.
- **c.** continental shelf.
- **d.** intertidal zone.

_____ 2. Free-swimming animals that move throughout the water column are called
- **a.** nekton.
- **b.** diatoms.
- **c.** benthos.
- **d.** plankton.

_____ 3. The only part of the open ocean that receives enough sunlight to support algae growth is the
- **a.** neritic zone.
- **b.** surface zone.
- **c.** deep zone.
- **d.** intertidal zone.

_____ 4. Over time, heat and pressure transform some remains of dead organisms buried on the ocean floor into
- **a.** nodules.
- **b.** mineral deposits.
- **c.** atolls.
- **d.** oil and gas deposits.

_____ 5. Two types of coastal wetlands are salt marshes and
- **a.** mangrove forests.
- **b.** tide pools.
- **c.** lagoons.
- **d.** kelp forests.

_____ 6. Coral reefs and kelp forests are usually found in the
- **a.** intertidal zone.
- **b.** open-ocean zone.
- **c.** neritic zone.
- **d.** deep zone.

_____ 7. The continuous range of mountains that passes through all of Earth's oceans is the
- **a.** mid-ocean ridge.
- **b.** abyssal plain.
- **c.** continental shelf.
- **d.** continental slope.

_____ 8. The smooth, nearly flat region of the ocean floor is called the
- **a.** mid-ocean ridge.
- **b.** abyssal plain.
- **c.** continental shelf.
- **d.** trench.

_____ 9. Exploring the deep zone is difficult because of its
- **a.** darkness.
- **b.** cold temperature.
- **c.** high water pressure.
- **d.** all of the above.

_____ 10. Pollutants such as pesticides, sewage, and industrial waste, are carried into estuaries by
- **a.** strong winds.
- **b.** rivers.
- **c.** ocean currents.
- **d.** waves.

Ocean Zones *(continued)*

True or False

If the statement is true, write true. *If it is false, change the underlined word or words to make the statement true.*

_____ **11.** Organisms that live in the <u>neritic</u> zone must be able to tolerate periods of being exposed to the air.

_____ **12.** An <u>estuary</u> is a coastal inlet or bay where fresh water from a river mixes with salty ocean water.

_____ **13.** The farming of saltwater and freshwater organisms is called <u>bioluminescence</u>.

_____ **14.** Seafloor spreading occurs where plates are <u>converging</u> at the mid-ocean ridge.

_____ **15.** Most ocean pollution comes from <u>human sources</u>.

_____ **16.** The <u>abyssal plains</u> are the deepest places on the ocean floor.

_____ **17.** <u>Animal</u> plankton form the base of open-ocean food webs.

Essay

Answer the following questions in the spaces provided.

18. How do hydrothermal vents support living things?

_____

_____

_____

19. How can changes in water temperature and clarity affect coral reefs?

_____

_____

_____

_____

_____

20. What factors allow the neritic zone to support a rich variety of organisms?

_____

_____

_____

_____

Using Science Skills: Interpreting Diagrams

The map below shows major mineral deposits in the ocean. Use the map to answer the questions that follow.

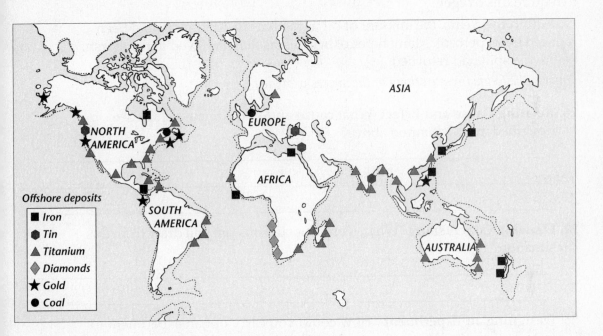

21. Where are ocean deposits of diamonds located? _____

22. Where are ocean deposits of coal found?

_____

_____

23. What minerals are found off the east coast of North America?

_____

24. What do the dotted lines on the map represent?

_____

25. Suggest why minerals are mined only in areas that are *inside* those lines.

_____

_____

Ocean Zones *(continued)*

Using Science Skills

In 1990, there was a large oil spill in the waters near Staten Island, New York. The pollution washed into an area of salt marsh called the Arthur Kill marsh. Unwilling to wait while the marsh very slowly repaired itself from pollution, the New York Parks Department tried a new approach—planting cord grass throughout the damaged marsh.

Animal plankton feed on cord grass. In turn, the animal plankton provide food for other organisms in the salt marsh food web, which includes mussels, crabs, fish, birds, and rodents. In addition, cord grass increases the amount of oxygen in the soil. Bacteria that naturally break down oil appear to require this oxygen.

Within five years, the amount of oil in the Arthur Kill marsh had been reduced by 70 percent. Many types of organisms that had lived in the marsh before the spill had returned.

Answer the following questions in the spaces provided.

26. Relating Cause and Effect What cause-and-effect relationships are described in the situation above?

_____

_____

_____

27. Drawing Conclusions What, if any, conclusions can you draw from this situation?

_____

_____

28. Designing an Experiment How could you carry out an experiment to test whether planting cord grass in a salt marsh speeds up recovery from an oil spill?

_____

_____

_____

_____

Essay

Answer the following items on a separate sheet of paper.

29. Explain why cleaning up an oil spill is so difficult.

30. Describe one idea for encouraging nations to cooperate in preventing ocean pollution.

Exploring the Ocean
Guided Reading and Study

Use Target Reading Skills

Building Vocabulary Check students' definitions for accuracy and understanding.

1. a
2. False
3. It has been explored only recently because the darkness, cold, and extreme pressure on the ocean floor required scientists to develop technology before they could study there.
4. False
5. a, b, c
6. b, c, d
7. **a.** Continental slope
   b. Seamount
   c. Continental shelf
   d. Abyssal plain
   e. Trench
8. f
9. d
10. b
11. a
12. c
13. e
14. a, c, d
15. magma; lava
16. plates
17. a, d
18. Along the mid-ocean ridge, magma squeezes up through cracks between the diverging plates. As the magma hardens, it adds a new strip of rock to the ocean floor. Over millions of years, seafloor spreading has produced the ocean floor.
19. Old rock farther away from the ridge sinks into trenches and back into Earth's interior, allowing the ocean floor to spread while Earth itself remains the same size.

Exploring the Ocean
Review and Reinforce

1. Darkness, cold, extreme pressure
2. Magma squeezes up through cracks between the diverging plates at the mid-ocean ridge. As the magma hardens, it creates new rock.
3. When two plates converge, one plate sinks under the other plate. Old rock sinks into trenches and back into Earth's interior.
4. D, a continuous range of mountains that winds around Earth
5. G, a steep-sided canyon in the deep ocean floor
6. A, a steep incline at the edge of the continental shelf
7. C, the smooth, nearly flat region of the ocean floor
8. B, a mountain that is completely under water
9. F, a gently sloping, shallow area of the ocean floor that extends outward from the edge of a continent
10. E, the peak of a volcano that breaks the ocean surface

Exploring the Ocean
Enrich

1. The boundary between two diverging plates at the mid-ocean ridge
2. Magma rising up
3. Strips of rock that formed when the magma hardened
4. *Oldest:* red *Newest:* green

The Shape of the Ocean Floor
Skills Lab

For answers, see Teacher's Edition.

Ocean Habitats
Guided Reading and Study

Use Target Reading Skills

Using Prior Knowledge This is one possible way to complete the graphic organizer. Accept all logical answers.

What You Know

1. Many organisms need sunlight.
2. Marine organisms obtain oxygen from the water.

What You Learned

1. The ocean is divided into three zones.
2. Marine organisms are classified by where they live and how they move.

1. False
2. Possible answer: clams, crabs, dolphins
3. intertidal zone
4. neritic zone
5. open-ocean zone

6. deep
7. False
8. near the surface of the ocean
9. high pressure
10. True
11. a
12. Plankton are tiny algae and animals that float in the water and are carried by waves and currents.
13. Possible answer: diatoms, microscopic crustaceans, some tiny young fishes
14. nekton
15. nekton
16. Benthos are organisms that inhabit the ocean floor.
17. Some benthos move from place to place. Others stay in one location.
18. Possible answer: crabs, sea stars, octopuses, lobsters, sponges, sea anemones
19. producers
20. b
21. wastes and remains of other organisms
22. A food web is made up of all of the feeding relationships that exist in a habitat.
23. d
24. Answers will vary, but should reflect information from the figure in the text.

Ocean Habitats
Review and Reinforce

1. They differ in amount of light, amount of pressure, and the organisms that inhabit them.
2. Scientists classify marine organisms according to where they live and how they move.
3. Dolphins are nekton because they are free-swimming animals.
4. Intertidal zone
5. Neritic zone
6. Open-ocean zone
7. b
8. c
9. a
10. a food web

Ocean Habitats
Enrich

Students' webs should include the 10 organisms listed in the table's left column, plus "remains of dead organisms" (eaten by crabs and clams). Make sure students draw each arrow *from* the organism being eaten *to* the organism doing the eating—for example, algae → plankton → small fish → octopus.

Intertidal Zone
Guided Reading and Study

Use Target Reading Skills This is one possible way to complete the graphic organizer. Accept all logical answers.
Intertidal Zone
I. Rocky shores
   A. Along the rocks
   B. In tide pools
II. Where river meets ocean
   A. Mangrove forests
   B. Salt marshes
   C. Protecting estuaries
   1. **a.** Pounding of the waves **b.** Changes in salinity **c.** Changes in temperature **d.** Living both underwater and exposed to the air
   2. a
   3. The area above the high tide line where the rocks are wet from breaking waves, but where the rocks are never under water
   4. **a.** It can close its hard shell, enclosing itself along with a drop of water to keep itself wet through dry periods. **b.** It has rows of tiny suction cups that help it cling to rocks. **c.** It has a large, muscular foot that allows it to hold on to rocks. **d.** It uses its spines to dig a hole and bury itself.
   5. True
   6. intertidal zone
   7. They must tolerate the pounding of waves, changes in salinity and temperature, and being underwater as well as being exposed to air.

8. tide pools
9. a, b, c
10. estuaries
11. brackish
12. **a.** Salt Marshes **b.** Mangrove Forests
13. Pollutants enter estuaries in river water.
14. **a.** They break the action of wind and waves, protecting the coastline during storms. **b.** Their roots trap sediment, creating a protected nursery, rich in nutrients, for many young animals.

Intertidal Zone
Review and Reinforce

1. Tide pools and estuaries
2. The highest high-tide line and the lowest low-tide line; *Any three:* pounding waves, changes in salinity, changes in temperature, periods of being underwater and periods of being exposed to air
3. Rivers that flow into estuaries carry pollutants from the land.
4. Students should describe a tide pool.
5. Groups of short, gnarled trees that fringe the coast of southern Florida.
6. Type of marsh that is made of sediments, animal and plant matter, and nutrients carried there by fresh water and tides.
7. salt marshes and mangrove forests
8. estuary

Intertidal Zone
Enrich

1. The yellow "river" water floated on the blue "ocean" water with little mixing. (Salt water is denser than fresh water.)
2. The yellow "river" water and blue "ocean" water mixed to form green water.
3. Like an estuary, river water flowed into ocean water and mixed to form brackish water—the green water.

Neritic Zone and Open Ocean
Guided Reading and Study

Use Target Reading Skills This is one possible way to complete the graphic organizer. Accept all logical answers.
a. Sunlight penetrates shallow water.
b. Nutrients from the land enter the ocean.
1. neritic zone; open-ocean zone
2. a, b, c
3. **a.** Kelp forests
   b. Coral reefs
4. True
5. 2, 1, 3
6. b
7. c
8. a
9. True
10. a, b, d
11. They eat sea urchins, which eat the kelp, and this prevents sea urchins from destroying the kelp forest.
12. True
13. True
14. Like a desert, the deep zone has harsh conditions.
15. bioluminescence
16. hydrothermal vent
17. a, b

Neritic Zone and Open Ocean
Review and Reinforce

1. It receives sunlight and has a steady supply of nutrients.
2. Algae need sunlight to make their own food, and the deepest parts of the ocean do not receive any sunlight.
3. Bacteria; chemical nutrients (gases and minerals) from the vent.
4. Intertidal zone: stretches from highest high-tide line to the lowest low-tide line

5. Neritic zone: extends from the low-tide line to the edge of the continental shelf

6. Open-ocean zone: beyond the edge of the continental shelf

7. Surface zone: extends as far as sunlight reaches below the surface

8. Transition zone: extends from the bottom of the surface zone to a depth of about 1 kilometer

9. Deep zone: extends from the bottom of the surface zone to the sea floor

Neritic Zone and Open Ocean
Enrich

1. Coral animals have sac-like bodies with a mouth surrounded by tentacles.

2. A coral colony is a structure that might look like a head or branching twig. Each coral colony contains large numbers of coral animals.

3. Space is limited on reefs. To be successful, a colony must occupy and keep space. The coral animals then can get sunlight and food from the water.

4. The colonies grow over neighboring colonies and block sunlight from reaching those colonies.

5. The animals in some coral colonies have sweeper tentacles that sting and kill animals in neighboring colonies. Filaments also are used to digest nearby coral animals.

Resources From the Ocean
Guided Reading and Study

Use Target Reading Skills This is one possible way to complete the graphic organizer. Accept all logical answers.

a. Water from desalination

b. Fuels from the remains of animals

c. Valuable minerals

1. False

2. a. herring b. tuna c. anchovy
   d. pollock e. mackerel

3. Nearly all fishes are caught on coastal waters or areas of upwelling.

4. aquaculture

5. Nonliving resources include gravel, sand, gold, diamonds, and metals such as manganese.

6. nodules

7. False

8. Magnesium is obtained from seawater by removing the fresh water and leaving the salts behind.

9. True

10. oil, natural gas

11. The richest deposits are located on the continental shelves because that is where many organisms in the ocean live, die, and become buried in sediment.

12. b, c

13. True

14. The sudden change in salinity may kill ocean animals that are unable to adjust to it.

15. a. Sewage b. Chemicals c. Trash

16. c

17. Certain bacteria that live in the ocean feed on the oil and multiply, eventually cleaning up the oil that was spilled.

18. It is difficult because the world ocean is a continuous body of water that has no boundaries.

19. False

20. False

Resources From the Ocean
Review and Reinforce

1. The catches of all three fish declined from 1970 to 1993.

2. The declines are probably caused by overfishing.

3. Limit catches so fish that are caught can be replaced by new fish that are born.

4. They sink to the ocean floor, are buried by sediments, and decompose. As sediments build up, heat and pressure from the overlying layers transform the remains into oil and gas.

5. The world's oceans are continuous, and no nation owns the high seas. Pollution in one nation's waters can reach the open ocean and spread to other nations' waters.

6. The farming of saltwater and freshwater organisms

7. Black lumps formed by metals concentrating around pieces of shell

Resources From the Ocean
Enrich

1. Thousands of metric tons of fish
2. A little more than 200,000 metric tons
3. About 60,000 metric tons
4. About 140,000 metric tons
5. 1986
6. To allow the fish populations to renew themselves naturally

Cleaning Up an Oil Spill
Skills Lab

For answers, see the Teacher's Edition.

Key Terms

1. holdfast
2. sonar
3. trench
4. magma
5. plankton
6. benthos
7. estuary
8. aquaculture
9. atoll
10. seamount
11. plates
12. brackish
13. nekton

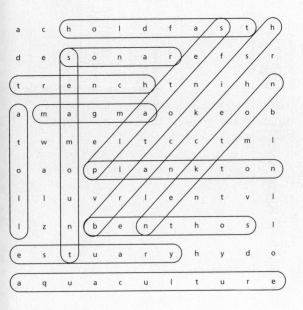

Connecting Concepts

This is one way to represent the main ideas and relationships in this chapter. Accept other logical answers from students.

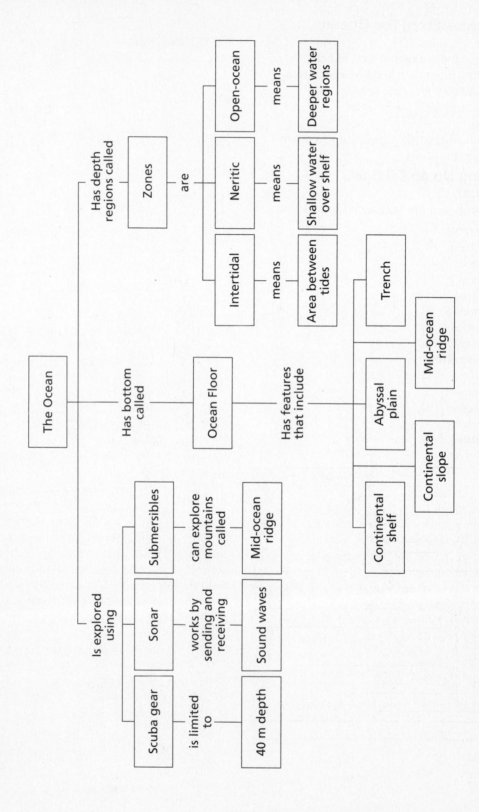

Laboratory Investigation

Microscopic Marine Life

Pre-Lab Discussion

1. Plankton are tiny algae and animals that float in water.

2. Algae plankton include diatoms and other organisms that make their own food. Animal plankton, such as copepods, crustacean larvae, and fish larvae, eat other organisms.

Analyze and Conclude

1. Answers will vary. Fish larvae, crustacean larvae, and copepods are multicellular.

2. Answers will vary. Sample answer: All are too small to be seen without a microscope, and all are made of cells.

3. Answers will vary. Sample answer: The organisms have different colors and shapes. Some have whip-like external structures. Some are algae plankton, and some are animal plankton.

Critical Thinking and Applications

1. Algae plankton, such as diatoms and dinoflagellates, make their own food. Algae contain chlorophyll.

2. Copepods, crustacean larvae, and fish larvae; any organism that does not have chlorophyll probably relied on other plankton as a food source.

3. Answers will vary. Sample answer: Some fish larvae are plankton. They are microscopic and are moved by waves and currents. When they grow larger, they become free-swimming animals that control their own motion.

More to Explore

Allow a classroom aquarium to become slightly overgrown with algae and monerans before the lab begins. Students should observe that the snails leave a clear trail on the aquarium sides as they scrape off and consume the underlying growth of protists and monerans. Students will observe a variety of algae, including different diatom species. Cyanobacteria should also be present.

Chapter Performance Assessment

1. The center slit represents a mid-ocean ridge; the side slits represent ocean trenches.

2. They represent plates.

3. Diverging plates are demonstrated at the mid-ocean ridge, and converging plates are demonstrated at the trenches.

4. Magma squeezes up through cracks between the diverging plates, and as it hardens, adds new strips of rock to the ocean floor.

5. Where plates converge, one plate sinks under the other and back into Earth's interior.

Chapter Test

1. c
2. a
3. b
4. d
5. a
6. c
7. a
8. b
9. d
10. b
11. intertidal
12. True
13. aquaculture
14. diverging
15. True
16. trenches
17. Algae
18. Hydrothermal vents release chemical nutrients that bacteria use to produce food. These bacteria are the base of the food web at a hydrothermal vent.
19. If the water becomes too warm, the coral animals release the algae that live inside them. If the water becomes cloudy, the algae inside the coral animals cannot survive. In both cases, the coral animals do not grow well without the algae and eventually die.
20. The shallow water in the neritic zone receives ample sunlight and nutrients washed from the land. The sunlight and nutrients support the growth of large, plantlike algae that provide food and shelter for many other organisms. In some areas, additional nutrients are brought from the bottom to the surface by upwelling currents. These nutrients support large numbers of plankton that form the base of ocean food webs.
21. Off the west coast of southern Africa
22. Off the east coast of North America and the northwest coast of Europe
23. coal, gold, titanium
24. The edge of the continental shelves

25. The ocean is shallow above the continental shelves; the open ocean is too deep for mining.

26. Answers may vary. Sample answer: oil spill (cause), polluted salt marsh (effect); planting cord grass (cause), speeded up recovery (effect); cord grass increases oxygen in soil (cause), supports oil-consuming bacteria (effect).

27. Answers may vary, although students should suggest that there may not be enough data to know for sure that planting cord grass speed up recovery of the salt marsh.

28. Students' experimental designs may vary. A typical design will suggest planting cord grass in one area of a polluted salt marsh and leaving the other area unplanted as a control. The responding variable will be the recovery of the salt marsh.

29. Students' answers should include the following major points: Oil adheres to marine animals' fur and feathers. Waves and tides wash the oil onto the beach. It is impossible to remove all the oil from the water.

30. Accept all reasonable responses. *Example:* Wealthier nations could provide financial aid to nations that cannot afford to build waste-treatment plants so that these less wealthy nations can stop dumping sewage and other contaminants into the ocean.

Transparencies

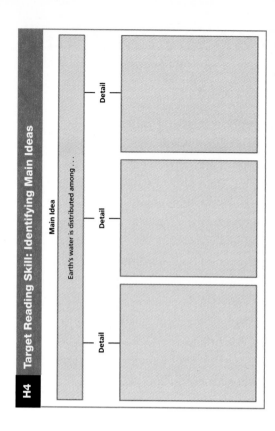

Main Idea

Earth's water is distributed among . . .

Detail

Detail

Detail

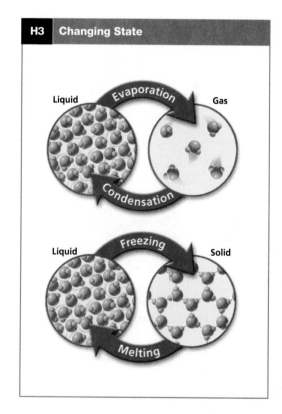

Hydrogen Atoms

Oxygen Atom

Water Molecules

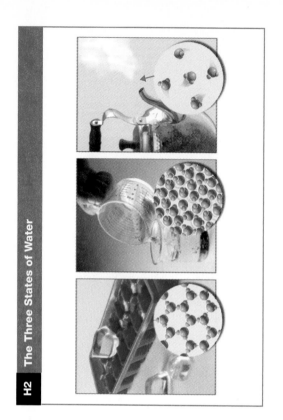

Liquid   Evaporation   Gas

Condensation

Liquid   Freezing   Solid

Melting

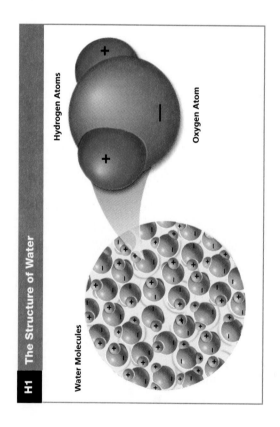

H6 Target Reading Skill: Outlining

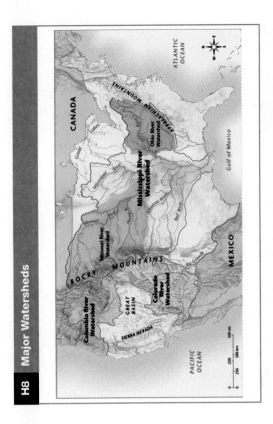

Surface Water

I. River systems

A. Tributaries

B.

C.

II. Ponds and lakes

A.

B.

C.

H8 Major Watersheds

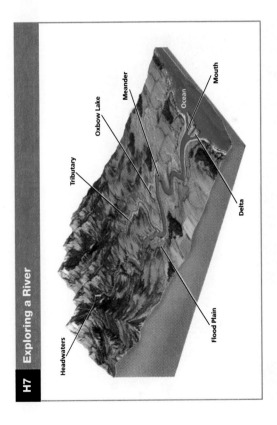

H5 The Water Cycle

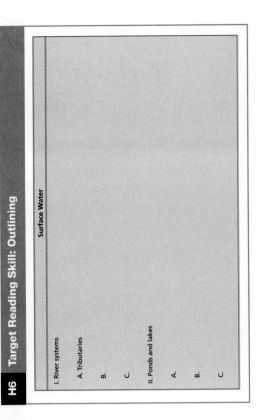

H7 Exploring a River

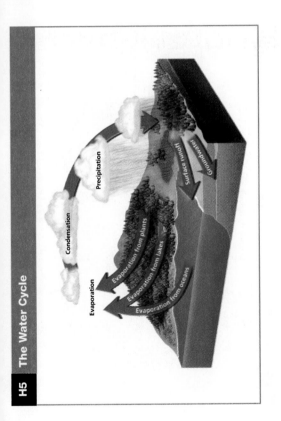

H9 · Long-Term Changes in a Lake

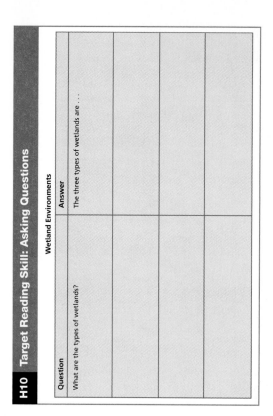

H10 · Target Reading Skill: Asking Questions

Wetland Environments

Question	Answer
What are the types of wetlands?	The three types of wetlands are . . .

H11 · Target Reading Skill: Previewing Visuals

Bringing Up Groundwater

Q. What is an artesian well?

A.

Q.

A.

Q.

A.

H12 · Groundwater Formation

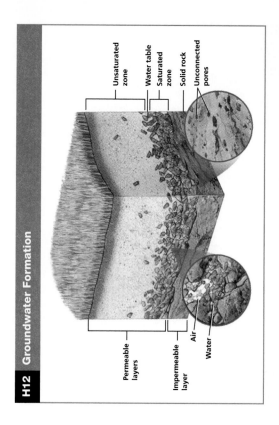

Permeable layers

Impermeable layer

Air

Water

Unsaturated zone

Water table

Saturated zone

Solid rock

Unconnected pores

H14 Organizing Information: Sequencing

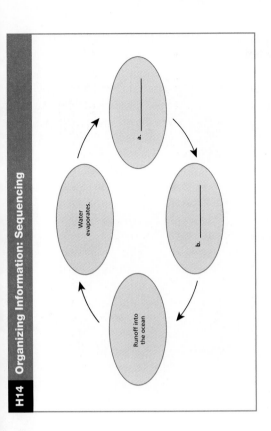

- Water evaporates.
- a. _____
- b. _____
- Runoff into the ocean

H13 Bringing Up Groundwater

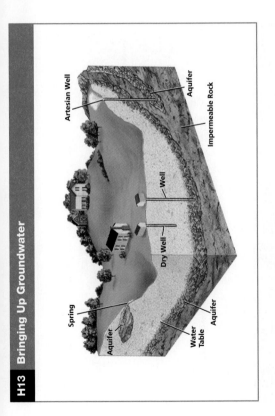

- Artesian Well
- Aquifer
- Impermeable Rock
- Well
- Dry Well
- Spring
- Aquifer
- Water Table
- Aquifer

H16 The Colorado River

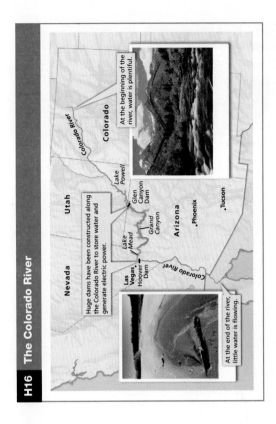

Nevada
Utah
Colorado
Arizona

Colorado River
Lake Powell
Glen Canyon Dam
Grand Canyon
Lake Mead
Las Vegas
Hoover Dam
Phoenix
Tucson
Colorado River

At the beginning of the river, water is plentiful.

Huge dams have been constructed along the Colorado River to store water and generate electric power.

At the end of the river, little water is flowing.

H15 Target Reading Skill: Using Prior Knowledge

What You Know

1. I can conserve water by taking shorter showers.
2.
3.

What You Learned

1.
2.
3.

Transparencies

H18 Drinking Water Treatment

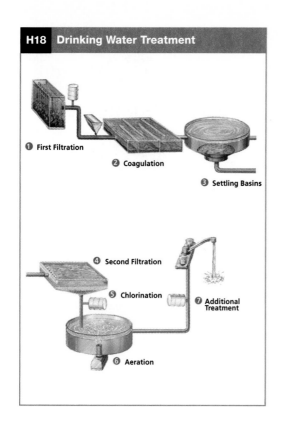

❶ First Filtration

❷ Coagulation

❸ Settling Basins

❹ Second Filtration

❺ Chlorination

❼ Additional Treatment

❻ Aeration

H20 Target Reading Skill: Outlining

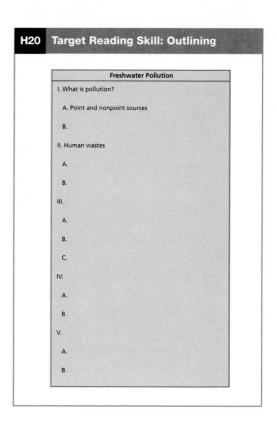

Freshwater Pollution

I. What is pollution?

  A. Point and nonpoint sources

  B.

II. Human wastes

  A.

  B.

III.

  A.

  B.

  C.

IV.

  A.

  B.

V.

  A.

  B.

H17 Target Reading Skill: Sequencing

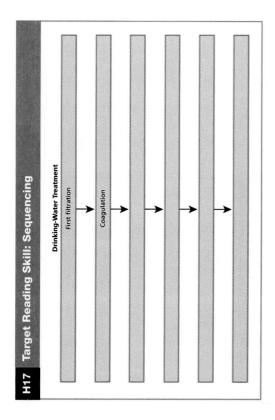

Drinking-Water Treatment

First filtration → Coagulation → → → →

H19 A Septic System

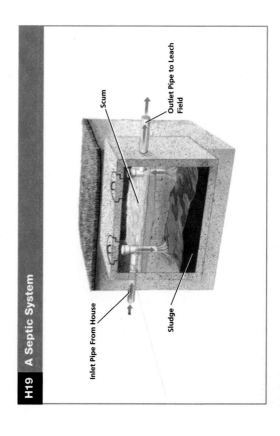

Scum

Outlet Pipe to Leach Field

Inlet Pipe From House

Sludge

H22 Pollution Solutions

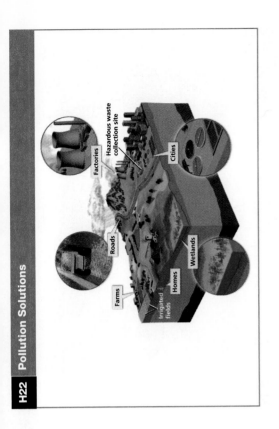

H24 Flash Floods

H21 Pesticides in the Water

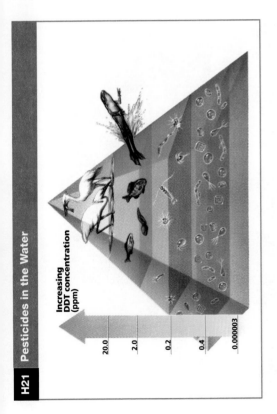

H23 Target Reading Skill: Comparing and Contrasting

Droughts and Floods

Feature	Droughts	Floods
Cause	Scarce rainfall	
Possible to predict?		
Preparation		
Major effects		

Water Power

Question	Answer
How are energy and moving water related?	Hydroelectric power . . .

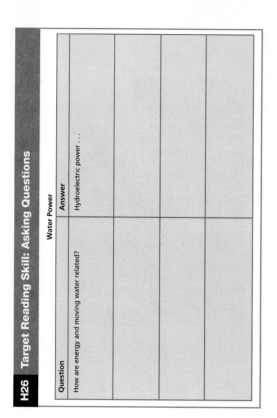

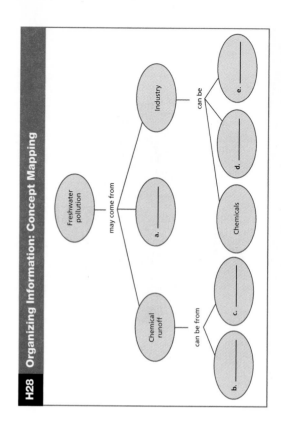

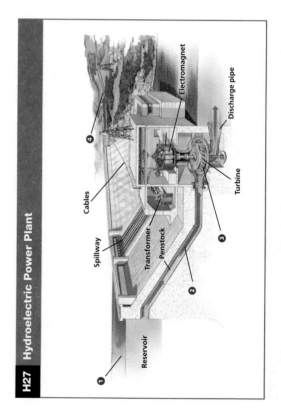

H29 Target Reading Skill: Using Prior Knowledge

What You Know

1. There are waves in the ocean.

2.

3.

What You Learned

1.

2.

3.

H30 Water Motion

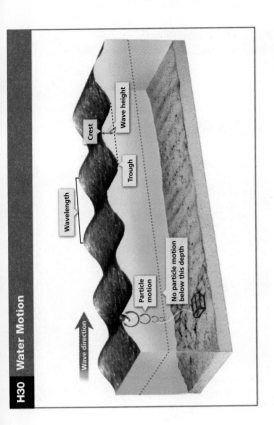

Wavelength

Crest

Wave height

Trough

Wave direction

Particle motion

No particle motion below this depth

H31 Breakers

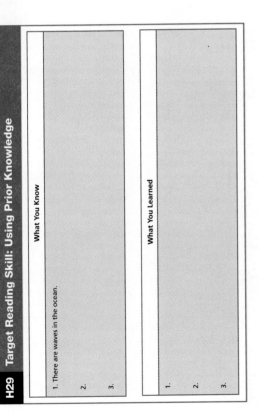

Swells

Surf Zone

Breaker

Beach

Wave height increases

Wave direction

H32 Longshore Drifts

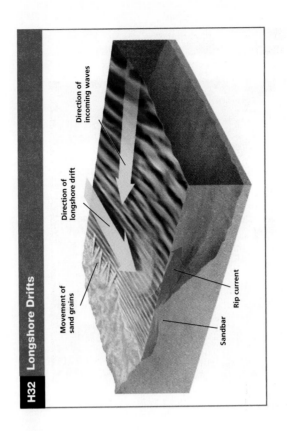

Direction of incoming waves

Direction of longshore drift

Movement of sand grains

Rip current

Sandbar

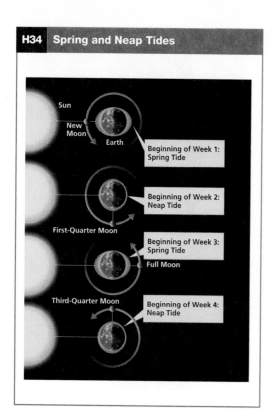

Sun

New Moon

Earth

Beginning of Week 1: Spring Tide

First-Quarter Moon

Beginning of Week 2: Neap Tide

Beginning of Week 3: Spring Tide

Full Moon

Third-Quarter Moon

Beginning of Week 4: Neap Tide

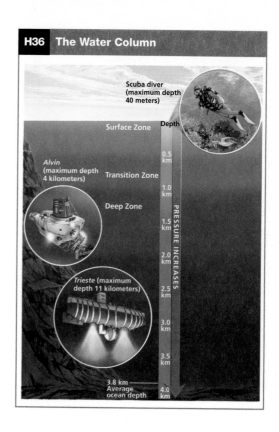

Scuba diver (maximum depth 40 meters)

Surface Zone

Depth

Alvin (maximum depth 4 kilometers)

Transition Zone

Deep Zone

0.5 km

1.0 km

1.5 km

2.0 km

PRESSURE INCREASES

Trieste (maximum depth 11 kilometers)

2.5 km

3.0 km

3.5 km

3.8 km Average ocean depth

4.0 km

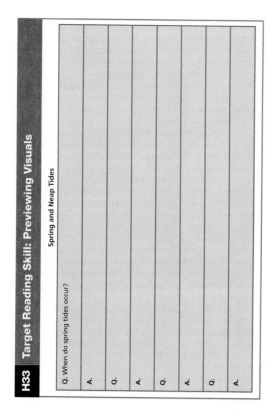

H33 Target Reading Skill: Previewing Visuals

Spring and Neap Tides

Q. When do spring tides occur?

A.

Q.

A.

Q.

A.

Q.

A.

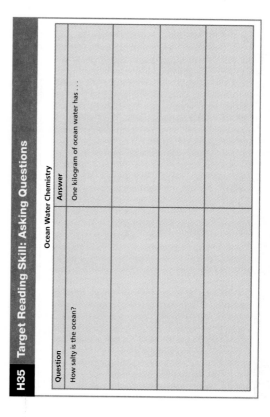

H35 Target Reading Skill: Asking Questions

Ocean Water Chemistry

Question	Answer
How salty is the ocean?	One kilogram of ocean water has . . .

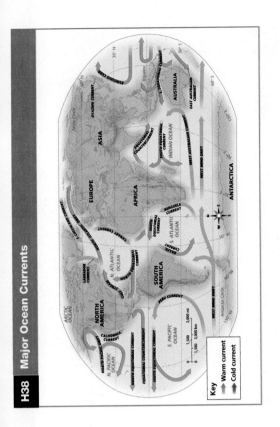

H38 Major Ocean Currents

Key
↑ Warm current
↑ Cold current

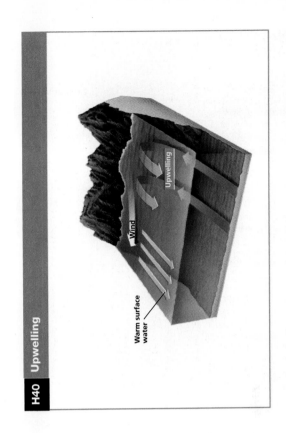

H40 Upwelling

Wind

Upwelling

Warm surface water

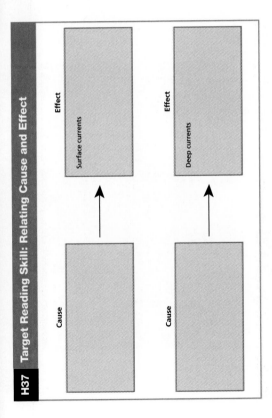

H37 Target Reading Skill: Relating Cause and Effect

Cause → Effect
Surface currents

Cause → Effect
Deep currents

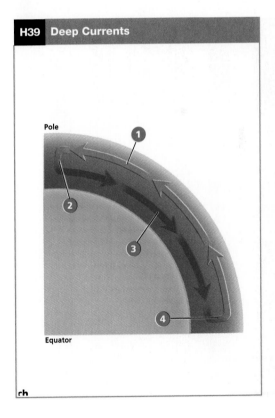

H39 Deep Currents

Pole

1
2
3
4

Equator

How Waves Move

Wind creates a ripple on the ocean surface.

a. _____

Wave touches the bottom in shallow water.

b. _____

c. _____

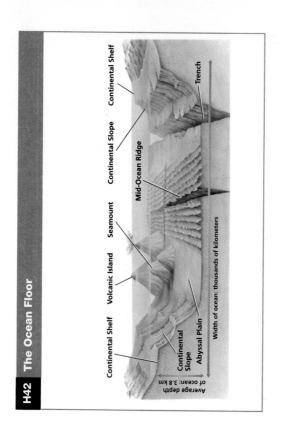

Continental Shelf

Volcanic Island   Seamount   Continental Slope   Continental Shelf

Mid-Ocean Ridge

Continental Shelf

Continental Slope

Abyssal Plain

Trench

Width of ocean: thousands of kilometers

Average depth of ocean: 3.8 km

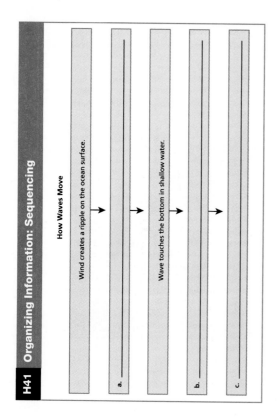

Eurasian Plate
Arabian Plate
African Plate
North American Plate
Caribbean Plate
South American Plate
Scotia Plate
Nazca Plate
Juan de Fuca Plate
Cocos Plate
Pacific Plate
Antarctic Plate
Philippine Plate
Indo-Australian Plate
Eurasian Plate

Key
Direction of plate movement

N W-E S

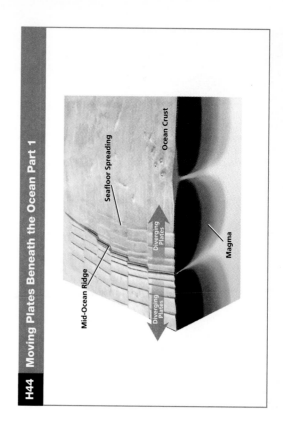

Mid-Ocean Ridge

Seafloor Spreading

Ocean Crust

Diverging Plates

Diverging Plates

Magma

H46 Target Reading Skill: Using Prior Knowledge

What You Know

1. Many organisms need sunlight.

2.

3.

What You Learned

1.

2.

3.

H48 Marine Organisms

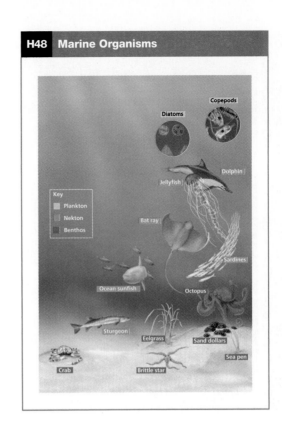

Key
- Plankton
- Nekton
- Benthos

Diatoms
Copepods
Dolphin
Jellyfish
Bat ray
Sardines
Ocean sunfish
Octopus
Sturgeon
Eelgrass
Sand dollars
Sea pen
Crab
Brittle star

H45 Moving Plates Beneath the Ocean Part 2

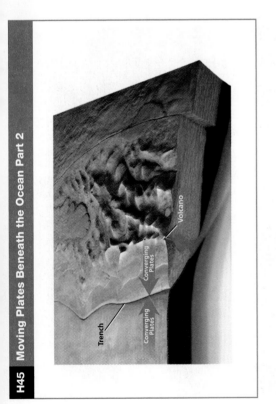

Trench
Converging Plates
Converging Plates
Volcano

H47 Ocean Zones

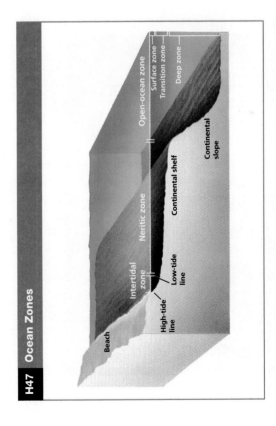

Open-ocean zone
Surface zone
Transition zone
Deep zone
Neritic zone
Continental shelf
Continental slope
Intertidal zone
Low-tide line
High-tide line
Beach

H49 Ocean Food Web

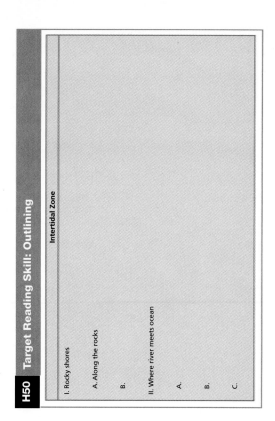

Polar bear

Ringed seal

Beluga whale

Arctic cod

Benthos

Loons

Silversides

Arctic tern

Animal plankton

Benthos

Sea duck

Algae plankton

H50 Target Reading Skill: Outlining

Intertidal Zone

I. Rocky shores

A. Along the rocks

B.

II. Where river meets ocean

A.

B.

C.

H51 A Rocky Shore

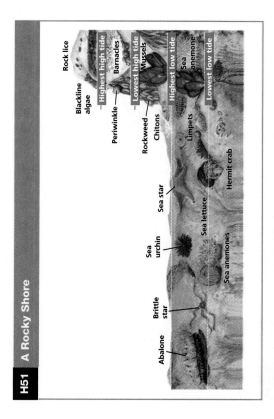

Rock lice

Blackline algae

Highest high tide

Barnacles

Periwinkle

Lowest high tide

Mussels

Rockweed

Chitons

Highest low tide

Sea anemone

Limpets

Lowest low tide

Sea star

Hermit crab

Sea urchin

Sea lettuce

Brittle star

Sea anemones

Abalone

H52 Target Reading Skill: Relating Cause and Effect

Causes

Effect

The neritic zone has a wide variety of organisms.

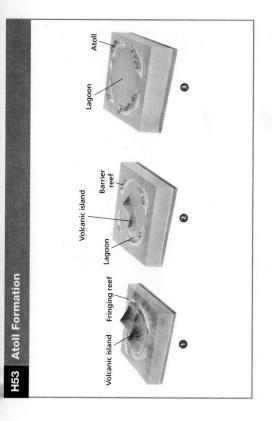

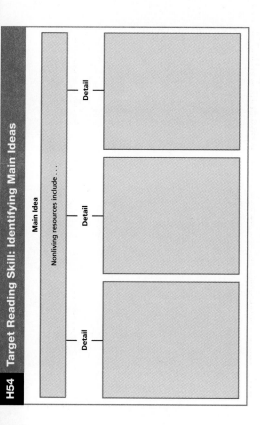

Volcanic island Fringing reef

1

Volcanic island

Lagoon

Barrier reef

2

Lagoon

Atoll

3

Main Idea

Nonliving resources include . . .

Detail	Detail	Detail

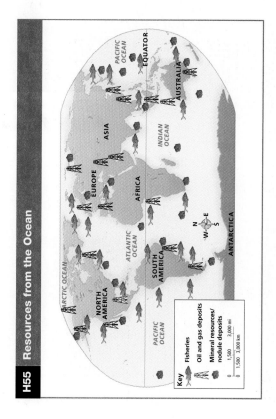

ARCTIC OCEAN
NORTH AMERICA
PACIFIC OCEAN
ATLANTIC OCEAN
SOUTH AMERICA
EUROPE
ASIA
AFRICA
PACIFIC OCEAN
INDIAN OCEAN
AUSTRALIA
EQUATOR
ANTARCTICA
N W E S

Key
Fisheries
Oil and gas deposits
Mineral resources/nodule deposits

0   1,500   3,000 mi
0   1,500   3,000 km

Habitat	Zone	Conditions	Organisms
Tide pool	Intertidal	a. ___	b. ___
Coral reef	c. ___	d. ___	Coral, fishes, shrimp, eels
Surface zone	Open ocean	e. ___	f. ___
Hydrothermal vent	g. ___	High pressure, dark, warm	h. ___